THE 1990 GUIDE

Contents

This 1990 edition published by Ebury Press
an imprint of Century Hutchinson Ltd
20 Vauxhall Bridge Road, London SW1V 2SA

ISBN 0 85223 853 3

Edited by: Mandy Morton-Smith and Annabel Lindsey Gray
Illustrations: Gary Brazier

Filmset by Flair Plan Phototypesetting Limited, Ware
Printed and bound in Great Britain at The Bath Press, Avon

FOREWORD

Welcome to the Routiers Guide to France, the ideal travelling companion for all those who wish to experience the real flavour of France, but on a reasonable budget.

For many travellers, France has the reputation of being an expensive country to visit. No doubt this is partly due to the temptation of all the superb wine and delicious cooking, a style of cuisine which is celebrated throughout Europe. However, it is more likely that the British traveller has not investigated a reliable source of reference to steer them clear of establishments whose "hidden extras" only become visible once they are on the bill and who make use of the inexperienced tourist to boost their own profits.

Routiers exists to point the traveller to places where they can eat and stay at real value for money. All "Relais Routiers" are regularly inspected to ensure that standards are maintained. Our philosophy is that value for money can be found in a variety of establishments, from family restaurants and local bars to lively brasseries; as long as they provide a warm welcome, serve good quality food, offer at least one fixed price menu, and observe rules of hygiene in kitchens, bathrooms and bedrooms. We are sure you will agree that travelling can be a far more enjoyable and relaxed affair if you know of a reliable place to eat and rest.

Whilst travelling, or after you have reached your destination and wish to explore, consult your Guide to find out where you can sample regional dishes and local wines and cheeses. Try the crisp white wines of the Loire Valley, or the rich reds of Bordeaux. Test the variety of cheeses in Normandy. Wherever you go, there will always be a "Relais Routiers" where you can rely on the quality of the produce.

The following pages will explain how to get the best from your Guide. There are many different flavours to France and Routiers will help you to explore them.

Bon voyage et bon appetit.

WHAT MAKES A RELAIS ROUTIERS

With the increase in the number of travellers through France, the Routiers establishments have adapted themselves to cater more readily for families and tourists. Despite this change in direction, the philosophy of Routiers remains unaltered – all Relais Routiers are inspected regularly to ensure they provide good food, a warm welcome, quality and value.

Routiers come in all shapes and sizes, from roadside cafe to locals' bar, pretty country hotel or lively town brasserie – but whatever the style of establishment, quality and value are served with a generous helping of authentic French cuisine and atmosphere.

The hallmark of the French Relais Routiers is the fixed-price menu. The menu will normally be for a 3 course meal and may or may not include drinks. It is displayed in the restaurant and comes with our recommendation. An a la carte menu may also be offered, but this will normally be slightly more expensive.

HOW TO FIND A RELAIS ROUTIERS

BY TOWN – establishments are listed by town on the alphabetical lists starting on page 69. The entry is followed by the department and number (the French equivalent of the county and postcode), the main road reference for the town and the map reference.

e.g. **Abbeville 80100 Somme RN1 Map 5-A3** This means that Abbeville is in the Somme Department on Route Nationale 1 and can be found on map 5 grid reference A3.

THE MAPS – start on page 17 with a list of all the maps provided and the page on which they can be found. On the following page there is a map of the whole of France showing the outline of the areas covered by the regional maps. The circled number refers to the map number and not to the department number. All towns where Routiers can be found are shown in blue, and the roads in red. The numbers of the roads are shown at the edge of the map and not on the map itself. The maps should assist in route planning rather than be relied on completely.

WITH ACCOMMODATION – Although most Relais Routiers in France are restaurants, many also have accommodation and are clearly indicated with the hotel symbol. Standards may vary considerably, and we have therefore included on page 54 a regional list of Relais Routiers approved by the French Tourist Board – the 'hotels de tourisme'. A map showing the location of these hotels is shown on page 52 with the relevant towns shown in red and the main roads in blue. The blue circled numbers on the map refer back to the more detailed maps on pages 18–44. The list of 'hotels de tourisme' which follows is in numerical order by department. So for example **01 Ain** means that the list of towns and establishments which follow are in the First Department – Ain. A map showing the location of the different departments is shown on page 45.

CASSEROLES – The 'Casserole' is the Les Routiers mark of excellence for those establishments offering exceptional quality. A map showing their location can be found on page 46, and a list of all 'Casseroles' on page 48. The map and the list follow the same principles as the map for 'hotels de tourisme' above.

SYMBOLS USED IN THIS GUIDE

⊗   BAR, CAFE

♈   RESTAURANT

🍲   CASSEROLE – the Les Routiers mark of excellence
awarded annually to those Relais Routiers where the
cuisine is exceptional.

🏠   HOTEL – bed and breakfast available.

☆   OFFICIAL CLASSIFICATION OF THE FRENCH
TOURIST BOARD – the number of stars indicates
degree of comfort.

☎   TELEPHONE NUMBER

NB. Each Routiers has a reference number e.g. (No RR AVR
1804). Please use it on all correspondence concerning
specific Relais Routiers.

WHEN IN FRANCE...

1. Take your Guide with you into restaurants – it will let the
owners know you have chosen the establishment by using
the Guide and that you expect a high standard of food and
service.

2. There are two types of meal available, "repas complet"
and "casse croute". "Repas complet" is a full meal and is
served at set times, i.e. lunch time and evening. "Casse
croute" is a snack meal and can be served at any time and is
usually fairly simple.

3. Two types of menu may be offered: The set menu is a
complete 3-course meal and may or may not include drinks.
There is no reduction if you do not eat all the courses. Many
restaurants offer several set menus at different prices and a
special lunchtime menu is often available at a lower cost than
in the evening.
    The a la carte menu offers a full choice of dishes and
courses and even if the meal chosen comprises the same
courses as the set menu, it will be more expensive.

4. If you order cheese or fruit, a cheeseboard or fruit basket may be set in front of you. Do not help yourself to more than a normal portion.

5. Following a change in the laws in 1987, the service charge must be included in the price of a meal. Tips are rarely expected and are usually given by rounding up the bill.

6. Soft drinks are much more expensive in France than in the UK. 'Sirops' which are mixed with water like a cordial or squash are a cheaper alternative to coke and lemonade.

7. The number of persons permitted to sleep in any one room is also governed by French law. It is illegal to rent a room to more than the permitted number of persons.

8. Many small hotels will lock their doors quite early at night, so if you wish to go out, do remember to advise the proprietors of this and they will make arrangements to lend you a key.

9. It is illegal to use any kind of cooking utensil in a French hotel room.

10. Many French people take their holiday between 14th July and 15th August and you may find some hotels and restaurants closed during this period. It is also advisable to book accommodation well in advance if you wish to travel at this time.

The British Embassy
Ambassade de Grande-Bretagne,
16 rue d'Anjou,
Paris 8,
France
TEL: 42 66 38 10 (prefix 010 33 1 if dialling from the UK).

AU RESTAURANT...

Choosing a restaurant and deciding what to eat can be one of the most enjoyable parts of your stay in France. One of the delights of eating in Relais Routiers lies in the discovery of authentic French Cuisine and atmosphere. In large hotels there is a tendency to serve 'continental French cuisine' whilst in Relais Routiers, providing the season is right, you can experiment with regional dishes and taste the true flavours of France. Some of the main regional specialities to look out for include:

BOEUF BOURGUIGNON – famous throughout France and well known in Britain, it originates from Burgundy. **Coq au vin** is another example. Due to the high quality of the wines many dishes either include wine or are designed to compliment the wines.

BOUILLABAISSE – a fish stew from Marseilles in Provence. Made with the characteristic southern ingredients of garlic, fennel, tomatoes and hot pepper sauce.

BROCHET AU BEURRE BLANC – pike from the Loire, cooked in a sauce made from shallots, white wine vinegar and butter. Shallots are as important an ingredient to Angevin cooking as garlic is to Provence. Many of the regional dishes are designed to compliment the dry, white wines of the Loire valley.

CASSOULET – regional stew from Toulouse, Carcassone and Castelnaudry in south west France. Made from confit d'oie (preserved goose), haricot beans, sausage, pork, mutton, garlic, herbs and tomatoes.

CHOUCROUTE – an Alsatian dish of special smoked sausage and pickled cabbage which reflects the German influence on the region.

QUICHE LORRAINE – a quiche containing smoked bacon, cream and egg. Popular in Britain and elsewhere in France where Gruyere cheese is often added. Cheese is not included in the original version, dating from the 16th century.

The hallmark of the French Relais Routiers is the fixed-price menu, which will normally be for a 3 course meal and may or may not include drinks. Whether you wish to sample regional dishes or one of the more traditional alternatives, the fixed-price menu is your guarantee of authentic French cuisine at good value for money.

BON APPETIT

A L'HOTEL...

Monsieur,

Votre hôtel m'a été recommandé par Les Routiers. Je vous prie de vouloir bien me retenir une chambre à un lit/pour deux personnes avec/sans salle de bain/douche pour la nuit du.../du...jusqu'au...

Soyez assez aimable de nous confirmer cette location et de nous dire s'il vous faut une caution.

Avec nos remerciements anticipés,

Veuillez agréer, Monsieur, nos sentiments les plus distinguées.

Dear Sir,

Your hotel has been recommended to me by Les Routiers. I would be grateful if you would reserve me a single/double room with/without bathroom/shower on the... for one night/from... to...

Please could you confirm this and let me know if a deposit is required.

Thanking you in advance,

Yours sincerely,

Single room – une chambre à un lit
Double room – une chambre pour deux personnes avec un grand lit
Twin room – une chambre avec deux lits
With/without en suite bathroom – avec/sans salle de bain
With/without en suite shower – avec/sans douche

Breakfast – le petit déjeuner
half board – demi-pension
full board – pension complète

I'd like to book/reserve...	– Je voudrais retenir/réserver...
How much does the room cost?	– Combien coûte/vaut la chambre?
How much will it cost?	– Combient est-ce que cela coûtera?

EN ROUTE...

1. Speed limits:
  60 km (approx 37 miles) per hour – in built up areas
  90 km (approx 56 miles) per hour – main roads
110 km (approx 68 miles) per hour – dual carriageways
130 km (approx 80 miles) per hour – motorways

NB: Some motorways may also have a **minimum** speed limit.

2. Tolls (péages) are charged on most motorways. Usually a
ticket is issued and a toll paid when you leave the motorway
or at intermediate points during the motorway journey. Some
motorway stretches have automatic collection where you
throw the change into a basket (like the Dartford Tunnel). If
you do not have the correct change, use the marked,
separate lane. Travellers cheques are NOT accepted but
Visa card can be used as an alternative.

3. To escape the motorway tolls and the most congested
routes, follow the Green Arrow routes (Itineraires Bis)
marked by green arrows. Traffic should be less and the
routes are designed to provide the holiday maker with a
more attractive route.

4. Minimum age for driving an imported car or motorbike in
France is 18. Insurance is compulsory and the additional
Green Card of Insurance is recommended.

5. Headlights must not dazzle oncoming drivers and may
need to be altered using either headlamp converters or
beam deflectors. Headlamps should have a removable
yellow plastic paint added to the lenses or deflectors with
yellow lenses to ensure that a yellow beam is emitted.

6. A warning triangle and hazard warning lights are
compulsory for all vehicles in the event of accident or
breakdown. Free emergency telephones are available
every 2 km on motorways and 24 hour services can be found
on motorways at regular intervals of about 40 kilometres.

7. PETROL – **L'ESSENCE**

| Super | **– de super** | ordinary | **– d'ordinaire** |
| lead-free | **– sans plomb** | diesel | **– gazole** |

BON VOYAGE

DISCOUNT LES ROUTIERS

As part of a unique deal for Club Routiers members and
Guide users, special concessions have been negotiated with
French Routiers' motorway restaurant chains. On production
of a current edition of this Guide, or your Club Routiers
membership card, you are entitled to a special 'Menu
Routier', priced at around 40FF, with wine, coffee, and
service included.

NB. To obtain this price concession, you must show your
Guide or card to the personnel concerned before ordering
your meal. If they show ignorance of this concession, ask for
the manager.

If you wish to make any comments about the Routiers
Motorway Service, please use the form which is available on
request from any motorway restaurant displaying the sign.

JOIN CLUB ROUTIERS FREE

You've bought the Guide – now join Club Routiers FREE – and save £5 on the registration fee.

The Club promotes quality and value in travel, food and wine in both Great Britain and in France. Membership benefits include:

- Your Club Routiers membership card which entitles you to special concessions at selected Relais Routiers in France and Britain.
- The quarterly 'Bon Viveur' magazine.
- A privileged price of £5.99 (including postage and packaging) when you buy additional copies of either Routiers guide.
- A special pre-publication offer on the 1991 Routiers guides to Britain and France.
- The Routiers Motoring Service – with discounts off Europ Assistance's overseas motoring services, personal travel insurance and U.K. motoring services.
- Discounts off all holidays in the Paris and France 1990 brochures through the French Travel Service.

To join Club Routiers simply complete the questionnaire on the opposite page.

CLUB ROUTIERS QUESTIONNAIRE

ABOUT LES ROUTIERS

In order to improve the package we offer you please complete the following:–

1. Have you bought a Routiers Guide Before?   [YES/NO]
If YES, in what year did you buy your last Routiers Guide?

_____

2. Was your last Routiers Guide?

The British Guide   ☐   (Please tick as applicable)

The French Guide   ☐

Both   ☐

3. How did you first find out about Les Routiers?

_____

4. Where did you buy this Guide from?

_____

5. How many times do you eat at a British Routiers each year?

_____

6. How many nights do you stay in a British Routiers each year?

_____

7. How often do you refer to this guide?

_____

8. How many people, apart from yourself, refer to this Guide?

_____

9. What other guides do you use? (Please specify)

_____

_____

10. What does the Les Routiers sign mean to you?

_____

ABOUT YOURSELF

We would like to get to know a little bit more about our members so that we can tailor the Club to cater for your specific needs:

1. Are you: Single ☐   Married ☐   (please tick as applicable)

2. Are you: Male ☐   Female ☐   (please tick as applicable)

3. Are you: 16–24 ☐   25–34 ☐   35–44 ☐   45–54 ☐   55+ ☐
   (tick as applicable)

4. What is your occupation?

_____

5. What type of car do you drive? What year?

_____

6. What Sunday newspaper do you read?

_____

7. How often do you visit France?

_____

8. How many times do you travel on a continental ferry? (e.g. once every three years.)

_____

NAME _____

ADDRESS _____

_____

_____ POSTCODE _____

Send your questionnaire to:

Routiers Limited, 354 Fulham Road, London SW10 9UH.

Closing date for receipt of this application form questionnaire for free Club Routiers registration; 31st December 1990.

Please allow at least 30 days for delivery of your registration pack.

LIST OF MAPS

17

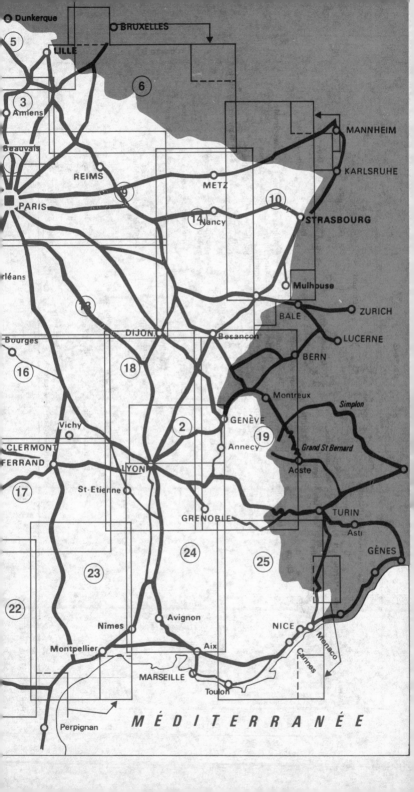

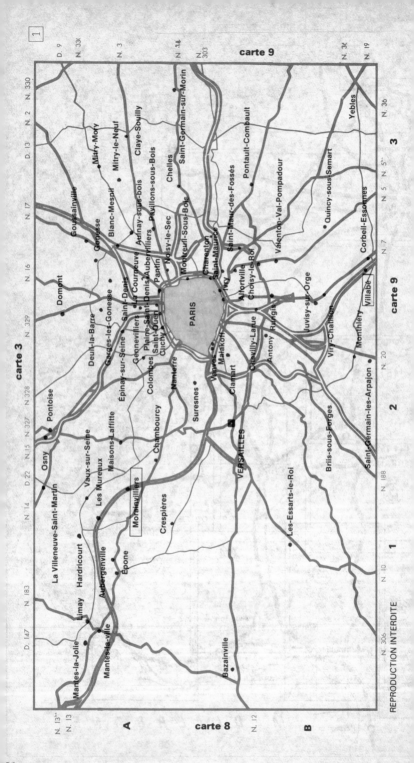

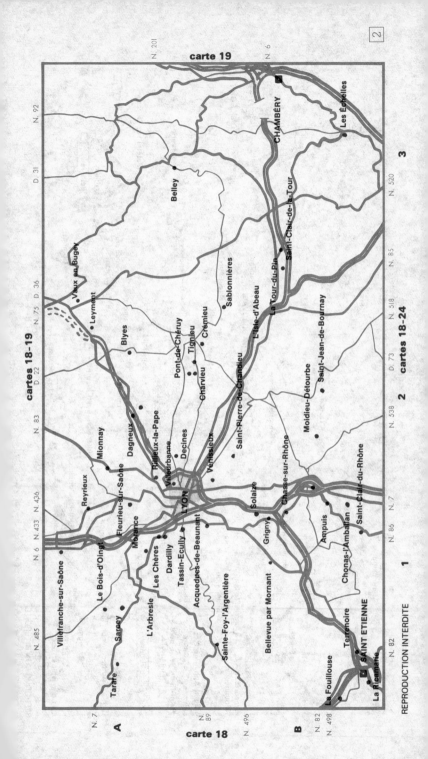

carte 19

cartes 18-19

carte 18

cartes 18-24

Villefranche-sur-Saône
Tarare
Sapey
Le Bois-d'Oingt
L'Arbresle
Reyrieux
Fleurieu-sur-Saône
Morancé
Les Chères
Dardilly
Tassin-Ecully
Acquedues-de-Beaunant
Sainte-Foy-l'Argentière
Bellevue par Mornant
Mionnay
Dagneux
Rillieux-la-Pape
Décines
Villeurbanne
LYON
Vénissieux
Solaize
Grigny
Ampuis
Chonas-l'Amballan
Saint-Clair-du-Rhône
Chasse-sur-Rhône
Terrenoire
SAINT ETIENNE
La Ricamarie
La Fouillouse
Leyment
Vaux-en-Bugey
Blyes
Pont-de-Chéruy
Tignieu
Charvieu
Crémieu
Sablonnières
Saint-Pierre-de-Chandieu
L'Isle-d'Abeau
La Tour-du-Pin
Saint-Jean-de-Bournay
Moidieu-Détourbe
Belley
Saint-Clair-de-la-Tour
CHAMBÉRY
Les Échelles

N. 201
N. 92
D. 31
D. 36
D. 75
D. 22
N. 83
N. 436
N. 433
N. 6
N. 485
N. 7
N. 89
N. 496
N. 82
N. 498
N. 82
N. 86
N. 7
N. 538
D. 73
N. 518
N. 85
N. 520
N. 6

A
B
1
2
3

21

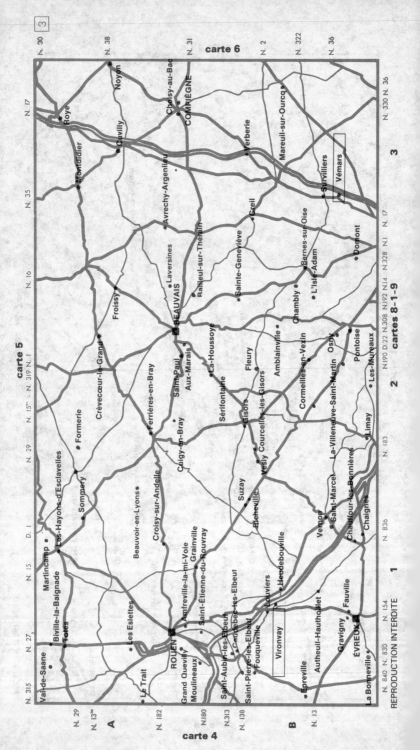

carte 5

carte 6

carte 4

cartes 8-1-9

3

2

1

A

B

N. 30

N. 38

N. 31

N. 2

N. 322

N. 36

N. 17

N. 35

N. 16

N. 15" · N. 319 N. 1

D. 1

N. 29

N. 15

N. 27

N. 315

N. 330 N. 36

N. 17

N. 328 N.1

N.190 D.22 N.308 N.192 N.14

N. 183

N. 836

N. 154

N. 840 N. 830

N. 13

N. 29

N. 13bis

NJ80

N.313

N. 138

N. 182

Noyon

Roye

Montdidier

Cuvilly

Choisy-au-Bac

COMPIÈGNE

Verberie

Mareuil-sur-Ourcq

Survilliers

Vémars

Creil

Bernes-sur-Oise

Dornont

L'Isle-Adam

Avrechy-Argenlieu

Laversines

Ralleuil-sur-Thérain

Sainte-Geneviève

Chambly

Froissy

BEAUVAIS

Saint-Paul-
Aux-Marais

La-Houssoye

Fleury

Amblainville

Cormeilles-en-Vexin

Osny

Pontoise

Les-Mureaux

Formerie

Crèvecœur-le-Grand

Ferrières-en-Bray

Sérifontaine

Gisors

Courcelles-les-Gisors

La-Villeneuve-Saint-Martin

Limay

Sommery

Les-Hayons-d'Esclavelles

Cuigy-en-Bray

Vesly

Suzay

Saint-Marcel

Vernon

Chaufour-les-Bonnières

Chaignes

Martincamp

Beauvoir-en-Lyons

Croisy-sur-Andelle

Bléheville

Boncheville

Heudebouville

Val-de-Saane

Biville-la-Baignade

Fotes

Les Eslettes

Autheville-la-mi-Voie

Grainville

Saint-Étienne-du-Rouvray

Louviers

Vernor

Le Trait

Grand Quevilly

Moulineaux

ROUEN

Saint-Aubin-les-Elbeuf

Caudebec-les-Elbeuf

Saint-Pierre-les-Elbeuf

Fouqueville

Vironvay

Epreville

Autheuil-Hauthollet

Gravigny

Fauville

ÉVREUX

La Bonneville

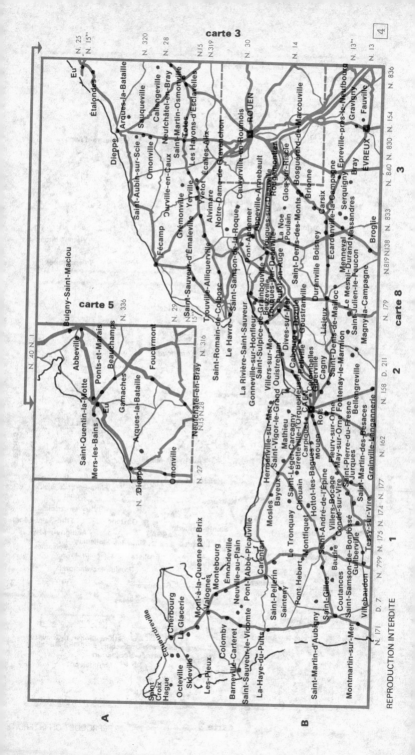

carte 3

carte 5

carte 8

REPRODUCTION INTERDITE

23

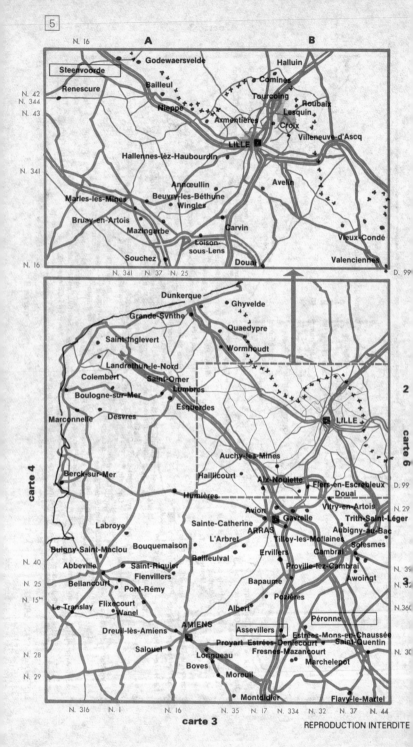

24

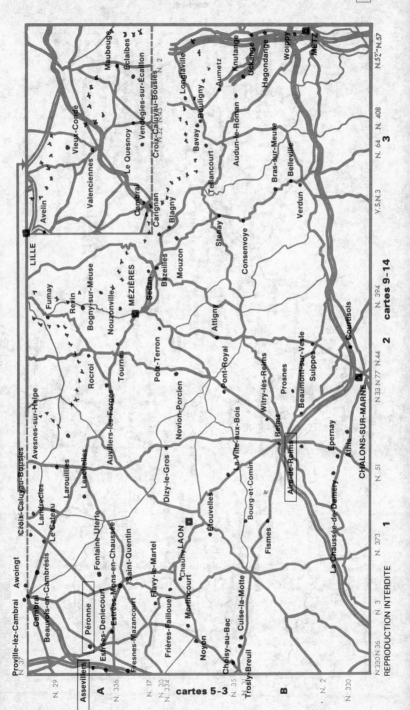

6

Proville-lez-Cambrai
Awoingt
N. 37

Croix-Caluyau-Bousies

Maubeuge
Éclaibes
Vendegies-sur-Écaillon
N. 2

Vieux-Condé
Valenciennes
Le Quesnoy
Cambrai

Avelin
LILLE

Longfaville
Bavay
Audun-e-Roman
Knutange
Uckange
Hagondange
Woippy
METZ

Télancourt
Blagny
Carignan

Aumetz
Boulligny

N. 52-N. 57

Fumay
Revin
Bogny-sur-Meuse
Nouzonville
MÉZIÈRES
Sedan
Bazeilles
Mouzon

Bras-sur-Meuse
Belleville
Verdun

N. 64   N. 408   3

Rocroi
Auvillers-les-Forges
Tournès
Poix-Terron
Attigny
Stenay
Consenvoye

V.S.N.3

Avesnes-sur-Helpe

N. 394

Novion-Porcien
Pont-Royal
Beaumont-sur-Vesle
Suippes
Courtisols

cartes 9-14

Landrecies
Le Cateau
Leschelles
Dizy-le-Gros
La-Ville-aux-Bois
Witry-lès-Reims
Prosnes
Reims

N. 33 N. 77 N. 44   2

Larouillies
Fontaine-Uterte

Bourg-et-Comin
CHALONS-SUR-MARNE

Beauvois-en-Cambrésis
Saint-Quentin
Chauny LAON
Élouvelles
Fismes
Épernay
Aÿhis

N. 51   1

Cambrai

Estrées-Mons-en-Chaussée
Flavy-le-Martel
Morlincourt
Cuise-la-Motte
La-Chaussée-de-Damery

N. 373

Estrées-Deniecourt
Péronne

Fresnes-Mazancourt
Frières-Faillouel
Noyon
Choisy-au-Bac

N. 3   REPRODUCTION INTERDITE

N. 29

Asseviller·s

N. 336

N. 17
N. 30
N. 334   cartes 5-3

N. 31
Trosly-Breuil

N330-N.36

A

B

N. 2

N. 330

25

carte 8

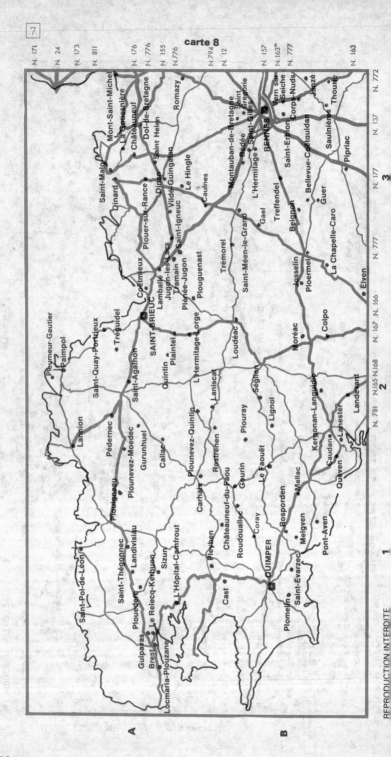

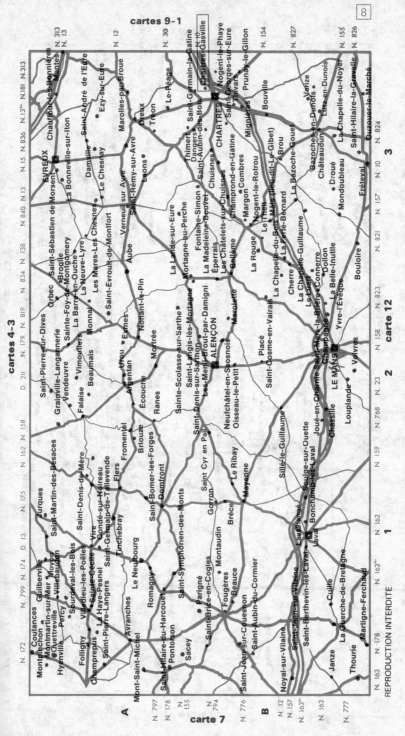

REPRODUCTION INTERDITE

carte 7

cartes 4-3

carte 12

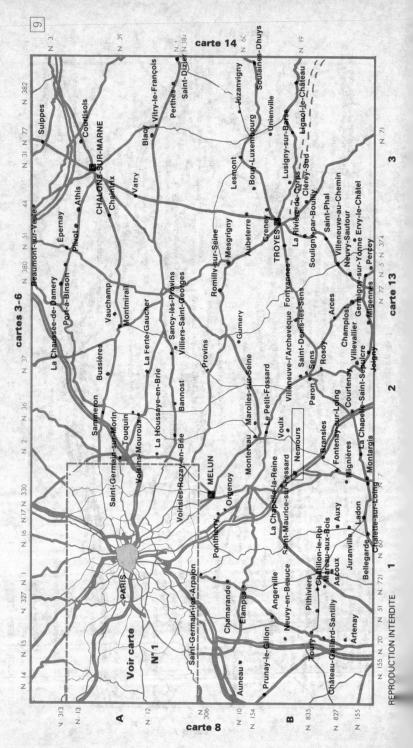

carte 14

cartes 3-6

N 3
N 35
N 1
N 384
N 60
N 19

N 77
N 31
N 382
44
N 51
N 380
N 37
N 36
N 2
N 330
N 17
N 16
N 1
N 327
N 15
N 20
N 14
N 13

Suippes
Cobrisols
Saint-Dizier
Jûzanvigny
Soulaines-Dhuys
Beaumont-sur-Vesle
Épernay
Vitry-le-François
Perthes
Unienville
Lesmont
CHALONS-SUR-MARNE
Chaintrix
Blacy
Bouy-Luxembourg
Lusigny-sur-Barse
Athis
Vatry
La Chaussée-de-Damery
Piwot
Ignol-le-Château
Port-à-Binson
Clérey-Sud
Vauchamp
Grenet
Montmirail
Aubeterre
La Rivière-de-Corps
Bussières
La Ferté-Gaucher
Romilly-sur-Seine
Mesgrigny
TROYES
Saint-Phal
Sancy-lès-Provins
Souligny-par-Bouilly
Villeneuve-au-Chemin
Villiers-Saint-Georges
Ervy-le-Châtel
Neuvy-Sautour
Sammeron
Gumery
Provins
Germigny-sur-Yonne
Perçey
Touquin
Fontvannes
Migennes
Saint-Denis-lès-Sens
Arces
La Houssaye-en-Brie
Bannost
Champlost
Voisins-Mouroux
Marolles-sur-Seine
Sens
Rosoy
Villevallier
Voisins-Rozay-en-Brie
Le Petit-Fossard
Paron
Courtenay
Joigny
Voulx
La Chapelle-Saint-Sépulcre
Monterau
Nemours
Montereau
Bransles
MELUN
Fontenay-sur-Loing
Orgenoy
La Chapelle-la-Reine
Mignières
Montargis
Saint-Germain-sur-Morin
La Chapelle-la-Reine
Pontthierry
Saint-Maurice-sur-Aveyron
Chatillon-le-Roi
Auxy
Saint-Germain-lès-Arpajon
Mareau-aux-Bois
Ladon
Ascoux
Juranville
Chamarande
Bellegarde
Angerville
Châlette-sur-Loing
PARIS
Neuvy-en-Beauce
Pithiviers
Étampes
Toury
Prunay-le-Gillon
Château-Gaillard-Santilly
Auneau
Artenay

Voir carte
N° 1

carte 13
carte 8

N 77
N 5
N 374
N 77
N 71
2
1
N 60
N 721
N 7
N 155
N 51
N 154
N 835
N 827
N 306
N 313
N 12
N 10
N 155

A
B

3
2
1

REPRODUCTION INTERDITE

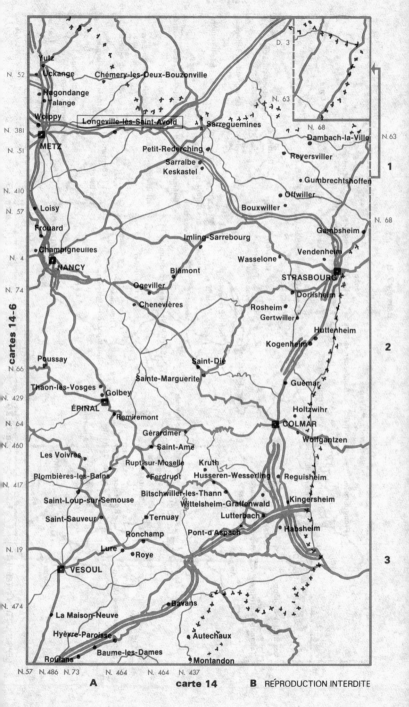

A carte 14 B RÉPRODUCTION INTERDITE

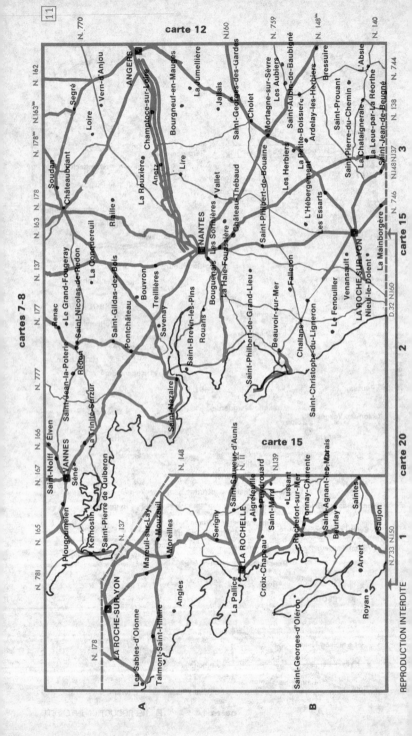

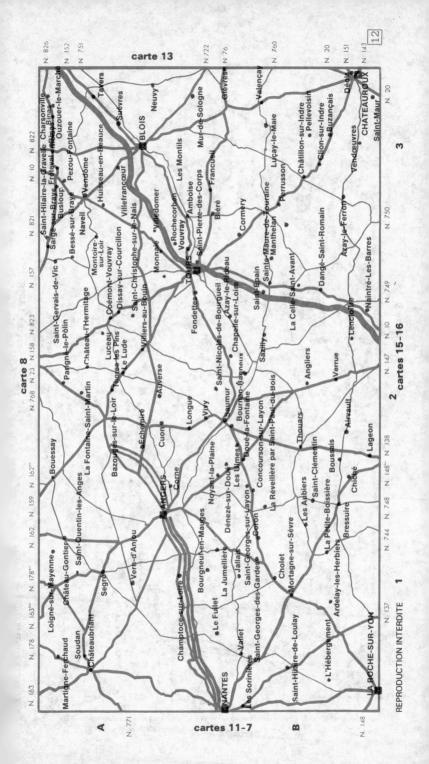

31

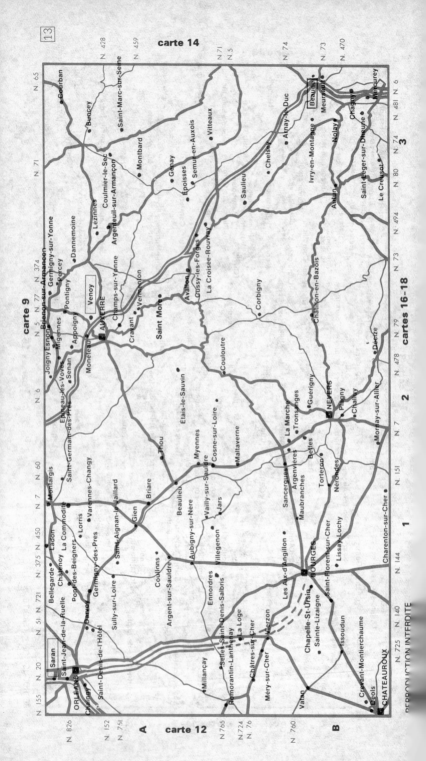

carte 14

carte 9

carte 12

cartes 16-18

N. 428
N. 459
N. 71
N. 5
N. 74
N. 73
N. 470
N. 65
N. 481 N. 6
N. 74
N. 80
N. 494
N. 73
N. 79
N. 478
N. 7
N. 151
N. 144
N. 140
N. 725
N. 71
N. 374
N. 77
N. 5
N. 6
N. 60
N. 7
N. 450
N. 375
N. 721
N. 51
N. 20
N. 155
N. 826
N. 152
N. 751
N. 765
N. 724
N. 76
N. 760

Courban
Buncey
Saint-Marc-sur-Seine
Coulmier-le-Sec
Montbard
Genay
Époisses
Semur-en-Auxois
Vitteaux
Atnay-le-Duc
Beaune
Meursault
Mercurey
Lézinnes
Argenteuil-sur-Armançon
Chelsea
Ivry-en-Montagne
Nolay
Chagny
Saint-Léger-sur-Dheune
Le Creusot
Autun
Dannemoine
Percey
Pontigny
Appoign
Venoy
Champs-sur-Yonne
Vermenton
Avallon
Crussy-les-Forges
La Croisee-Rouvray
Saulieu
Chatillon-en-Bazois
Germigny-sur-Yonne
Brienon-sur-Armançon
Joigny Esnon
Migennes
Senan
Saint-Germain-des-Pres
Moneteau
AUXERRE
Cravant
Saint More
Corbigny
Dietze
Montargis
La Commodité
Chatenoy
Pop. des-Beignets
Lorris
Varennes-Changy
Briare
Gien
Beaulieu
Vailly-sur-Sauldre
Jars
Thou
Myennes
Cosne-sur-Loire
Maltaverne
Couloutre
Etais-le-Sauvin
NEVERS
Plagny
Challuy
Mornay-sur-Allier
La Marche
Tronsanges
Guerigny
Sancergues
Argenvières
Belfes
Nérondes
Mornay-sur-Aller
Bellegarde
Ladon
Saint-Aignan-le-Jaillard
Germigny-des-Pres
Ouzer
Sully-sur-Loire
Coullons
Argent-sur-Sauldre
Villegenon
Aubigny-sur-Nere
Maubranches
Torteron
Charenton-sur-Cher
Saran
Saint-Jean-de-la-Ruelle
Saint-Denis-de-l'Hôtel
Chancy
ORLEANS
Millançay
Remorantin-Lanthenay
La Loge
Châtres-sur-Cher
Selles-Saint-Denis-Salbris
Mery-sur-Cher
Vierzon
Chapelle-St-Ursin
Sainte-Lizaigne
BOURGES
Les Aix-d'Angillon
Saint-Florent-sur-Cher
Lissay-Lochy
Issoudun
Valon
Crevant-Montierchaume
Déols
CHATEAUROUX
Ennordres

A

B

1

2

3

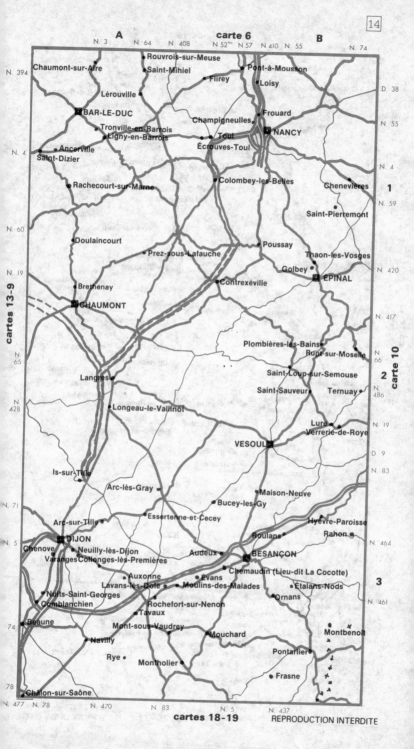

carte 6

N. 3   A   N. 64   N. 408   N. 52 bis   N. 57   N. 410   N. 55   B   N. 74

N. 394
Chaumont-sur-Aire
Rouvrois-sur-Meuse
Saint-Mihiel
Flirey
Pont-à-Mousson
Loisy
D. 38
Lérouville
N. 55
BAR-LE-DUC
Champigneulles
Frouard
NANCY
Tronville-en-Barrois
Ligny-en-Barrois
Toul
Écrouves-Toul
N. 4
Ancerville
Saint-Dizier
N. 4
Rachecourt-sur-Marne
Colombey-les-Belles
Chenevières
1
N. 59
Saint-Pierremont
N. 60
Doulaincourt
Prez-sous-Lafauche
Poussay
Thaon-les-Vosges
N. 420
Golbey
EPINAL
N. 19
Brethenay
Contrexéville
N. 417
CHAUMONT
Plombières-les-Bains
Rupt-sur-Moselle
N. 66
N. 65
Langres
Saint-Loup-sur-Semouse
2
Saint-Sauveur
Ternuay
N. 486
N. 428
Longeau-le-Vallinot
Lure
N. 19
Verrerie-de-Roye
VESOUL
D. 9
Is-sur-Tille
N. 83
N. 71
Arc-lès-Gray
Maison-Neuve
Bucey-lès-Gy
Essertenne-et-Cecey
Hyèvre-Paroisse
Arc-sur-Tille
Roulans
Rahon
N. 464
N. 5
DIJON
Chenôve
Neuilly-lès-Dijon
Audeux
BESANÇON
Varanges Collonges-lès-Premières
Chemaudin (Lieu-dit La Cocotte)
Auxonne
Evans
Étalans-Nods
3
Lavans-lès-Dole
Moulins-des-Malades
N. 461
Nuits-Saint-Georges
Ornans
Comblanchien
Rochefort-sur-Nenon
74   Beaune
Tavaux
Mont-sous-Vaudrey
Montbenoît
Navilly
Mouchard
Rye
Pontarlier
Montholier
78
Chalon-sur-Saône
Frasne
N. 477   N. 78   N. 470   N. 83   N. 5   N. 437

cartes 18-19   REPRODUCTION INTERDITE

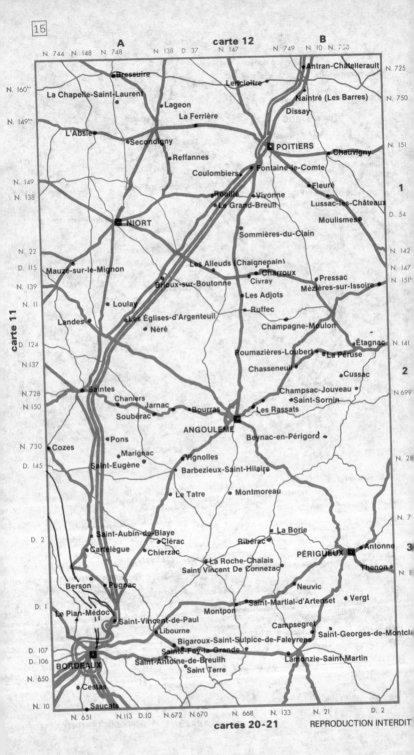

carte 12

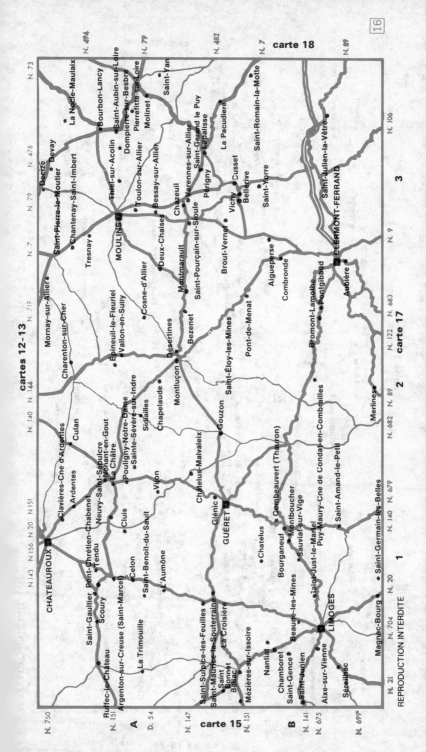

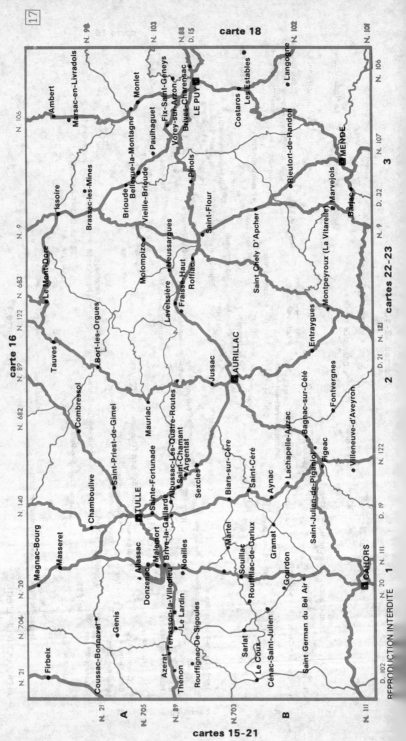

carte 18

carte 16

cartes 22-23

cartes 15-21

N. 98
N. 103
N. 88
D. 15
N. 102
N. 101
N. 106
N. 106
N. 9
N. 122
N. 683
N. 89
N. 682
N. 140
N. 20
N. 704
N. 21
N. 705
N. 89
N. 703
N. III
N. 107
D. 32
N. 9
N. 121
D. 21
D. 19
N. 122
N. III
N. 20
D. 102

REPRODUCTION INTERDITE

Ambert
Marsac-en-Livradois
Monlet
Fix-Saint-Geneys
Brives-Charensac
LE PUY
Les Estables
Langogne
Costaros
Paulhaguet
Vorey-sur-Arzon
Brioude
Bellevue-la-Montagne
Vieille-Brioude
MENDE
Rieutort-de-Randon
Brassac-les-Mines
Issoire
Pinols
Saint-Flour
Marvejols
Bagnac
Le Mont-Dore
Molompize
Neussargues
Lavensière
Fraisse-Haut
Roffiac
Saint Chely D'Apcher
Montpeyroux (La Vitarelle)
Tauves
Bort-les-Orgues
Entraygues
AURILLAC
Jussac
Fontvergnes
Combressol
Mauriac
Baniac-sur-Célé
Villeneuve-d'Aveyron
Saint-Priest-de-Gimel
Albussac-Les-Quatre-Routes
Saint-Chamant
Argentat
Biars-sur-Cère
Lachapelle-Auzac
Figeac
Chamboulive
Sainte-Fortunade
Sexcles
Saint-Céré
Aynac
Saint-Julien-de-Piganiol
TULLE
Magnac-Bourg
Masseret
Malemort
Brive-la-Gaillarde
Noailles
Martel
Souillac
Gramat
Gourdon
Allassac
Rouffignac-de-Carlux
CAHORS
Genis
Donzenac
Terrasson-la-Villedieu
Le Lardin
Firbeix
Coussac-Bonneval
Azerat
Thenon
Rouffignac-De-Sigoules
Sarlat
Le Coux
Cénac-Saint-Julien
Saint German du Bel Air

A

B

1

2

3

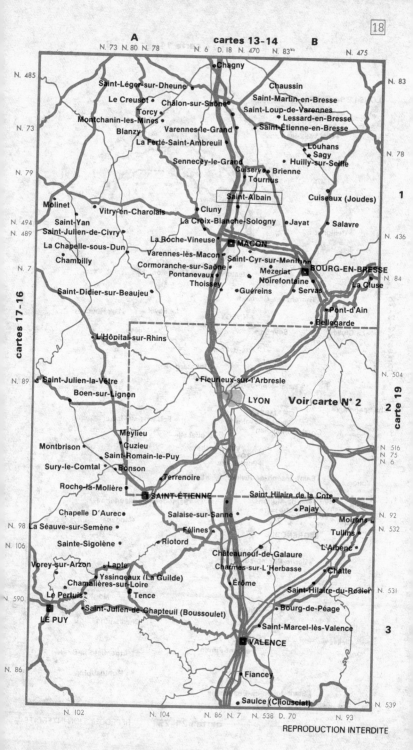

cartes 13-14

A   N. 73 N. 80 N. 78   N. 6 D. 18 N. 470   N. 83bis   B   N. 475

N. 485

Chagny

N. 83

Saint-Léger-sur-Dheune
Chaussin

Le Creusot
Saint-Martin-en-Bresse

Torcy   Chálon-sur-Saône
Saint-Loup-de-Varennes

N. 73

Montchanin-les-Mines
Lessard-en-Bresse

Blanzy   Varennes-le-Grand
Saint-Étienne-en-Bresse

N. 78

La Ferté-Saint-Ambreuil
Louhans

Sagy

Sennecey-le-Grand
Huilly-sur-Seille

N. 79

Cuisery   Brienne

Tournus

Saint-Albain

Cuiseaux (Joudes)   1

Molinet
Vitry-en-Charolais   Cluny

N. 494   Saint-Yan
La Croix-Blanche-Sologny   Jayat   Salavre

N. 489   Saint-Julien-de-Civry

La Chapelle-sous-Dun   La Roche-Vineuse   MACON   N. 436

N. 7   Chambilly   Varennes-lès-Macon
Saint-Cyr-sur-Menthon

Cormoranche-sur-Saône   Mezeriat   BOURG-EN-BRESSE   N. 84

Pontanevaux   Noirefontaine

Saint-Didier-sur-Beaujeu   Thoissey   Servas   La Cluse

Guéreins

Pont-d'Ain

Bellegarde

cartes 17-16

L'Hôpital-sur-Rhins

N. 504

N. 89   Saint-Julien-la-Vêtre
Fleurieux-sur-l'Arbresle

Boen-sur-Lignon
LYON   Voir carte N° 2   **carte 19**   2

Meylieu
Guzieu

Montbrison
N. 516

Saint-Romain-le-Puy   N. 75

Sury-le-Comtal   Bonson   N. 6

Roche-la-Molière   Terrenoire

SAINT-ÉTIENNE   Saint Hilaire de la Côte

Chapelle D'Aurec   Salaise-sur-Sanne   Pajay   N. 92

N. 98   La Séauve-sur-Semène   Félines   Moirans

Tullins   N. 532

Sainte-Sigolène   Riotord   L'Albenc

N. 106

Vorey-sur-Arzon   Lapte   Châteauneuf-de-Galaure   Chatte

Yssingeaux (La Guilde)   Charmes-sur-L'Herbasse

Chamalières-sur-Loire   Érôme   Saint-Hilaire-du-Rosier   N. 531

Le Pertuis   Tence

N. 590   Saint-Julien-de-Chapteuil (Boussoulet)   Bourg-de-Péage

LE PUY   Saint-Marcel-lès-Valence

3

VALENCE

N. 86

Fiancey

N. 102   N. 104   N. 86 N. 7   N. 538 D. 70   N. 93   Saulce (Cliousclat)   N. 539

37

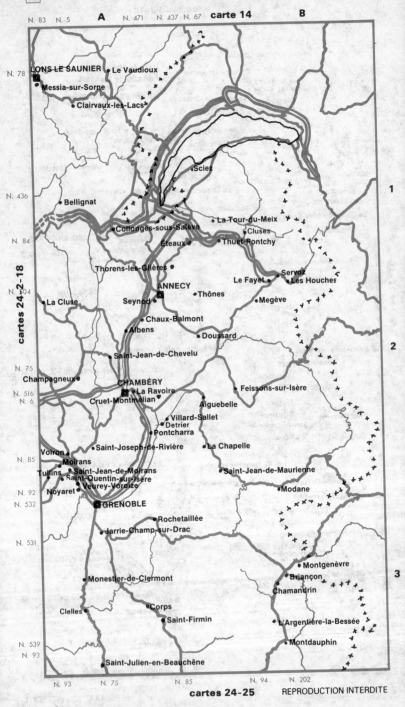

N. 78
LONS LE SAUNIER　● Le Vaudioux
● Messia-sur-Sorne

● Clairvaux-les-Lacs

● Sciez

N. 436
● Bellignat

N. 84
● Collonges-sous-Salève
● La Tour-du-Meix
● Cluses
● Eteaux　● Thuet-Pontchy

cartes 24-2-18

N. 04
● Thorens-les-Glières
● Le Fayet　● Servoz
ANNECY　● Thônes　● Les Houches
● La Cluse　● Seynod　● Megève
● Chaux-Balmont
● Albens
● Doussard
● Saint-Jean-de-Chevelu

N. 75
● Champagneux
CHAMBÉRY
N. 516　● La Ravoire
N. 6　● Cruet-Montmélian　● Feissons-sur-Isère
● Aiguebelle
● Villard-Sallet
● Detrier
● Pontcharra
N. 85
● Voiron　● Saint-Joseph-de-Rivière　● La Chapelle
● Moirans
● Saint-Jean-de-Moirans
● Tullins　● Saint-Jean-de-Maurienne
N. 92　● Saint-Quentin-sur-Isère
● Noyaret　● Veurey-Voroize
N. 532　● Modane
■ **GRENOBLE**

N. 531　● Rochetaillée
● Jarrie-Champ-sur-Drac

● Montgenèvre
● Briançon
N. 93　● Monestier-de-Clermont　● Chamandrin
● Corps
● Clelles　● Saint-Firmin
● L'Argentière-la-Bessée
N. 539
N. 93　● Montdauphin

● Saint-Julien-en-Beauchêne

N. 93　N. 75　N. 85　N. 94　N. 202　1 2 3

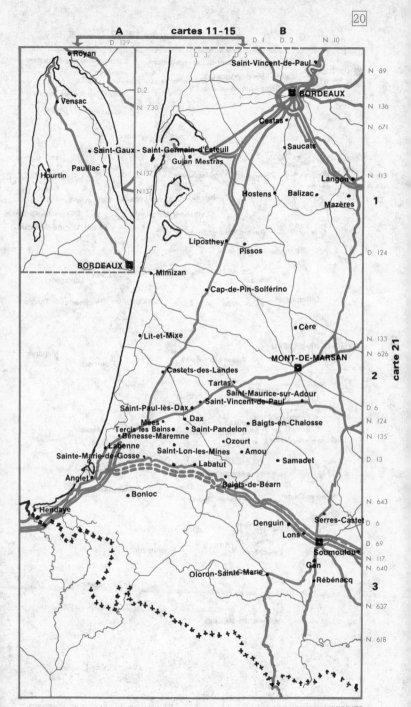

cartes 11-15

A D 129 **B** D 1 D 2 N 10

Royan

D 3 D 5

Saint-Vincent-de-Paul

N 89

Vensac

D.2 BORDEAUX

N 730 N 136

Cestas N 671

Saucats

Saint-Gaux - Saint-Germain-d'Esteuil

Gujan Mestras

N 137 Langon N 113

Paulllac N 137

Hostens Balizac 1

Hourtin Mazères

BORDEAUX

Liposthey D 124

Pissos

Mimizan

Cap-de-Pin-Solférino

Cère

Lit-et-Mixe N 133

N 626

MONT-DE-MARSAN

Castets-des-Landes 2

Tartas

Saint-Maurice-sur-Adour

Saint-Paul-lès-Dax Saint-Vincent-de-Paul D 6

Mées Dax N 124

Tercis les Bains Saint-Pandelon Baigts-en-Chalosse N 135

Benesse-Maremne

Labenne Ozourt

Sainte-Marie-de-Gosse Saint-Lon-les-Mines Amou D 13

Anglet Labatut Samadet

Bonloc N 643

Baigts-de-Béarn

Hendaye Serres-Castet D 6

Denguin

Lons

Soumoulou D 69

Gan N 117

N 640

Oloron-Sainte-Marie Rébénacq 3

N 637

N 618

REPRODUCTION INTERDITE

carte 21

39

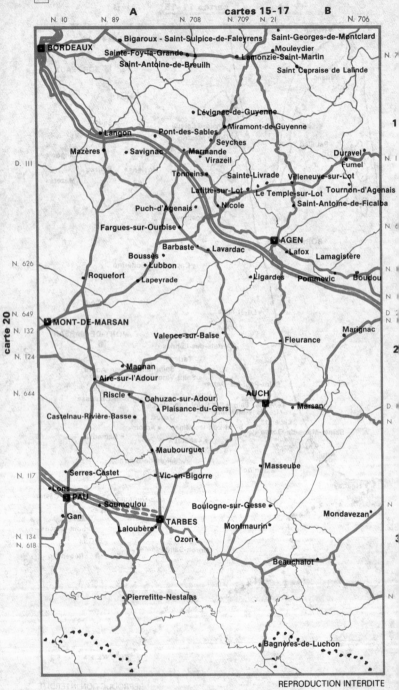

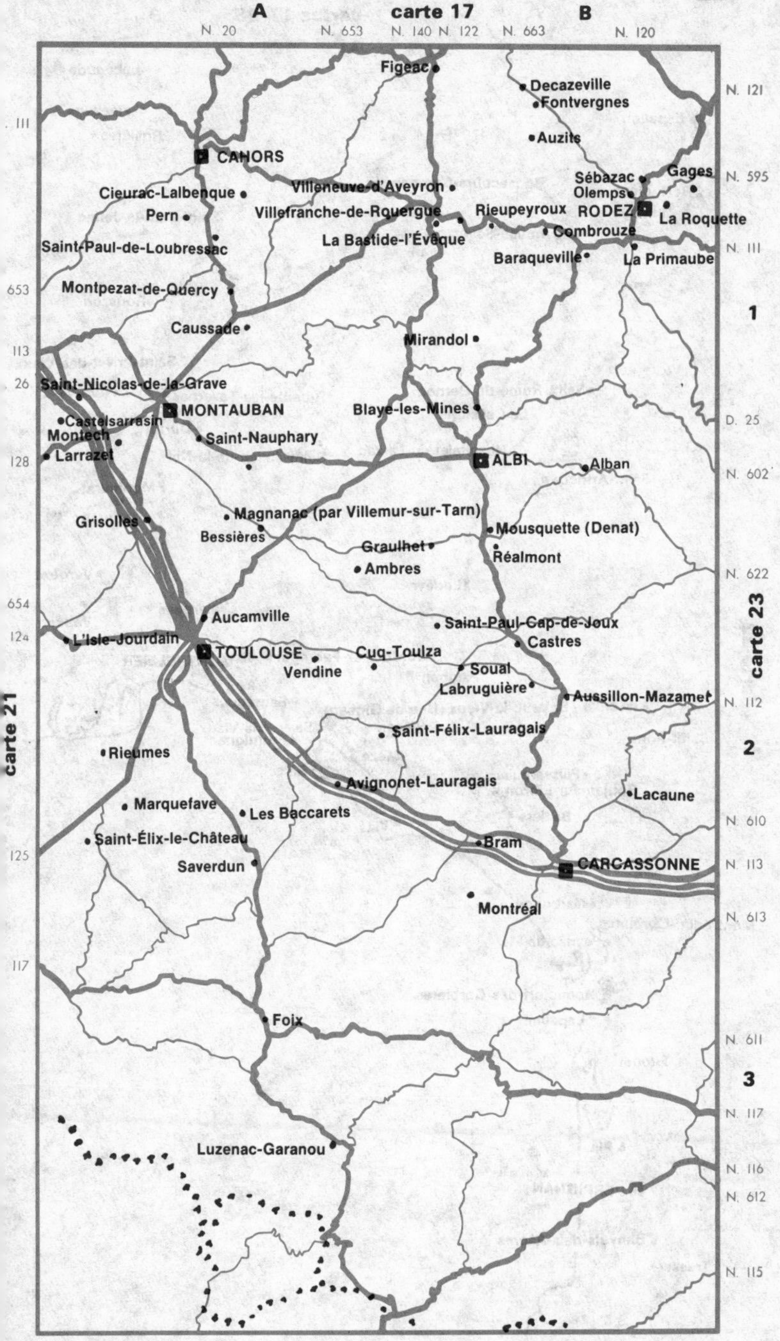
A
carte 17
B
N. 20
N. 653
N. 140
N. 122
N. 663
N. 120
N. 121
N. 595
N. 111
1
D. 25
N. 602
N. 622
carte 23
N. 112
2
N. 610
N. 113
N. 613
N. 611
3
N. 117
N. 116
N. 612
N. 115
111
653
113
26
128
654
124
carte 21
125
117
Figeac
Decazeville
Fontvergnes
Auzits
CAHORS
Sébazac
Gages
Olemps
RODEZ
La Roquette
Cieurac-Lalbenque
Villeneuve-d'Aveyron
Pern
Villefranche-de-Rouergue
Rieupeyroux
Combrouze
La Bastide-l'Évêque
Saint-Paul-de-Loubressac
Baraqueville
La Primaube
Montpezat-de-Quercy
Caussade
Mirandol
Saint-Nicolas-de-la-Grave
MONTAUBAN
Blaye-les-Mines
Castelsarrasin
Montech
Saint-Nauphary
Larrazet
ALBI
Alban
Grisolles
Magnanac (par Villemur-sur-Tarn)
Bessières
Mousquette (Denat)
Graulhet
Réalmont
Ambres
Aucamville
Saint-Paul-Cap-de-Joux
L'Isle-Jourdain
Castres
TOULOUSE
Cuq-Toulza
Vendine
Soual
Labruguière
Aussillon-Mazamet
Saint-Félix-Lauragais
Rieumes
Avignonet-Lauragais
Lacaune
Marquefave
Les Baccarets
Saint-Élix-le-Château
Bram
Saverdun
CARCASSONNE
Montréal
Foix
Luzenac-Garanou

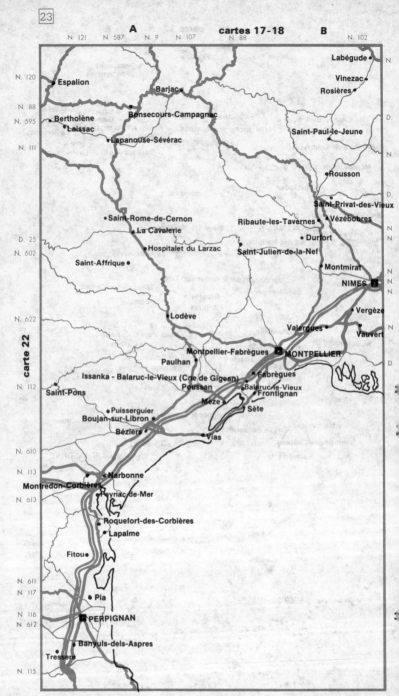

REPRODUCTION INTERDITE

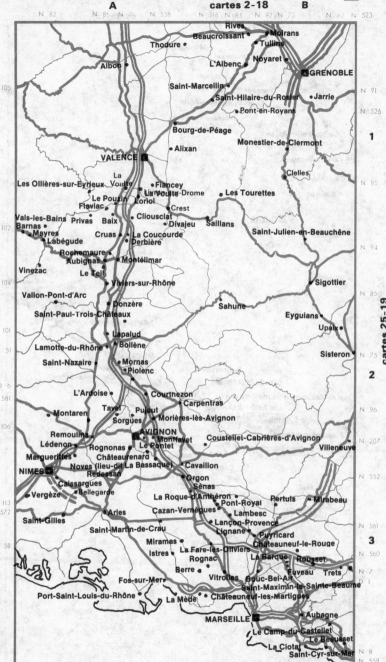

A **B**

N 82 N 86 N 538 N 518 N 85 N 92 N 75 N 93 N 523

Rives
Beaucroissant • • Moirans
Thodure • • Tullins
L'Albenc • Noyaret •
Aibon • • GRENOBLE

N 105
Saint-Marcellin •
Saint-Hilaire-du-Rosier • • Jarrie N 91
Pont-en-Royans • N 526

Bourg-de-Péage •
Monestier-de-Clermont • **1**
• Alixan

VALENCE •
Clelles • N 85

La
Les Ollières-sur-Eyrieux • Voulte
• Flancey
La Voulte-sur-Drome • Les Tourettes
Le Pouzin • Loriol
Flaviac • • Crest
Vals-les-Bains • Privas • Baix • Cliousclat
Barnas • • Divajeu • Saillans
Mayres • Cruas • La Coucourde Saint-Julien-en-Beauchêne N 102
Labégude • • Derbière N 94
Rochemaure •
Aubignas • • Montélimar
Vinezac •
Le Teil • N 104
• Viviers-sur-Rhône Sigottier • N 85
Vallon-Pont-d'Arc •
• Donzère Sahune • Eyguians • N 101
Saint-Paul-Trois-Châteaux • Upaix •
D 51
• Lapalud
Lamotte-du-Rhône • • Bollène Sisteron • N 75
Saint-Nazaire • • Mornas **2**
D 6 • Piolenc
N 581
L'Ardoise • • Courthezon
Montaren • Tavel • Pujaut • Carpentras N 96
Sorgues • Morières-lès-Avignon
N 106
Remoulins • • AVIGNON
Lédenon • • Montfavet Coustellet-Cabrières-d'Avignon
Rognonas • Le Pontet • Villeneuve N 207
Marguerittes • Châteaurenard
Noves (lieu-dit La Bassaque) • • Cavaillon
NIMES • Redessan
Caissargues • • Orgon N 552
Vergèze • • Bellegarde Sénas
N 113 La Roque-d'Anthéron • • Pertuis • Mirabeau
N 572 • Cazan-Vernègues Pont-Royal
Saint-Gilles • Arles • • Lambesc
Saint-Martin-de-Crau Lançon-Provence • N 561
Miramas • Lignane • Puyricard
D 58 Istres • La Fare-les-Oliviers Châteauneuf-le-Rouge • **3**
Rognac • La Barque • Rousset N 560
Berre • Fuveau • Trets
Vitrolles • Bouc-Bel-Air N 7
Fos-sur-Mer • Saint-Maximin-la-Sainte-Beaume
Port-Saint-Louis-du-Rhône • La Mède • • Châteauneuf-les-Martigues
MARSEILLE •
• Aubagne
Le Camp-du-Castellet
Le Beausset
La Ciotat N 8
Saint-Cyr-sur-Mer N 559

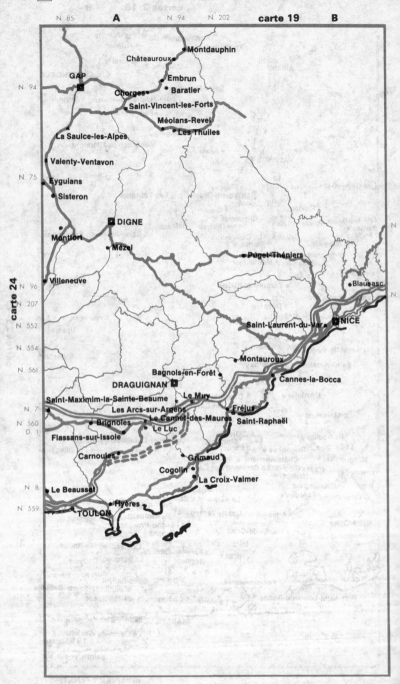

CASSEROLE RELAIS
AND TOURIST HOTELS
BY REGION

French Regions (Départements) by number

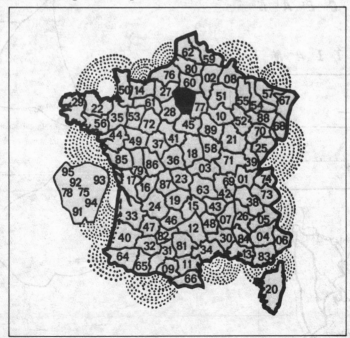

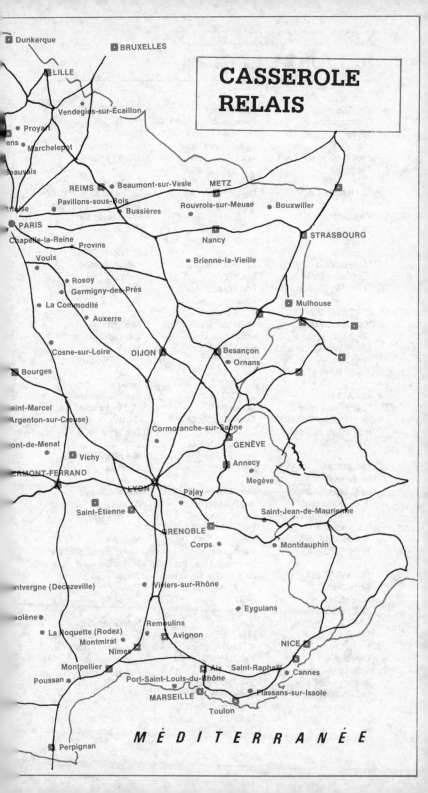

CASSEROLE RELAIS

LIST OF CASSEROLE RELAIS BY REGION

01 – AIN
Cormoranche-s-Saône
Auberge
chez la Mère Maritinet
Tel: 85-36-20-40

05 – HAUTES-ALPES

Eyguians
Le Relais de la Gare
Tel: 92-66-20-08

Montdauphin
Hôtel de la Gare
Tel: 92-45-03-08

07 – ARDECHE
Viviers sur Rhône
Chez-Espérardieu
Les Relais du Vivarais
Les Sautelles
Tel: 75-52-60-41

10 – AUBE
Brienne-la-Vieille
Le Relais des Routiers
Route Nationale 443
Tel: 25-77-81-94

11 – AUDE
Narbonne
La Caille qui Chante
Pont de Montredon
4 km Nle 113 Towards
Carcassonne
Tel: 68-42-04-36
Telex: 505097

12 – AVEYRON
Bertholène
Hôtel Bancarel
Forêt des Palanges
Route Nationale 88
Tel: 65-69-62-10

Espalion
Relais des Quatre
Routers ★ NN
Tel: 65-44-01-69

Fontvergnes-Decazeville
Rest des Usines
23, Fg. Desseligny
Tel: 65-43-15-88

La Roquette – Rodez
La Rocade
Anet-le-Château-4 Saisons
Tel: 65-67-10-44
and 67-17-12

13 – BOUCHES-DU-RHONE
Port St-Louis-du-Rhône
Hôtel Lazzeri –
Le Relais des Ouvriers
et des Routiers
59/64, Rue Jean-Jaurès
Tel: 42-86-01-28

14 – CALVADOS
Bayeaux –
Saint-Vigor-le-Grand
La Colombe
13, Route de Caen
Tel: 31-92-13-65 and
21-12-28

Saint-Martin-des-Besaces
La Renaissance
Tel: 31-68-72-65

Vandeuvre
Le Relais de la Gare
Saint-Pierre-sur-Dives
Tel: 31-40-32-77 or
92-77

Vire
Hôtel de France
4, Rue d'Aignaux
Tel: 31-68-00-35

16 – CHARENTE
Barbezieux
Le Relais de la Billette
Ladiville
Tel: 45-78-57-09

22 – COTES-DU-NORD
Dinan
La Marmite
Tel: 96-39-04-42

Lamballe
La Tour d'Argent
2, Rue du Dr Lavergne
Route Nationale 12
Tel: 96-31-01-37

24 – DORDOGNE
Cenac-St-Julien
La Promenade
Route Nationale 703
Tel: 53-28-36-87

Saint-Martial
L'Auberge de Saint-Martial
Tel: 53-80-35-74

Ornans
Hôtel le Progrès
11, Rue Jacques-Gervais
Tel: 81-62-16-79

28 – EURE-ET-LOIR
Chartres
Le Relais
Saint-Maurice
20, Rue Saint-Maurice
Tel: 37-21-13-89

Marolles
Au Relais de Marolles
44 Rue Georges
Bréant
Route Nationale 12
Tel: 37-43-20-50

Mignières
Le Relais Beauceron
Situated at junction of
Chartres autoroute
and the RN10
Tel: 37-26-46-21

Cast
Le Relais Saint-Gildas
11–13, Rue de
Kreisker
Tel: 98-73-54-76
and 73-55-43

Landivisiau
Le Terminus
94, Av. Foch
Tel: 98-68-02-00

Pont-Aven
Chez Mélanie et
Monique
Croissant-Kegoz
Tel: 98-06-03-09

Sizun
Hôtel des Voyageurs
2, Rue de l'Argaot
Tel:98-68-80-35

30 – GARD
Montmirat
Le Castelas
Route Nationale 110
Tel: 66-77-81-33

Remoulins
Auberge les Platanes
Castillon-du-Gard
Les Croisées
Tel: 66-37-10-69

33 – GIRONDE
Langon
Hôtel Restaurant
Darot
10, Rue Dotézac
Tel: 56-63-01-36

Poussan
Le Chalet
Chez Castor OS
La Douliere
Route Nationale 113
Tel: 67-78-24-74

35 – ILE-ET-
VILAINE
Bédée
Hôtel du Commerce
14, Place de l'Eglise
Tel: 99-07-00-37
and 07-00-76

La Guerche-de-
Bretagne
Relais du Pont
d'Anjou
11, Faubourg d'Anjou
Tel: 99-96-23-10

Montauban-de-Bretagne
L'Hôtel de France
34, Av. du Gl-de-
Gaulle
Tel: 99-06-40-19

36 – INDRE
Argenton-sur-Creuse
Saint-Marcel
Le Relais de Routiers
7, Route de
Châteauroux
Tel: 54-24-01-77

37 – INDRE-ET-
LOIRE
Villedomer
Le Relais des grands
vins de Touraine –
La Grande Vallée
Route Nationale 10
Tel: 47-55-01-05

38 – ISERE
Corps
Hôtel du Tilleul
Rue des Fosses
La Salette
Tel: 76-30-00-43

Pajay
Ma Petite Auberge
La Côte Saint-Audie
Tel: 74-54-26-06

40 – LANDES
Cap de Pin
Au Routier
Route Nationale 20
Tel: 58-07-20-54

Sainte-Marie-
de-Gosse
Les Routiers
Route Nationale 17
Tel: 59-56-32-02 and
56-34-17

41 – LOIR-ET-CHER
La Loge par Theillay
Relais de la Loge
Route Nationale 20
Tel: 54-83-37-20

Suèvres
La Providence
Chez Jacques
1, Place de la Mairie
Tel: 54-87-80-88

44 – LOIRE-
ATLANTIQUE
Pontchâteau
Auberge du Calvaire
6, Route de la Brière
Le Calvaire
Tel:40-01-61-65

Pontchâteau
Le Relais de Beaulieu
Tel: 40-01-60-58
and 01-63-58

Saint-Brévin-les-Pins
Le Relais du Marche
Place Henri-Bosle
Tel: 40-27-22-21

Saint-Gildas-
des-Bois
Le Relais des Routiers
27, rue du Pont
Tel: 40-01-42-15
and 01-44-70

45 – LOIRET
Commodité (La)
(par Solterre)
Auberge de la Route
Bleue
Route Nationale 7
Tel: 38-94-90-04

Germigny-des-Prés
Hôtel de la Place
Le Bourg
Châteauneufsur Loire
Tel: 38-58-20-14

46 – LOT
Gramat
Le Relais du Centre
(S.A.)
Place de la
République
Tel: 65-38-73-37

Saint-Paul-de-Loubressac
Le Relais de la
Madeleine
Tel: 62-21-98-08

49 – MAINE-ET-LOIRE
Jallais
Le Relais de la Croix
Verte
1. Rue Jean-de-Sagmond
Tel: 41-64-10-12
and 64-20-22

Saumur
Hôtel de la Gare
16, Av. David-d'Angers
Tel: 41-67-34-24

Vivy
Le Relais Saint-Paul
30, Rue Nationale
Tel: 41-52-50-13
and 52-41-65

50 – MANCHE
Coutances
Le Relais du Viaduc
25, Av. de Verdun
Tel: 33-45-02-68

Folligny
Le Lion d'Or
Le Repas
Tel: 33-61-32-77

Saint-Pierre-Langers
A la Grillade
La Havaudière
Tel: 33-48-83-71

Saint-Symporien-des-Monts Lapenty
Le Relais
du Bois Léger
Tel: 33-49-01-43

51 – MARNE
Beaumont sur-Vesle
La Maison du
Champagne
2, Rue du Port
Route Nationale 44
Tel: 26-03-92-45

54 MEURTHE-ET-MOSELLE
Nancy
Le Relais du Port
Chez Claude
5, Rue Henri-Bazin
Tel: 83-35-49-85

55 – MEUSSE
Rouvrois-sur-Meuse
Les Chaudrons Fleuris
Route Départ. 964
Tel: 29-90-13-43

56 – MORBIHAN
Elven
Le Relais de l'Argouët
36, Rue de l'Argouët
Tel: 97-53-32-98

Landevant
Le pelican
Route Nationale 165
Tel: 97-56-93-12

Sene
Le Poulfanc
Route de Vonnes
Route Nationale 165
Tel: 97-47-47-77

58 – NIEVRE
Cosne-sur-Loire
Les Trous Couleurs
21, Rue Saint Agnan
Tel: 86-28-23-50

59 – NORD
Vendegies s/Écaillon
Relais des Belles Filles
1111 Rte de Solesmes
Tel: 27-27-12-47

61 – ORNE
Domfront
Le Relais St-Michael
5, Rue du Mont-Saint-Michel
Place de La Gare
Route Nationale 176
Tel: 33-38-64-99

Nonant-le-Pin
Le Relais des Haras
Grande-Rue
Tel: 33-39-93-35

63 – PUY-DE-DOME
Pont-de-Menat
Chez Roger
Tel: 73-85-50-17

67 – BAS-RHIN
Bouxwiller
Le Soleil
71, Grande-Rue
Tel: 88-70-70-06

73 – SAVOIE
St-Jean-de-Maurienne
Restaurant du Champ
de Foire
Pl. du Champ-de-Foire
66 Rue Louis Sibue
Tel: 79-64-12-03

74 – HAUTE-SAVOIE
Mégève
Le Chalet des Fleurs
Rte Sallanches
Pont d'Arbon
Tel:50-21-21-46

76 – SEINE-MARITIME
Louvetot
Auberge du Grand
Méchant Loup
Caudebec-en-caux
Tel: 35-96-01-44

77 – SEINE-ET-MARNE
Bussières
Au Sans-Gêne
32, Rue de la Ferte-sous-Jouarre
Route Nationale 33
Tel: 60-22-50-18

Chapelle-la-Reine (La)
Le Relais
de la Salamandre
5, Rue du Dr Battesti
Tel: 64-24-30-03

Provins
La Cure d'Air
54, Av. du Gl-de-
Gaulle
Tel: 64-00-03-21

Vouex
La Bruyère
72, Grande-Rue
Tel: 64-31-92-41

80 – SOMME
Marchelepot
Restaurant oriental
Chez Dahmane
Route Nationale 17
Tel: 22-84-04-85

Proyart
La Raperie
Tel: 22-85-37-30

82 – TARN-ET-
GARONNE
Moissac
Le Relais Auvergnat
31, Bd. Camille-Delthil
Place du Palais
Tel: 63-04-93-02 and
63-04-02-58

Pommevic
Bonne Auberge
Route Nationale
Tel: 63-39-56-69

63 – VAR
Flassans Sur Issole
La Nocturne
Spualtier de la
Bourette
Route Nationale 7
Tel: 94-69-71-33

St. Raphael
Relais Bel Azur
247, Bld. de Provence
Tel: 94-95-14-08

84 – VAUCLUSE
Piolenc
Bar Restaurant
Le Commerce
Place Cours Coursin
Tel: 90-37-60-14

86 – VIENNE
Trimouille
Auberge Fleurie
Rue Octave-Bernard
Tel: 49-91-60-64

89 – YONNE
Auxerre
Le Saint-Nitasse
Route de Lyon-Auxille
Tel: 86-46-95-07

Rosoy
La Maison Blanche
Route Nationale 6
Tel: 86-97-13-01

93 – SEINE-SAINT-
DENIS
Pavillon-sous-Bois
Restaurant du Stade
31, Av. A.-France
Tel: 48-48-10-98

95 – VAL D'OISE
Pontoise
Restaurant de la Poste
68, Rue Pierre Butin
Tel: 30-32-47-72

BELGIQUE
Gerpinnes
(6280 Prov Hainaut)
Relas Routiers
Comme Chez Soi
251 Chaus de
Phillipeville
Route Nationale 5
Tel: 071-21-65-22

LUXEMBOURG
Wiltz
Auberge
Amsterdam-Wiltz
114, Rue du Dix-
Septembre
Tel: 95-73-24

51

TOURIST HOTELS

Dunkerque
Bailleul
BRUXELLES
LILLE
Bruay-en-Artois · Fumay
Amiens
Sedan
Beauvais
REIMS · Beaumont-sur-Vesle
Knutange
METZ
Rohrbach-les-Bitche
Bouxwiller
Courgivaux
Ancerville
Keskastel
PARIS
Corbeil-Essonne
Nancy
Kogenheim
STRASBOURG
Saint-Pierremont
Souligny
Doulaincourt
Sainte-Marguerite
rtenay
Percey
Gérardmer · Kruth
Bellegarde
Ronchamp
Mulhouse
Auxerre
Hyèvre-Paroisse
Cosne-sur-Loire
Bourges
DIJON
Ornans · Besançon
Chenove · Nuits-Saint-Georges
Ivry-en-Montagne
Nérondes
Nolay
Cormoranche-sur-Saône
Lapalisse
GENÈVE
Clairvaux-les-Lacs
Sciez
Vichy
Seynod · Meythet
Annecy
CLERMONT-FERRAND
LYON · Décines
Albens
Megève
Bonson
Chaux-Balmont
Saint-Étienne
Aiguebelle
arsac-en-Livradois
GRENOBLE
Le Vernet-la-Varenne
Monlet (près d'Allègre)
Vieille-Brioude
iac
Fraisse-Haut
Le Pouzin
Rochetaillée (par le Bourg-d'Oisans
Boussoulet
Aubignas
Saint-Firmin
Le Puy-en-Velay
Montdauphin
Félines
Embrun
Langogne
Rosières
Chorges
Marvejols · Balsièges
Alixan
Sahune
La Saulce-les-Alpes
lion
Bertholène
Saint-Nazaire
Le Lauzet
ges
Eyguians
Montauroux
Saint-Julien-de-la-Nef
Bollène
Avignon
Mézel
NICE
Nimes
Montfavet
Fréjus · Cannes
aint-Pons
Pont-Royal
Saint-Raphaël
Montpellier
Aix
Cuq-Toulza
Rognac
Balaruc-le-Vieux (Issanka)
Les Arcs-sur-Argens
Pont-Saint-Louis-du-Rhône
MARSEILLE
Labruguière
Fos-sur-Mer
Narbonne
Toulon
Perpignan
MÉDITERRANÉE

LIST OF TOURIST HOTELS BY REGION

01 – AIN
Cormoranche-s-Saône
Le Bourg
Auberge Chez le Mère Martinet
★★NN
Tel: 85-36-20-40

03 – ALLIER
Lapalisse
Le Chapon Doré
★NN
Av. du 8 Uisi 17 45
Route Nationale 7
Tel: 70-99-09-51

04 – ALPES DE HAUTE-PROVENCE
Le Lauzet
Le Relais du Lac
★NN
Le village
Tel: 92-85-51-07

Mezel
Le Relais de la Place
★NN
Tel: 92-35-51-05

05 – HAUTES-ALPES
Chorges
Le Relais des Alpes
★NN
Route Nationale 94
Tel: 92-50-60-08

Eyguians
Le Relais de la Gare
★NN
Tel: 92-66-20-08

Mont-Dauphn
Hôtel de la Gare
★NN
Tel: 92-45-03-08

La Saulce-les-Alpes
Le Relais de France
★NN
Tel: 92-54-20-08

Saint-Firmin
Le Relais
de la Trinité
★NN
Tel: 92-55-21-64

★07 – ARDÈCHE
Aubignas
Relais de la Gare
★NN
Opuartier de la Gare
Tel: 75-52-43-89

Felines
Relais de la Remise
★NN
Route Nationale 82
Tel: 75-34-82-22

Le Pouzin
Les Routiers
★NN
64, Rue Olivier de Serres
Tel: 75-63-83-45

Rosières
Les Cévennes
★NN
CD 104
Tel: 75-39-52-07

Vivieres Sur Rhone
Le Relais du Vivârais
Chez Esperandieu
★NN
Route Nationale 86
Lieu Dit les Sautelles
Tel: 75-52-60-41

08 – ARDENNES
Fumey
Le Relais du Lion
★NN
41, Rue de la Gare
Tel: 24-41-10-27

Sedan
Hôtel Bellevue
★NN
56, Av. Philippoteaux
Tel: 24-27-03-96

10– AUBE
Souligny par Bouilly
Le Relais de Montaigu
★NN
30, Rue aux Fèbres
Tel: 25-40-20-20

11 – AUDE
Narbonne
Le Relais des Deux-Mers
★NN
Route de la Nautique
Croix-du-Sud
de Narbonne
Tel: 68-41-00-21

Narbonne
La Caille qui Chante
★★NN
Pont de Montredon
4 km N 113 towards Carcassonne
Tel: 68-42-04-36

12 –AVEYRON
Bertholène
Hôtel Bancarel
★NN
Tel: 65-69-62-10

Espallion
Le Relais de France
★NN
Bd. Joseph-Poulenc
Tel: 65-44-06-13

Espallion
Le Relais de Quatre Routes
Quatre Route
★NN
Tel: 65-44-01-69

Gages
Relais de la Plaine de Gages
Tel: 65-42-29-03

Roquette par Rodez
Le Relais de la Rocade
★N
Tel: 65-67-10-44
and 67-17-12

13 – BOUCHES-DU-RHONE
Fos-sur-Mer
Ma Campagne
★NN
42, Av. Jean-Jaurès
Tel: 42-05-01-66
and 42-05-00-11

Pont-Royal
Le Relais Provençal
★NN
Tel: 90-57-40-64

Port-Saint-Louis-du-Rhône
Le Relais des Ouvriers
Hôtel Lazzeri
★NN
59–64, Rue Jean-Jaurès
Tel: 42-86-01-28

Rognac
Cade Roussel
★★NN
Tel: 42-87-00-33

14 – CALVADOS
Cagny
Hôtel des Routiers
★NN
22, Route de Paris
Tel: 31-23-4-27

Saint-Martin-des-Besaces
La Renaissance
★NN
Tel: 31-68-72-65

Villiers-sur-Mer
Le Normand
★NN
44, Re de Maréchal Foch
Tel: 31-87-04-23

Vire
Hôtel de France
★★NN
4, Rue d'Aignaux
Tel: 31-68-00-35

15 – CANTAL
Fraisse-Haut
Hôtel des Cimes
★NN
Tel: 71-20-07-42

Mauriac
Les Routers
★NN
27, Rue St-Mary
Tel: 71-68-00-79

16 – CHARENTE
Champagne-Mouton
Le Relais de Plaisance
★NN
Tel: 45-31-80-52
and 31-98-19

17 – CHARENTE-MARITIME
Soujon
Hôtel de la Gare
2 Rue Clemenceau
Tel: 46-02-80-33

18 – CHER
Culan
Hôtel du Berry
★NN
Tel: 48-56-65-93

Nérondes
Le Lion d'Or
★NN
Place de la Mairie
Tel: 48-74-87-81

19 – CORRÈZE
Albussac
Aux Quatre-Routes
★★NN
L'Hostellerie de la Roche du Vic
Tel: 55-28-15-87

Combressol
Le Chatel
★★NN
La Chapelle
Tel: 55-94-22-04

21 – COTE-D'OR
Chenove
Au Bon Coin
★NN
54, Route de Dijon
Tel: 80-52-58-17

Ivry-en-Montagne
Restau Motel
★NN
Route Nationale 6
Tel: 80-20-21-18

Nolay
Hôtel du Chevreuil
★★NN
Place de l'Hôtel-de-Ville
CD 973
Tel: 80-21-71-89

Nuits-Saint-Georges
Les Cultivateurs
★★NN
12, Rue du Général de Gaulle
Tel: 80-61-10-41

22 – COTES-DU-NORD
Lamballe
La Tour d'Argent
★★NN
2, Rue du Dr Lavergne
Tel: 96-31-01-37

Loudeac
Hotel les Routiers
7 Rue Lavergne
Tel: 96-28-01-44

Saint-Agathon
Hôtel Bellevue
★NN
Bel-Orme Route Nationale 12
Tel: 96-43-80-53

Saint-Breiuc
Le-Beaufeuillage
★NN
2, Rue de Paris
Tel: 96-33-09-16

24 – DORDOGNE
Beynac-en-Périgord
Hôtel Pontet
★★NN
Route Depart 703
Tel: 53-29-50-06

Rouffillac-de-Carfux
Aux Poissons Frais
★★NN
Tel: 53-29-70-24

25 – DOUBS
Hyèvres-la-Paroisse
Le Relais de la
Géneaillère
Hôtel Ziss
∗∗∗NN
Tel: 81-84-07-88

Ornans
Hôtel le Progrès
∗NN
11, Rue Jacques-
Gervais
Tel: 81-62-16-79

Rahon
Auberge
du Château
∗NN
Tel: 81-86-82-27

26 – DROME
Alixan
Alpes Provence
∗∗NN
Route Nationale 532
Tel: 75-47-02-84

Sahune
Le Relais Dauphine-
Provence
∗NN
Tel: 75-27-40-99

27 EURE
Bosguerard-de-
Marcouville
La Tête d'Or
∗NN
Route de Lisieux
route Nationale 138
Tel: 35-87-60-24

28 – EURE-ET-LOIR
Chartres
Le Relais Beauceron
∗∗NN
Mignières
Situated at junction of
Chartres autoroute
Chartres autoroute
and Route Nationale
10

29 – FINISTÈRE
Cast
Le Relais Saint-Gildas
∗NN
11–13 Rue Kreisker
Tel: 98-73-54-76
and 73-55-43

Sizun
Hôtel des Voyageurs
∗NN
2, Rue de l'Argot
Tel: 98-68-80-35

Saint-Évarzec
Au Bon Repos
∗NN
Poullogoden
Tel: 38-56-20-09

30 – GARD
Saint-Julien-de-
La-Nef
Auberge de la
Cascade d'Aigues
Folles
∗∗NN
Sarl 6
Between Ganges and
Le Sumene
Tel: 67-82-42-78

Saint-Nazaire
Les Terailles
∗NN
Route Nationale 86
Tel: 66-89-66-14

31 HAUTE-
GARONNE
Bagnères-de-Luchon
L'Escapade
∗NN
27, Av. Jean-Jaurès
Tel: 61-79-01-85

Marquefave
Chez Roger
∗NN
Route Nationale 117
Tel: 61-87-85-07

Saint Elix le Château
Relais du Chateau
∗NN
Le Fouseret
Tel: 61-87-60-23

32 – GERS
Auch
Modern Hôtel
∗NN
10 bis, Av. Pierre
Nandis France
Tel: 62-05-03-47

Riscle
Le Relais de l'Auberge
∗NN
Place de la Mairie
Tel: 62-69-70-49

33 – GIRONDE
Cartelègue
L'Escale
∗NN
Tel: 56-42-71-18

Saint-Vincent-
de-Paul
Chez Anatole
∗NN
Ambarés
Route Nationale 10
Tel: 56-38-95-11

34 – HÉRAULT
Balaruc-le-Vieux
Le Relais Garrigou
∗∗NN
Issanka-Gigean
Tel: 67-78-71-30

Saint-Pons
Le Somail
∗NN
2, Av. de Castre
Tel: 67-97-00-12

35 – ILE-ET-
VILLAINE
Bedee
Hôtel du Commerce
∗NN
14, Place de l'Eglise
Tel: 99-07-00-37
and 07-00-76

Fougères
Aux Amis de la Route
∗NN
6. Bd. St-Germain
Tel: 99-99-07-62

Le Grand-Fougeray
Relais de la Belle
Ètoile – La Belle Éoile
*NN
Tel: 99-08-42-59

Montauban-de-Bretagne
Le Relais de France
**NN
34, Av. du Gl-de-Gaulle
Tel: 99-06-40-19

Montauban-de-Bretagne
Relais de la Hucherais
**NN
Tel: 99-06-40-29
and 06-54-31

Pipriac
Hôtel de la Tour
d'Auvergne
*NN
7, Rue de l'Avenir
Tel: 99-34-41-34

Redon
Le Relais
*NN
Route de Rennes
Tel: 99-71-46-54

36 – INDRE
Châteauroux
La Rallye
*NN
9, Rue Bourdillon
Tel: 54-34-37-41

La Châtre
SARL du Lion
d'Argent
**NN
2, Av. du Lion-d'Argent
Tel: 54-48-15-67
and 49-11-69

37 – INDRE-ET-LOIRE
Villiers-au-Bouin
Le Grand Cerf
**NN
La Porrerie
Tel: 47-24-11-06

38 – ISÉRE
Rochetaillee, par Le Bourge-d'Oisans
Le Relais de
Belledonne
*NN
Tel: 76-80-07-04

39 – JURA
Clairvaux-les-Lacs
L'Hôtels de l'Horloge
*NN
15, Grande Rue
Tel: 84-48-30-09

40 – LANDES
Aire-sur-l'Adour
Les Routiers
Chez Sierrett
*NN
15, rue du 4-Septembre
Tel: 58-71-63-01

Benesse-Marenne
Hôtel des Pins
*NN
Tel: 58-72-56-41
and 72-50-80

Saint-lon-les-Mines
Hôtel du Fronton
*NN
Le Bourg
Tel: 58-57-80-45

Sainte-Marie-de-Gosse
On Mange, on Boit, on
Dort
*NN
Route Nationale 117
Tel: 59-56-32-02

41 – LOIRE-ET-CHER
La Loge
Le Relais de la Loge
*NN
Theillay
Tel: 54-83-37-20

Mur de Sologne
Rest la Croix Blanche
Le Bourg
Tel: 54-83-81-11

Ouzourer-le-Marché
La Halte Beauceronne
18, Place de l'Eglise
Tel: 54-82-41-26

Romorantin
Les Aubiers
*NN
1, Av. de Blois
Tel: 54-76-05-59

42 – LOIRE
Bonson
Le Relais des Sports
*NN
Av. de St Rambert
Tel: 77-55-20-12
43 – HAUTE-LOIRE
Boussoulet
Auberge du Meygal
*NN
Saint-Julien-Chapteuil
Tel: 71-08-71-03

Molet près Allègro
Le Roulis
*NN
Le Bourg
Tel: 71-00-73-54

Le Puy-en-Velay
La Verveine
*NN
6, Place Cadelade
Tel: 71-02-00-77 and
02-14-66

Vieille-Brioude
Les Glycines
**NN
Av. de Versailles
Tel: 71-50-91-80

44 – LOIRE-ATLANTIQUE
Chateaubriant
Le Paris/Ocean
*NN
25–29, Rue d'Ancenis
Tel: 40-81-21-79

Pontchâteau
L'Auberge du
Calvaire
★NN
6, Route de la Brière
Le Calvaire
Tel: 40-01-61-65

Saint-Brévin-les-Pins
Relais du Marché
★NN
Place Henri Bosle
Tel: 40-27-22-21

45 – LOIRET
Artenay
Relais d'Artenay
★★NN
Rue de Chartres
Tel: 38-80-40-78

Bellegarde
Le Relais du
Commerce
★NN
1, Rue de la
République
Tel: 38-90-10-45

46– LOT
Gramat
e Relais du Centre
★★NN
Place de la République
Tel: 65-38-73-37

L'Europe
★NN
8, Av. Louis-Mazet
Tel: 65-38-71-68

Souillac
Le Relais de l'Escale
★NN
41, Av. Louis Jean
Nelroy
Tel: 65-37-82-65

Saint-Paul de
Loubressac
Le Relais de la
Madeleine
★NN
Tel: 65-21-98-08

47 – LOT-ET-
GARONNE
Au Relais Toulousain
★NN
113, Route de
Toulouse
Tel: 53-68-54-83

Lévignac-de-
Guyenne
Chez Denise
★NN
Allée des Promenades
Tel: 53-83-72-12

Saint-Livrade
Au Bon Accueil
★NN
Route de Villeneuve
Tel: 58-01-02-34

Tournon-d'Agenais
Le Relais des
Voyageurs
★NN
Rue de Cahors
Tel: 58-71-70-28

48 – LOZÉRE
Balsièges
Relais de Luxembourg
★N
Quartier du
Luxembourg
Tel: 66-47-00-01

Langogne
Le Relais du
Luxembourg
★NN
Place de la Gare
Tel: 66-69-00-11

Marvejols
Hôtels de la Paix
★★NN
2, Av. Brazza
Tel: 66-32-10-17

Le Monastier
Les Ajustons
★NN
Carrefour Nles 9 and
88
Marvejols
Tel: 66-32-70-35

49 – MAINE-ET-
LOIRE
Jallais
Le Relais de la Croix-
Verte
Hôtel du Vert Galant
★★NN
1, Rue Jean de
Sagmond
Place de la Mairie
Tel: 41-64-10-12 and
64-20-22

Saumur
Hôtel de la Gare
★★NN
16, Av. Dorio d'Angers
Tel: 41-67-34-24

Vivy
Le Relais Saint-Paul
★NN
30, Rue Nationale
Tel: 41-52-50-13 and
52-51-65

50 – MANCHE
Coutances
Le Relais du Viaduc
★NN
24, Av. de Verdun
Tel: 33-45-02-68

Montmartin-sur-Mer
L'Hôtellerie du Bon
Vieux Temps
★★NN
Tel: 33-47-54-44

St-Hilaire-du-
Harcouet
Les Routiers
Chez Jacques
★NN
Le Relais du Chemin
de Fer
La Gare
Tel: 33-49-10-55

Saint-Symphorien-
des-Monts
Relais du Bois Léger
★NN
Tel: 33-49-01-43

51 – MARNE

Beaumont-sur-Vesle
La Maison du
Champagne
∗∗NN
2, Rue du Port
Tel: 26-03-92-45

Cougivaux
Auberge du
Chaperon Rouge
∗NN
Route Nationale 4
Tel: 26-81-57-09

52 – HAUTE-MARNE

Doulaincourt
Hôtel de Paris
∗NN
Place du Géneral-de-
Gaulle
Tel: 25-94-61-18

53 – MAYENNE

Gorron
Au Rendez-vous des
routier
∗NN
9, Rue Corbeau-Paris
Tel: 43-08-61-74

**St. Berthevin-lès-
Laval**
Restaurant de l'Aulne
International
∗∗NN
Lieu-dit L'Aulne
Route Nationale 157
Tel: 43-69-31-74

55 – MEUSE

Ancerville
Le Relais
59, Route de Saint
Dizier
Tel: 29-75-30-13

56 – MORBIHAN

Elven
Le Relais de l'Argouet
∗NN
36, Rue de l'Argouet
Tel: 97-53-32-98

Lancaster
Le Relais de la
Rotonde
∗NN
120, Rue Jean-Jaurès
Tel: 97-76-06-37

Sene
Le Poulfanc
∗NN
Route de Vannes
Tel: 97-47-47-97

57 – MOSELLE

Knutange
Relais du Stade
∗NN
180, Rue Victor-
Rimmel
Tel: 87-84-12-47

Rohrbach-les-Bitche
L'Auberge de la Croix
d-Or
∗NN
6, Rue de la Liberation
Tel: 87-09-73-01

58 – NIÈVRE

Cosne-sur-Loire
Relais des Trois
Couleurs
∗NN
21, Rue Saint Agnes
Tel: 86-28-23-50

59 – NORD

Bailleul
Auberge du Seau
∗NN
CD 933
Tel: 20-48-62-00

61 – ORNE

Domfront
Relais St-Michel
NN
5, Rue du Mont-St-
Michel
Place de la Gare
Route Nationale 176
Tel: 33-38-64-99

Mortagne-au-Perche
Hôtel des Voyageurs
∗NN
60, Fg. St.-Éloi
Tel: 33-25-25-46

62 – PAS-DE-CALAIS

Bruay-en-Artois
Restaurant
Chez Michel
∗NN
114, Rue Raoul
Bripuet
Tel: 21-53-42-07

63 – PUY-DE-DOME

Clemont-Ferrand
Le Relais des Routiers
Auvergne-Pyrénées
∗NN
12 Bis, Place Carme
Tel: 73-92-35-73

Marsac en Livradois
Hotel le Kallisté
∗NN
Tel: 73-95-60-78

**Verndet-la-Varenne
(Le)**
Hôtel du Commerce
∗NN
Place St-Roch
Tel: 73-71-31-73

**64 – PYRÉNÉES-
ATLANT**

Denguin
Les Routiers de
Denguin
∗∗NN
Tel: 59-68-85-15

Gan
L'Hôtel Moderne
∗NN
43, Place de la Mairie
Tel: 59-21-54-98

Oloron-Gurmencon
Le Relais Aspois
∗∗NN
Route d'Espagne –
Route Nationale 134
Tel: 59-39-09-50

Oloron-Sainte-Marie
Le Terminus
∗NN
Place de la Gare
Tel: 59-39-01-72

Pau
Hostellerie du Bois
Louis
*NN
18, Av. Gaston-
Lacoste
Tel: 59-27-34-98

**65 – HAUTES-
PYRÉNÉES**
Laloubère
Hôtel des Pyrénées
*NN
13, Rue du Mi-Foch
Tel: 62-93-19-62

Tarbes
Le Relais Victor-Hugo
*NN
52, Rue Victor-Hugo
Tel: 62-93-36-71

**66 PYRÉNÉES
ORIENTALES**

67 – BAS-RHIN
Bouxwiller
Le Soleil
**NN
71, Grande-Rue
Tel: 88-70-70-06

Keskastel
Le Relais d'Alsace
*NN
11, Rue de Faubourg
Tel: 88-00-11-04

Kogenheim
A l'Etoile
36, Route de
Strasbourg
Tel: 88-74-70-02

68 – HAUT-RHIN
Kruth
**NN
20, Grande-Rue
Tel: 89-92-28-02

69 – RHONE
Decines
Le Relais de la Poste
**NN
11, Rue d'Alsace
Tel: 78-49-19-03

70 – HAUTE-SAONE
Ronchampe
La Pomme d'Or
*NN
Rue Le Corbusier
Tel: 84-20-62-12

**71 – SAONE-ET-
LOIRE**
Mercurey
Le Mercurey
*NN
Grande-Rue
Tel: 85-45-13-56

Varennes-le-Grand
Relais de la Gare
*NN
Tel: 85-44-22-76

72 – SARTHE
La Belle Inutile
La Biche Dorée
*NN
Route Nationale
Tel: 43-76-70-45

Besse-sur-Braye
Le Relais de la Gare
*NN
19, Av. de la Gare
Tel: 43-35-30-22

Jové-en-Charnie
Restaurant du Cheval
Blanc
*NN
Route Nationale 157
Tel: 43-88-42-13

73 – SAVOIE
Aiguebelle
Le Relais de la Poste
**NN
Grande-Rue
Tel: 79-36-20-05

Albens
Hôtel de France
*NN
Rue du 8 Mai 1945
Tel: 79-54-17-04

74 – HAUTE SAVOIE
Chaux-Balmont
L'Auberge
*NN
Route Nationale 201
Tel: 50-46-71-02

Doussard
La Tour du Lac
*NN
Nle 508 La Gare
Tel: 50-44-30-37

Megève
Le Chalet des Fleurs
**NN
Route de Sallanches
Pont d'Arbon
Tel: 50-21-21-46

Meythet
Les Routiers
*NN
22, Route de Frangy
Tel: 50-22-02-93

Sciez
Le Leman
*NN
Bonatrait
Tel: 50-72-60-04

Seynod
Le Relais
Sainte-Catherine
*NN
181, Route d'Aux
Tel: 50-59-00-86

Thones
L'Hermitage
Av. du Vieux Pont
Tel: 50-02-00-31

81 – TARN
Ambres
Les Pommiers
*NN
Le Grès
Tel: 63-58-05-56

Cuq Touiza
Chez Alain-La
Bombardière
*NN
Tel: 63-75-70-36

Labrugière
La Marmite
*NN
35, Av. Henri Simon
Tel: 63-50-21-19

Mosquette
Auberge du Sanglier
★★NN
Denat/Réalmont
Tel: 63-45-50-80

82 – TARN-ET-GARONNE
Caussade
Relais d'Auvergne
21R. de Meaux
Tel: 63-93-03-89

Moissac
Le Relais Auvergnat
★NN
31, Bd. Camille-Delthil
Place du Palais
Tel: 63-04-93-02
and 63-04-02-58

Montpezat-de-Quercy
Le Relais de l'etape
Quercy
★NN
Route Nationale 20
Tel: 63-02-07-58

83 – VAR
Arcs sur Argens (Les)
Hôtel de l'Avenir
★NN
Rue Jean Jaurès
Quartier de la Gare
Tel: 94-73-30-58

Fréjus
Les Trois Chènes
★NN
Route de Cannes
Route Nationale 7
Tel: 94-53-20-08

Montauroux
Le Relais du Lac
★★NN
Tel: 94-76-43-65

Saint-Raphaël
Le Relais Bel Azur
★NN
247, Bd. de Provence
Tel: 94-95-14-08

Saint Raphael
Hotel Moderne
★★NN
329, Av. du Gl Leclerc
Tel: 94-51-22-16

84 – VAUCLUSE
Bellene
La Croisière
★NN
Tel: 90-30-20-05

Montfavet
Relais de Bonpas
Pont de Bonpas
★NN
Route Nationale 7
Tel: 90-23-07-01

85 – VENDÉE
Les-Herbiers
L'Orée des Bois Verts
★NN
Route des Sables
Route Nationale 160
Tel: 51-91-00-18

La Roche-sur-Yon
Hôtel Sully
★★NN
Bd Sully
Tel: 51-37-54-02
and 51-37-18-21

Saint-Philbert-de-Bouaine
Le Relais des Étangs
★★NN
Route du
Rocheserniére
Tel: 51-41-92-44

Venansault
Le Moulin de la
Bergerie
★NN
Carrefour de la Grolle
Route de Landeronde
Tel: 51-40-39-64

86 –VIENNE
Chaunay
Hotel du Commerce
★★NN
Le Bourg
Tel: 49-59-02-71

Moulisme
La Table Ouverte
★NN
Montmorillon
Route Nationale 147
Tel: 49-91-90-68

87 – HAUTE-VIENNE
Sauviat-sur-Vige
Hôtel 400 de la Poste
★NN
Tel: 55-75-30-12

88 – VOSGES
Geradmer
Le Gai Realis
★NN
59, Bd de la Jarnogne
Tel: 29-63-05-96

Plombières-les-Bains
Le Relais
Strasbourgeois
★NN
3, Place Beaumarchais
Tel: 29-66-00-70

St Pierremont
'Le Belais Vosgien'
★★NN
Tel: 29-65-02-46

Sainte-Marguerite
Le Relais des Amis
★NN
486, Rue d'Alsace
Tel: 29-56-17-23

89 – YVONNE
Arces
Le Relais de la Forêt
d'Othe
★NN
Tel: 86-88-10-44

Auxerre
Le Relais le Vaulabelle
★NN
36, Bd Vaulabelle
Tel: 86-52-04-48

Le Sainte-Nitasse
★NN
Route de Lyon/
Auxerre
Tel: 86-49-95-07

Percey
Auberge
des Pêcheurs
★NN
Departmentale 905
Tel: 86-35-01-55

91 – ESSONNE
Corbell-Essonne
Relais de l'Hermitage
★NN
137, Bd de
Fontainebleau
Tel: 64-96-29-42

Montlhéry
Le Sologne
★NN
65, Route d'Orléans
Tel: 96-01-00-98

MOTORWAY RELAIS ROUTIERS

AUTOROUTE – A1

Vemars
95470 Val-d'Oise
Tel: 34-68-39-20

Assevillers par Péronne
80200 Somme
Towards Sens
Provence/Paris
Tel: 22-85-20-35

Péronne
80200 Somme/
Provence
Tel: 22-85-26-08
Telex: 140828

Wancourt
62128 Pas-de-Calais
Tel: 21-55-97-83

AUTOROUTE – A4

**Rheims –
Aire de Rheims
Champagne**
51400 Marne
Tel: 26-61-63-57

Verdun Saint-Nicolas
55100 Meuse
Tel: 29-86-41-18

Le Fère-en-Tardenois
Relais du Tardenois
02130 Fresnes-en-
Tardenois
Tel: 23-70-23-16

AUTOROUTE – A6

Les Lisses par Villabe
91100 Essonne
Tel: 60-86-22-51

Nemours
77140 Seine-et-Marne
Tel: 64-28-11-97

Venoy par Auxerre
8900 Yonne
Towards Paris/
Provence
Tel: 86-52-31-71

**Venoy/Auxerre
(Venoy 2)**
8900 Yonne
Towards Provence/
Paris
Tel: 86-52-35-52
Telex: 800921

Guillon
89420 Yonne
Tel: 86-32-11-34

**La Ferté Saint-
Ambreuil par
Sennecy-le-Grand**
71240 Saône-et-Loire
Towards Provence/
Paris
Tel: 85-44-20-64

La Ferté-St-Ambreuil
71420 Saône-et-Loire
Towareds Paris/
Provence
Tel: 85-44-21-79

**Saint-Albain par
Mâcon**
71260 Saône-et-Loire
Tel: 85-33-19-00

AUTOROUTE – A7

Solaize
69360 Rhône
Tel: 78-02-82-63

Montélimar
26200 Drôme
Tel: 78-46-60-00

Lancon de Provence
13680 B.-du-R.
Tel: 90-53-90-25

Morières-les-
Avignon
84310 Vaucluse
Tel: 90-22-59-68

Mornas
84420 Vaucluse
Towards Paris/
Provence
Tel: 90-37-03-09

AUTOROUTE – A7

Sorgues
84700 Vaucluse
Tel: 90-39-10-72

AUTOROUTE – A9

Tavel
30126 Gard
Tel: 66-50-04-19

Montpellier –
Fabrègues
34690 Hérault
Towards Passerelle
Tel: 67-85-15-06

AUTOROUTE – A10

Antran –
Châtellerault
86100 Vienne
Towards Provence/
Paris
Tel: 49-02-72-04

Fleury-les-Aubrais
Aire de Bais Picard
45400 Loiret
Tel: 38-73-34-89
Telex: 780959

Saran par Orléans
45400 Loiret
Tel: 38-91-30-12

Tours
3700 Indre-et-Loire
Towards Passerelle
Tel: 47-56-15-49

Pons
Aire de Saint-Léger
17800 Charente
Maritime
Tel: 46-94-25-30

Briis-sous-Forges
91640 Essonne
Tel: 64-90-77-18

Blois
41000 Loir-et-Cher
Tel: 54-46-84-73

AUTOROUTE – A11

Chartes –
Aire de la Fosse
Blanche
28300 Eure-et-Loire
Tel: Paris/Provence
37-31-62-41
Tel: Provence/Paris
37-31-62-41

La Ferté-Bernard
72400 Sarthe
Tel: 43-93-41-02

AUTOROUTE – A13

Morainvilliers par
Orgeval
78630 Yvelines
Tel: 39-75-92-25

Vironvay
27400 Eure
Towards Passerelle
Tel: 32-40-21-51

AUTOROUTE – A25

Steenvoorde
59114 Nord
Towards Paris/
Provence
and Provence/Paris
Tel: 28-42-04-67

AUTOROUTE – 31

Loisy
Aire de Pont-á-
Mousson
54700 Meurthe-et-
Moselle
Tel: 83-81-18-89

AUTOROUTE – A32

Longeville-les-
St-Avold
57740 Moselle
Tel: 87-92-23-89

AUTOROUTE – A43

L'Isle d'Abeau
par Bourgoin-Jallieu
38300 Isère
Towards Passerelle
Tel: 74-27-27-91

AUTOROUTE – A63

Cestas
33610 Gironde
Tel: 56-21-80-68

THE ROUTIERS SIGN

The red and blue Les Routiers sign is recognised internationally as a mark of quality and value and is awarded annually to restaurants and hotels which pass the strict Routiers inspection.

In order to maintain the right to be listed and display the sign, establishments are reinspected regularly. For the most part, standards are maintained; however, there are inevitably a few who let their standards drop and have to be withdrawn. There may have been a change of ownership or reinspection following a complaint.

In spite of our efforts, some establishments continue to display the sign after they have been withdrawn. Authentic Relais Routiers are issued with an annual certificate which should be displayed on the premises, and only if this certificate is valid should the sign be displayed.

If you visit an establishment displaying the Routiers sign without an entry in the Guide or a valid certificate, please write and tell us and we will investigate. Finally, if you have any comments or complaints about a current Relais Routiers, then please let us know – you will find a questionnaire on the following page.

YOUR RECOMMENDATION

If you know of an establishment not already
a Relais Routiers but worthy of nomination,
please send us details on the form below.
We will arrange for an inspector to call

Send to: ROUTIERS, 354 Fulham Road,
LONDON SW10 9UH

Name of Establishment:

_____

Address

_____

_____

Name of Proprietor (if known):

_____

Restaurant/Pub/Hotel/Bed and breakfast

(Please delete as applicable)

Comments

_____

_____

_____

_____

_____

_____

Your Name:

_____

Address:

_____

_____

YOUR OPINION

If you are dissatisfied or alternatively would like to praise a Relais Routiers, please write and tell us. Although our establishments are reinspected regularly, your comments help us maintain Routiers' high standards. All correspondence will be treated in confidence.

Send to: ROUTIERS, 354 Fulham Road, LONDON SW10 9UH

Name of Relais Routiers:

_____

Address

_____

_____

on (date) ___ for lunch/dinner/bed and breakfast

Comments

_____

_____

_____

_____

_____

_____

_____

Your Name:

_____

Address:

_____

_____

FRANCE

ABBEVILLE 80100 Somme **RN 1 Map 5-A3**
Ⓨ ⊗ **AUBERGE FLEURIE** (N° RR OCT 25 672) (M. and Mme Michel **Rubin**) 294, Côte de la Justice ☎ 22-24-88-22 ⊶ 3 Showers.

ABBEVILLE 80132 Somme **RN 25 Map 5-A3**
Ⓨ ⊗ **AU CHEVAL NOIR** (N° RR JANV 26 779) (M. and Mme Bernard **Lafargue-Fortier**) Petit Miannay ☎ 22-24-20-17 Closed Fri. A little English spoken.

ABSCON 59215 Nord **RN 45 Map 5-B3**
Ⓨ ⊗ ⌂ **LE MOULIN D'OR** (N° RR MAR 25 846) (Mme Monique **Bauduin**) 17, place de Gaulle ☎ 27-36-30-33 ⊶ 9 Closed Aug. Coaches welcome (rest. seats 80). Evening meals.

ABSIE (L') 79240 Deux-Sèvres **Maps 11-B3, 15-A1**
Ⓨ ⊗ **BAR RESTUARANT DE LA POSTE - LES ROUTIERS** (N° RR AOU 26 984) (M. Eugène **Bignon**) 21, rue de la Poste ☎ 49-95-90-21 Closed Sun. Filling stations near.

ACQUEDUCS DE BEAUNANT 69110 Rhône **Map 1-A1**
Ⓨ ⊗ **MARYSE ET ANNIE** (N° RR JUL 25 053) (Mme Maryse **Bert**) 66, av. de la Libération Ste-Foy-Lès-Lyon ☎ 78-59-03-05 Closed Sat, Sun; 15 July to 15 Aug. Italian spoken.

ADJOTS (LES) 16700 Charente **RN 10 Map 15-B2**
Ⓨ ⊗ **PARIS-IRUN-CHEZ BRANGE** (N° RR JUN 19 796) (M. Jacky **Sommier**) ☎ 45-31-02-44 Closed midday Sat to Sun.

AGEN 47000 L.-et-G. **RN 21 and 113 Map 21-B1**
Ⓨ   **CHEZ MARIO - Snack bar** (N° RR JUN 24 614) (M. Mario **Ghibaudo**) 30, bd de la Liberté ☎ 53-96-89-42 **Minitel** Closed Sun; Aug.

AIGREFEUILLE 17290 Charente-Maritime **RD 939 Map 11-B1 (see PUYDROUARD)**

AIGUEBELLE 73220 Savoie **RN 6 Map 19-A2**
Ⓨ ⊗ ⌂ **2 Stars NN LE RELAIS DE LA POSTE** (N° RR AOU 18 816) (Mme Germaine **Vincent**) Grande-Rue ☎ 79-36-20-05 ⊶ 21 Closed Sat; 20 December to 1 February.
Ⓨ ⊗ **LA CHAPELLE** (N° RR OCT 26 353) (Mme Christiane Magnin) Restoroute La Chapelle ☎ 79-36-17-09 **Minitel** Coaches welcome (rest. seats 80). Evening meals until 11pm. German, English, Italian spoken.

AIGUEPERSE 63260 P.-de-D. **RN 9 Map 16-B3**
Ⓨ ⊗ **LE ROUTIER DE ST-GENEST** (N° RR JUN 22 396) (M. Camille **Chalbos**) Les Littes **Saint-Genest-du-Retz** ☎ 73-63-68-35 Closed Sun; Aug. Open 5am-7pm.

AIRE-sur-L'ADOUR 40800 Landes **RN 134 Map 21-A2**
Ⓨ ⊗ ⌂ **1 Star NN LES ROUTIERS-CHEZ PIERRETTE** (N° RR OCT 24 377) (M. Joël **Daste**) 15, rue du 4 septembre ☎ 58-71-63-01 ⊶ 10 from 70 to 110F. Breakfast from 12 to 15F. Closed Saturday

A

Aire-sur-L'Adour continued
from 1 October to 31 December. Coaches welcome (rest. seats 150). Evening meals. Dogs allowed.

AIRVAULT 79600 Deux-Sèvres **RD 46**
♟ ⊗ ⌂ **HOTEL DE LA GARE** (N° RR FEV 26 818) (Mme Anne-Marie **Bourgois**) 26, rue Sablières ☎ 48-64-70-16 ⊷ 7. Closed Sun; Aug.

AIX-D'ANGILLON (LES) 18220 Cher **Map 13-B1**
♟ ⊗ **LE PARISIEN** (N° RR JANV 26153) (M. Jacques **Blanchet**) Place du Général-de-Gaulle ☎ 48-64-43-62 ⊷ 4 Closed Sun; Aug. Coaches welcome (rest. seats 100). Meals served till 9 pm.

AIXE-SUR-VIENNE 87700 Hte-Vienne **RN 21 Map 16-B1**
♟ ⊗ ⌂ **LE RELAIS DE LA CHAUMIERE** (N° RR JUL 15 314) (M. J.-L. **Pechalat**) 5, avenue de la Gare ☎ 55-70-12-12 **Minitel** ⊷ 5 Closed Wed; 15 Aug to 7 Sept. Coaches welcome (rest. seats 35). Evening meals.

AIX NOULETTE 62160 Pas de Calais **Map 5-B2/3**
♟ ⊗ **RELAIS D'EPINETTE** (N° RR JUIL 26 963) (M. and Mme François **Lefebvre**) 181, route de Béthunes ☎ 21-29-93-48 Filling stations near.

ALBAN 81250 Tarn **CD 999 Map 22-B1**
♟ ⊗ **LES QUATRE SAISONS** (N° RR DEC 27 127) (M. et Mme Jean-François **Galvan**) 2, Grande-Rue ☎ 63-55-83-22 Arabic, Spanish and Italian spoken.

ALBENC (L') 38470 Isère **Maps 24-B1 and 18-B3**
♟ ⊗ **AUBERGE DU VERCORS** (N° RR MARS 25 335) (Mme Claudette **Torri**) Place Jean-Vinay ☎ 76-64-75-17 Closed Sun.

ALBENS 73410 Savoie **RN 201 Map 19-A2**
♟ ⊗ ⌂ **1 Star NN HOTEL DE FRANCE** (N° RR JAN 25 773) (M. Robert **Stacchetti**) rue du 8 Mai 1945 ☎ 79-54-17-04 ⊷ 9 Closed Wed except in Jul/Aug. Full-board 150-160 F per night. Coaches welcome (rest. seats 40). Evening meals. German, English, Italian spoken.

ALBERT 80300 Somme **Map 5-B3**
♟ ⊗ ⌂ **LA CLOCHE D'OR** (N° RR SEPT 27 009) (M. Daniel **Macarez**) 53, rue Victor Hugo ☎ 22-75-09-68 ⊷ 6 English spoken.

ALBI 81000 Tarn **RN 88 and D 81 Map 22-B1**
♟ ⊗ **LE RELAIS FLEURI** (N° RR DEC 25 225) (M. Pedro **Casado**) 25, av. François-Verdier ☎ 63-54-07-09 Closed Sun. Full board 150-170F per night. Coaches welcome (rest. seats 60). Meals served till midnight. Spanish spoken.

♟ ⊗ **RELAIS CATALAN** (N° RR AVR 26 878) (M. Raymond **Thar-reau**) RD 999 Route de Millau (Barrière de Montplaisir) ☎ 63-60-27-00 ⊷ 3 Closed Sat, Sun.

♀ ⊗ **AUBERGE LANDAISE DE CHEZ MARCEL** (N° RR FEV 27 189) (M. Marcel **Gauzère**) Rte de Montplaisir La Rivayrolle ☎ 63-45-03-11 Closed Sun.

ALBON 26140 Drôme **N7 Map 24-A1**
♀ ⊗ 🏠 **RELAIS DE LA TOUR ALBON** (N° RR DEC 26 745) (M. Camille **Bertrand**) Nationale 7 ☎ 75-03-11-22 ⊷ 13 Closed Sun (unless by arrangement); 15-31 Aug.

ALBUSSAC-AUX-QUATRE-ROUTES 19400 Corrèze **D 940 RN 121 Map 17-A1**
♀ ⊗ 🏠 **2 Stars NN HOSTELLERIE DE ROCHE-DE-VIC** (N° RR MAI 11 509) (Mme **Pailler**) Les Quatre Routes ☎ 55-28-15-87 **Minitel** ⊷ 14 (85-210F, breakfast 18F) Closed Mon low season; Feb. Full-board 160-180F per night. Coaches welcome (rest.seats 100). Evening meals. Parking, terrace, grill, bar, dogs allowed. Places to visit: Roche-de-Vic, Collonges la Rouge, Meyssac Turenne. English spoken.

ALFORTVILLE 94140 Val de Marne **Map 1-B2/3**
♀ ⊗ **LA TERRASSE** (N° RR OCT 27 059) (M. Boualem **Belamri**) 173, rue Etienne Dolet ☎ 43-75-17-02 Closed Sun and 15/8 to 15/9. English spoken.

ALIXAN 26300 Drôme **RN 532 Map 24-A1**
♀ ⊗ 🏠 **2 Stars NN ALPES PROVENCE** (N° RR JUN 25 462) (M. Jean-Claude **Bocaud**) RN 532 ☎ 75-47-02-84 ⊷ 23 Closed 15 to 30 Nov. Full-board 130-250F per night. Coaches welcome (rest. seats 190) Evening meals. English, German spoken.

ALLASSAC 19240 Corréze **CD 901 Map 17-A1**
♀ ⊗ **RELAIS CHEZ BABETTE** (N° RR NOV 27 079) (Mme Elisabeth **Dublanche**) Varetz ☎ 55-84-21-79 Spanish and English spoken.

ALLEUDS (LES). Lieu-dit Chaignepain 79190 D.-Sèvres **RN 148 Map 12-A1 (see SAUZE-VAUSSAIS)**

ALVIMARE 76640 S.-Mme **RN 15 Map 4-A3**
♀ ⊗ **CHEZ DENISE** (N° RR MAI 26 545) (Mme Denise **Letailleur**) **Fauville-en-Caux** ☎ 35-96-01-50 Closed Sat afternoon, Sun; 15 days in summer and 15 days in winter. Coaches welcome (rest. seats 80).

AMBERT 63600 P.-de-D **RN 106 Map 17-A3**
♀ ⊗ 🏠 **LE RELAIS DES ROUTIERS** (N° RR MAI 16 065) (M. Robert **Pichoir**) 4, place du Général-Courtial ☎ 73-82-15-82 ⊷ 10 Closed Oct. Coaches welcome (rest. seats 30). Evening meals.

AMBLAINVILLE 60110 Oise **RN 327 Map 3-B2**
♀ ⊗ 🏠 **CHEZ MARIE ODILE** (N° RR JUL 23 393) (Mme Marie-Odile **Prunier**) 40, rue Nationale ☎ 44-52-03-10 Closed Sun.

AMBOISE 37400 I.-et-L. **RD 151 Map 12-A3**
♀ ⊗ 🏠 **LE CHANTECLERC** (N° RR DEC 26 773) (M. Eric **Boitelle**)

Amboise continued

34, Avenue de Tours ☎ 47-57-11-94 ⬤ 5 Closed Sun in winter. English spoken.

AMBRES 81500 Tarn **RD 87 Map 22-A2**

⟡ ⊗ ⌂ **1 star NN LES POMMIERS** (N° RR MAI 26 887) (M. Alain **Sore**) Le grès ☎ 63-58-05-56 ⬤ 8 Closed Fri evenings and February or March. Spanish and English spoken.

AMFREVILLE LA MI VOIE 76920 S-Mme **RN 13 bis Map 3-A1**

⟡ ⊗ **LE BOUT DU MONDE** (N° RR AOUT 26 979) (M. Rémy **Piquot**) 2, route de Paris ☎ 35-23-31-47. Filling stations near.

⟡ ⊗ **LE RELAIS CHANTECLAIR** (N° RR SEPT 26 636) (M. Roger **Ridel**) 19, route de Paris ☎ 35-23-70-24.

AMIENS 80000 Somme **RN 16 Map 5-A3**

⟡ ⊗ ⌂ **SAINT ROCH** (N° RR FEV 21 411) (Mme **Halter**) 2, place Foch ☎ 22-91-38-69 ⬤ 7 Closed Sun pm. English spoken.

AMILLY 45200 Loiret **RN 443 Map 13-A1/2**

⟡ ⊗ **LE RELAIS DU GROS-MOULIN** (N° RR SEP 19 905) (Mme Bernadette **Grégoire**) 371, rue du Gros-Moulin ☎ 38-85-46-62 Closed Sun; 15 to 31 Aug.

AMOU 40330 Landes **RD 15 Map 20-B2**

⟡ ⊗ ⌂ **AU FEU DE BOIS** (N° RR JANV 26 430) (M. Joël **Martinet**) Avenue des Pyrénées ☎ 58-89-00-86 ⬤ 5 Closed Fri evenings, midday Sat and Jan. Evening meals.

AMPUIS 69420 Rhône **RN 86 Map 2-B1/2**

⟡ ⊗ ⌂ **AUX PORTES DE PROVENCE** (N° RR JUN 20 215) (M. Maurice **Terpend**) RN 86 Les Allées ☎ 74-56-10-31 ⬤ 14 Closed Wed in Feb.

ANCERVILLE 55170 Meuse **RN 4 Map 14-A1**

⟡ ⊗ ⌂ **1 Star NN LE RELAIS** (N° RR JUN 25 958) (Mme Renée **Lange**) 59 Rte de St-Dizier ☎ 29-75-30-13 ⬤ 10 Closed Sat afternoon and Sun mornings and part of Sept or Oct. Coaches welcome (rest. seats 80). Evening meals.

ANETZ 44150 Loire-Atlantique **RN 23 Map 11 A3**

⟡ ⊗ **LE RELAIS DE LA BARBINIÈRE** (N° RR JANV 27 169) (Mme Sylvie **Dronet**) La Barbinière ☎ 40-83-11-25 ⬤ 4 Closed Sun, and between Christmas and New Year. English spoken.

ANGERS 49000 M.-et-L. **RN 31 Maps 21-A1 and 11-A3**

⟡ ⊗ ⌂ **CHEZ GEORGES** (N° RR AVR 24 926) (M. Georges **Janneau**) 47, rue Guillaume-Lekeu ☎ 41-43-86-25 ⬤ 7 Evening meals.

⟡ ⊗ **CHEZ MICHEL** (N° RR MAI 26 836) (M. Michel **Guerin**) 7, bld Ayrault ☎ 41-43-82-43 ⬤ 11 Closed Sat and Aug. English spoken.

ANGERVILLE 91670 Essonnes **RD 838 Map 9-B1**

⟡ ⊗ **RESTO-RAPIDE** (N° RR MARS 26 486) (M. Daniel **Saragosa**) Rte d'Authon-la-Plaine ☎ 64-95-29-40 Open 24 hours. English, Spanish, Portuguese, Arabic spoken.

ANGLES 85750 Vendée **RN 747 Map 11-A1**
Ⓨ ⊗ **AUBERGE DU BON ACCUEIL Chez Cathy** (N° RR MAR 21 816) (Mme Catherine **Gaborit**) Rue Nationale ☎ 51-97-52-20 Closed 3 weeks in Sept. Coaches welcome (rest. seats 195). Evening meals. English spoken.

ANGLET 64600 Pyr.-Atl. **RN 10 Map 20-A3**
Ⓨ ⊗ ⌂ **LES MOUETTES** (N° RR AVR 24 180) (M. Reñe **Anneix**) 5, avenue de l'Adour ☎ 59-52-46-08 ⊶ 8 Closed Sat, Sun; 15 Aug to 6 Sept. Evening meals until 10.30 pm.

ANGLIERS 86330 Vienne **RN 147 Map 12-B2**
Ⓨ ⊗ **LA GALUCHE** SARL (N° RR NOV 25 729) (M. Claude **Poupard**) RN 147 ☎ 49-98-19-26 Closed Sat afternoon. Coaches welcome (rest. seats 55). Evening meals, until midnight. English spoken.

ANNOEULLIN 59112 Nord **Map 5-A1**
Ⓨ ⊗ **CHEZ MAUMO** (N° RR JUL 26 006) (M. Maurice **Desailly**) 32, Rue de Touraine ☎ 20-85-75-92 Closed Sun; Aug. Coaches welcome (rest. seats 50).

ANTONNE 24420 Dordogne **RN 21 Map 15-B3**
Ⓨ ⊗ ⌂ **LE RELAIS DE LAURIÈRE** (N° RR MAI 26 899) (M. Jean-Claude **Condaminas**) Laurière ☎ 53-06-00-28 ⊶ 5 Closed Sun and 1/5 to 15/5. Full board 140 to 160F. Coaches welcome (rest seats 80).

ANTONY 92160 Hauts-de-Seine
Ⓨ ⊗ **LES ROUTIERS** (N° RR OCT 13 147) (Mme Ginette **Laurence**) 86, av. de la Division Leclerc ☎ 46-66-02-62 Closed Sun.

ANTRAN see **CHATELLERAULT**

APPEVILLE (called ANNEBAULT) 27290 Eure
Ⓨ ⊗ **LE RELAIS DE LA POSTE** (N° RR AVR 26 503) Rte de Pont-Audemer ☎ 32-56-11-13 Closed Mon afternoons. Coaches welcome (rest. seats 60).

APPOIGNY 89380 Yonne **RN 6 Map 13-A2**
🏆 **Les Routiers Shell Service Station LE RELAIS DE L'AMITIE** (N° RR OCT 55 0000 101) (M. Philippe **Saur**) 21, Rte d'Auxerre ☎ 86-53-21-76- Open 24 hours exept Fri, Sat evenings.

ARBRESLE (L') 69210 Rhône **RN 7 Map 2-A1**
Ⓨ ⊗ **LES ROUTIERS** (N° RR NOV 22 989) (Mme M.-A. **Durix-Michaud**) 91, rue Gabriel-Péri ☎ 74-01-05-81 Closed Sat afternoon. Meals served until 7.30 pm.
Ⓨ ⊗ **LE RELAIS DES ROUTIERS** (N° RR NOV 26 364) (Mme Monique **Giraudier**) 27 Rte de Paris ☎ 74-01-07-59 Closed Sun afternoon. English, Spanish spoken.

⊗ **AUX VOSIGIENS** (N° RR MARS 27 283) (M. EVelyne **Péchard**) 49, rue Gabriel-Péri ☎ 74-01-00-13 Closed pm and Sun.

ARBRET (L') 62158 P.-de-C. **RN 25 Map 5-B3**
 ⊗ **LE RELAIS DE LA GARE** (N° RR JUN 17 290) (M. Maurice **Vicart**) 44, route Nationale ☎ 21-48-24-33 Open 24 hours, except Sat, Sun. Closed Sat, Sun. Full board 145-150F per night. Coaches welcome (rest. seats 60). Evening meals.

ARC-LES-GRAY 70100 Haute- Saône **Map 14-A3**
 ⊗ **LES ROUTIERS** (N° RR SEP 23 928) (Mme Henriette **Demoulin**) 4, place Aristide-Briand La Croisée ☎ 84-65-37-23 Closed Sun. Coaches welcome (rest. seats 60). Evening meals.

ARC-SUR-TILLE 21560 Côte-d'Or **Map 14-A3**
 ⊗ ⌂ **LE POELON** (N° RR MAR 25 850) (Mme Roberte **Gauthey**) 13 Rte Nationale ☎ 80-37-21-52 ⊷ 5 Closed Sat afternoon; Aug. Evening meals.

ARCS-SUR-ARGENS (LES) 83460 Var **Map 25-A2**
 ⊗ ⌂ **1 Star NN HOTEL DE L'AVENIR** (N° RR AVR 25 902) (Mme Marie-Jeanne **Hortal**) SARL, rue Jean-Jaurès. Quartier de la Gare ☎ 94-73-30-58 ⊷ 10 Closed Sat low season. Full board 150F per night. Coaches welcome (rest. seats 45). English, Italian spoken.

ARCES 89320 Yonne **RD 905 Map 9-B2**
 ⊗ ⌂ **1 Star NN LE RELAIS DE LA FORET D'OTHE** (N° RR JUN 18 747) (Mme Yolande **Misura**) 15, Place de l'Eglise. ☎ 86-88-10-44 ⊷ 8. Full board 150-200F per night. Coaches welcome (rest. seats 100).

ARDELAY-LES-HERBIERS 85500 Vendée **RD 38 Maps 12-B1 and 11-B3**
 ⊗ ⌂ **2 Stars NN CHEZ CAMILLE** (N° RR JAN 20 079) (M. Camille **Masse**) 2, rue Monseigneur-Massé ☎ 51-91-07-57 ⊷ 13 Full-board 200-250F per night. Coaches welcome (rest.seats 200). Evening meals.

ARDENTES 36120 Indre **Map 16 A1**
 ⊗ ⌂ **CAFÉ DES SPORTS** (N° RR MAI 27 287) (Mme Cécile **Pascaud**) 21, avenue de Verdun ☎ 54-36-21-19 ⊷ 5 Evening meals served until 9pm.

ARDOISE (L') 30290 Gard **Map 24-A2**
 ⊗ ⌂ **LE CHALET** (N° RR OCT 26 350) (M. Jacky/Martine **Char-masson**) Rte d'Avignon ☎ 66-50-22-22 **Minitel** ⊷ 7 Closed Sun, Christmas, New Year. Full-board 140-180F per night. Coaches welcome (rest. seats 55). Evening meals until 8 pm.

ARGENLIEU 60130 Oise **D916 Map 3-A3**
 ⊗ **LE RELAIS D'ARGENLIEU** (N° RR MARS 26 860) (M. Alain **Meyer**) 45, rue Thierry d'Argenlieu, Avrechy ☎ 44-51-72-18 Closed Sun. English spoken.

ARGENT-SUR-SAULDRE 18410 Cher **RD 940 Map 13-A1**
♀ ⊗ **AUBERGE DES BRUYÈRES** (N° RR JUN 25 959) (M. Jean-Yves **Muelle**) 10, Rue Nationale ☎ 48-73-60-20. Evening meals.

ARGENTAN 61200 Orne **RN 24 Bis and 158 Map 8-A2**
♀ ⊗ ⌂ **LE NORMANDY** (N° RR AVR 21 870) (M. René **Dutertry**) 35, avenue de la 2ᵉ Division Blindée ☎ 33-67-05-87 ⊷ 20 Closed Sat, Sun and 1-15 Aug. Full board 145F per night. Coaches welcome (rest. seats 90). Evening meals until 11 pm.

ARGENTAT 19400 Corrèze **RN 120 Map 17-A1/2**
♀ ⊗ ⌂ **CHEZ RAYMOND** (N° RR MAI 22 325) (Mme Monique **Pouzaud**) Place du 14 Juillet ☎ 55-28-01-97 Closed Sun; Jun. Full board 150-180F per night Coaches welcome (rest. seats 160). Evening meals.

ARGENTEUIL-SUR-ARMANÇON 89160 Yonne **CD 118 Map 13-A3**
♀ ⊗ **CAFÉ DE LA MARE** (N° RR OCT 27 052) (Mme Marie-Madeleine **Mestanier**) ☎ 86-75-08-60 Closed Fri.

ARGENTIÈRE-LA-BESSEE(L') 05120 Hautes-Alpes **Map 19-B3**
♀ ⊗ ⌂ **HOTEL DE LA MAIRIE** (N° RR AVR 26 506) (M. Zohra **Benkhaled**) 32, avenue Charles de Gaulle ☎ 92-23-10-33.

ARGENTON-SUR-CREUSE 36220 Indre **RN 20 Map 16-A1**
♀ ⊗ ⌂ **LE RELAIS DES ROUTIERS** (N° RR NOV 17 413) (Mme Mauricette **Calmel**) Saint-Marcel, 7, Rte de Châteauroux ☎ 54-24-01-77 ⊷ 6 Closed Sun. Menus 45-80F; specialties: *coq au vin, coquilles de crabes, andouillettes grillées.* English, Spanish spoken.

ARGENVIERES (L') 18140 Cher **RD 45 Map 13-B2**
♀ ⊗ ⌂ **CAFE DE LA MARINE** (N° RR OCT 15 815) (Mme **Sautereau**) l'Ecluse-d'Argenvières ☎ 36-74-47-14.

ARLES 13200 B.-du-R. **RN 113 Map 24-A3**
♀ ⊗ ⌂ **LE RELAIS DU PASSAGE A NIVEAU** (N° RR AVR 25 893) (Antoine and Laurence **Pech-Faure**) Route de Tarascon 31, av. de la Libération ☎ 90-96-06-64 ⊷ 8 Closed Sun (restaurant). Full-board 140-160F per night. Coaches welcome (rest. seats 52). Evening meals. English, Italian, German, Spanish spoken.

ARMENTIERES 59280 Nord **RN 42 Map 5-A1**
♀ ⊗ **AUBERGE DE LA LYS** (N° RR FEV 26 183) (Mme Jacqueline **Leflon**) 110, rue des Résistants ☎ 20-77-21-83 ⊷ 4 Closed Sun. Evening meals.
♀ ⊗ **Café-Restaurant LA TERRASSE** (N° RR MARS 26 194) (Mme Évelyne **Delporte**) 112, rue des Résistants ☎ 20-77-37-57 Closed Sun afternoon.

ARNAY-LE-DUC 21250 Côte-d'Or **RN 6 Map 13-B3**
♀ ⊗ **RELAIS DU ST-PRIX** (N° RR AVR 26 510) (M. Robert **Tonelli**) ☎ 80-84-81-74 Closed Sat afternoon, Sun. Full board 160-180F per night. Evening meals. Italian spoken.

A

ARQUES-LA-BATAILLE 76880 Seine-Maritime **RD 154 Map 4-A2/3**
♀ ⊗ **CHEZ ANDREE** (N° RR MAI 21 940) (Mme Andrée **Guerrier**) 77, rue du 11 novembre ☎ 35-85-54-00 Closed Sun; 1 to 30 Aug.

ARRAS 62000 P.-de-C. **RN 25 Map 5-B3**
♀ ⊗ ⌂ **AU POINT DU JOUR** (N° RR OCT 24 707) (SARL M. Patrick **Renier**) 13, avenue Michonneau ☎ 21-59-96-42 ⊷ 4 Closed Sat 2pm, Sun.

ARTENAY 45410 Loiret **RN 20 Map 9-B1**
♀ ⊗ ⌂ **2 stars NN RELAIS D'ARTENAY** (N° RR SEPT 26 670) (M. Lucian **Lichet**) rue de Chartres ☎ 38-80-40-78 ⊷ 34 English spoken.

ARVERT 17530 Chte-Marit. **RD 14 Map 11-B1**
♀ ⊗ ⌂ **LE RELAIS DES 3 CANARDS** (N° RR JUIL 26 938) (Mme Pascale **Branco**) ☎ 46-36-40-43 ⊷ 5 + 8 bungalows Closed Fri afternoons, Sat mornings. English spoken.

ASCOUX 45300 Loiret **RN 721 Map 9-B1**
♀ ⊗ **AUBERGE SAINT-ELOI** (N° RR MAI 26 543) (SDF **Robillard-Daroux**) 1, rue de Pithiviers ☎ 38-33-00-20 ⊷ 3 Closed Sun; 15-31 July. Coaches welcome (rest. seats 140).

ASSEVILLERS 80200 Somme **Autoroute A1 Maps 5-B3 and 6-A1 see PERONNE**

ATHIS 51150 Marne **RN 37 Map 6-B2**
♀ ⊗ **AU BON ACCUEIL** (N° RR SEP 17 895) (Mme Ginette **Bourscheidt**) 12, Route Nationale ☎ 26-59-62-61.

ATTIGNY 08130 Ardennes **Map 6-B2**
♀ ⊗ ⌂ **SPORT BAR** (N° RR JANV 26 792) (Mme Nicole **Pienne**) 16, place Charlemagne ☎ 24-71-20-69 ⊷ 3.

AUBAGNE 13400 B. du R **RN 8 Map 24-B3**
♀ ⊗ **LES ROUTIERS** (N° RR OCT 26 058) (M. Saïd **Sidi Boucif**) RN 8 La Tourtelle ⊷ 5 Closed Sun afternoon. Arabic spoken.

AUBE 61270 Orne **RN 26 Map 8-A2**
♀ ⊗ **LE PETIT QUEBEC** (N° RR MAI 26 903) (M. Jean-Claude **Rialland**) 47, route de Paris ☎ 33-24-55-34 Closed Sun and Aug. English and Spanish spoken.

AUBERGENVILLE 78410 Yvelines **RN 13 and 190 Map 1-A1**
♀ ⊗ **L'AMI RENÉ** (N° RR AVR 24 212) (M. Michel **Bellotto**) 21, rue Gaston Jouillerat ☎ 30-95-70-07 Closed Sun.

AUBERIVES-SUR-VARÈZE 38550 Isère **RN 7 Map 18-B3**
♀ ⊗ ⌂ **LE RELAIS DES ROUTIERS — Chez François et Marie-Hélène** (N° RR AVR 21 498) (Mme Marie-Hélène **Graziano**) ☎ 74-84-90-71 ⊷ 8 Closed Sun afternoon; 1-15 Sept. Full board 155F per night. Coaches welcome (rest. seats 60). Evening meals.

AUBERVILLIERS 93300 S.-St-Denis **Porte d'Aubervilliers Map 1-A2**
♀ ⊗ **LE RELAIS CRÉOL** (N° RR AOUT 26 623) (M. Alain **Mercien**) 119, avenue Victor Hugo ☎ 48-33-68-99.
♀ ⊗ **AU RENDEZ-VOUS DES CAMIONNEURS** (N° RR SEP 24 330) (M. Akil **Ayadi**) 17, rue, de la Haie-Coq ☎ 43-52-09-15.

AUBETERRE 10150 Aube **RN 77 Map 9-B3**
♀ ⊗ **LES TILLEULS** (N° RR DEC 26 401) (M. Raymond **Mielle**) ☎ 25-37-51-11 Closed Sun.

AUBIÈRE 63170 Puy-de-Dôme **Map 16-B3**
♀ ⊗ ⌂ **L'EUROPE** (N° RR OCT 27 069) (M. Michel **Mouestier**) SARL, 41 av. du Roussillon ☎ 73-26-34-61 ⊸ 10 Closed Sat afternoon and Sun. English spoken. Service Station open 6am to 10pm.

AUBIERS (LES) 79250 Deux-Sèvres **RN 759 Maps 12-B1 and 11-B3**
♀ ⊗ **HOTEL DU CHEVAL BLANC** (N° RR JUN 11 565) (M. Claude **Sauer**) 9, place St-Melaine ☎ 49-65-60-51 ⊸ 2 Closed Sat afternoon; Sun afternoon; Aug.

AUBIGNAS 07400 Ardeche **RN 540 Map 24-A2**
♀ ⊗ ⌂ **RELAIS DE LA GARE** (N° RR NOV 26 392) (Melle **Borne**) Quartier de la Gare ☎ 75-52-43-89 ⊸ 6 Closed Sundays from 1 Nov to Easter. Full-board 90-120F per night. (1 room + dinner 2 pers 190F). Coaches welcome (rest.seats 60). Evening meals. English, Spanish spoken.

AUBIGNY-AU-BAC 59265 Nord **RN 17 Map 5-B3**
♀ ⊗ ⌂ **LE BERTREISIEN** (N° RR JUL 25 990) (M. Didier **Wattelet**) 21, route Nationale ☎ 27-80-96-40 **Minitel** ⊸ 5 Full-board 165-195F per night. Coaches welcome (rest. seats 140). Evening meals. English spoken.

AUBIGNY-SUR-NÈRE 18700 Cher **RD 940 Map 13-A1**
♀ ⊗ ⌂ **LE RELAIS DES ROUTIERS** (N° RR JAN 17 168) (M. Bernard **Ollier**) 17, av. Charles Lefebvre ☎ 48-58-01-42 ⊸ 9 Closed Sun; public holidays; August. Full board 125-135F per night. Evening meals.

AUCAMVILLE 31140 Haute-Garonne **Map 22-A2**
♀ ⊗ ⌂ **REST LE TOIT** (N° RR JUIN 26 259) (M. Jean-Pierre **Lablanchi**) 50 Chaussée des Mazuries ☎ 61-70-46-37 Coaches welcome (rest. seats 150). Spanish spoken.

AUCH 32000 Gers **RN 124 Map 21-B2**
♀ ⊗ ⌂ **1 Star NN MODERN HOTEL** (N° RR SEP 19 908) (M. Henri **Thibault**) 10 bis, avenue Pierre Mendis-France ☎ 62-05-03-47 ⊸ 14 from 80-200F, breakfast 16-25F, telephone in room, access for disabled. Closed Sat; Sun. Restaurant and bar closed Sat, Sun lunchtime. Meals served until 9 pm. Parking, dogs allowed. Places to visit: Museum, Cathedral. Some English spoken.

AUCHY-LES-MINES 62138 P.-de-C **RN 41 Map 5-B1**
♀ ⊗ **ROUTIERS ARTÉSIENS** (N° RR MAR 26 832) (M. Daniel **Fon-**

A

Auchy-les-Mines continued
 taine) 120, Rte Nationale ☎ 21-66-74-81.

AUDEUX 25170 Doubs **CD 67 Map 14-B3**
 ♈ ⊗ **LE CHANAT** (N° RR SEPT 26 986) (M. Bernard **Jeandenant**) 6,
 Grande Rue-Au Village ☎ 81-58-05-87 English spoken. 5km from
 filling station.

AUDUN-LE-ROMAN 54560 M.-et-M. **RD 156 Map 6-B3**
 ♈ ⊗ ⌂ **HOTEL DE LA POSTE** (N° RR DEC 25 244) (M. Patrick
 Schwarz) 25/27, rue Albert Lebrun ☎ 82-21-61-53 ⊷ 8 Closed
 Sun. German, Italian spoken.

AULNAY-SOUS-BOIS 93600 S.-St-Denis **Autoroute A1 Map 1-A3**
 ♈ ⊗ ⌂ **BISTRONORD** (N° RR AVR 24 923) (M. Jean-Claude **Pradal-
 ler**) Garonor BP 660 ☎ 48-65-63-41 ⊷ 14 Closed Sat, Sun. English
 spoken.

AUMONE (L') par MOUHET 63490 Indre **RN 20 Map 16-A1**
 ♈ ⊗ ⌂ **A L'ARRET DES ROUTIERS** (N° RR OCT 21 658) (M. Pierre
 Boussely) ☎ 54-47-55-11 ⊷ 6 Closed Sat; Sun (except Jun-Sept).
 Evening meals. English, German spoken.

AUMETZ 57710 Moselle **RN 52 Map 6-B3**
 ♈ ⊗ ⌂ **CAFÉ DE LA POSTE** (N° RR JANV 27 145) (Mme Linda
 Cossa) 15, rue Roch ☎ 82-91-91-71 ⊷ 6 Closed Tues pm. Italian
 spoken.

AUNEAU 28700 E.-et-L. **RD 177 Map 9-B1**
 ♈ ⊗ ⌂ **HOTEL DES TROIS MARCHES** (N° RR SEP 26 309) (M.
 André **Lesage**) 2, rue Emile-Labiche ☎ 37-31-70-49 ⊷ 6 Closed
 Sun afternoon; Aug. Half board 110-140F per night. Coaches
 welcome.

AURILLAC 15000 Cantal **RN 126 Map 17-B2**
 ♈ ⊗ **L'ÉTAPE DU ROUTIER** (N° RR MARS 26 219) (M. Michel
 Muller) Rue des Frères Lumières Zl de Sistrières ☎ 71-64-66-70
 Closed Sun; Sat afternoon. Coaches welcome (rest. seats 150).
 Evening meals.

AUSSILLON MAZAMET 81200 Tarn-et-Garonne **RN 112/118 Map 22-
B2**
 ♈ ⊗ **LE RELAIS DU COMMERCE CHEZ LOULOU** (N° RR 25 991)
 (M. Louis **Blavy**) 21, av. Charles-Sabatié ☎ 63-61-26-16 **Minitel**
 Closed Sun; 11 to 25 Aug. Coaches welcome (rest. seats 120).
 Spanish spoken.

AUTECHAUX 25110 Doubs **near to the Péage de Beaume-les-Dames
motorway Map 10-A3**
 ♈ ⊗ **RELAIS DE L'AUTOROUTE LA DÉTENTE** (N° RR DEC 26 112)
 (Mme Simone **Courtial**) Beaume-les-Dames ☎ 81-84-01-14 Closed Fri afternoons 3-6pm. Full board. Coaches welcome (rest.
 seats 80). Meals until 2 am.

AUTHEUIL 27490 Eure **RN Map 3-B1**
♀ ⊗ **LA MARMITE** (N° RR OCT 26 075) (M. André **Person**) 17, Rue de Pacy ☎ 32-34-67-67 Closed Sat; Aug.

AUTHIEUX (LES) 27220 Eure **RD 835 Map 8-A3**
♀ ⊗ **LE RELAIS DES AUTHIEUX** (N° RR NOV 22 569) (M. Claude **Lecomte**) St-André-de-l'Eure ☎ 32-37-31-03 Evening meals.

AUTUN 71400 S.-et-L. **Map 13-B3**
♀ ⊗ **LE CLUB** (N° RR NOV 25 169) (Mme Eva **Rizzo**) **Pizzeria** 13, route de Beaune Pont-l'Evêque ☎ 85-52-27-72 ⇥ 4 Closed Sun.

AUVERSE 49490 M. et L. **Map 12-A2**
♀ ⊗ **LES ROUTIERS** (N° RR AOUT 26 030) (M. Michel **Chasseau**) Route de Noyant à Beauge ☎ 41-82-20-13 Closed Sat, Sun; 15 days in Oct. Evening meals until 9.30pm.

AUVILLERS-LES-FORGES 08260 Ardennes **RN 43 Map 6-A2**
♀ ⊗ ⌂ **ARRET DES ROUTIERS** (N° RR JAN 23 608) (Mme Nicole **Bonnaire**) Mon Idée ☎ 24-36-32-77 ⇥ 5 Closed Sat; 15 Dec to 1 Jan. Coaches welcome (rest. seats 70). Meals served until 10pm.

AUXERRE 89000 Yonne **RN 6 Map 13-A2**
♀ ⊗ ⌂ **1 Star NN LE SAINTE-NITASSE** (N° RR AVR 17 517) (Mme **Courault**) Rte de Chablis ☎ 86-46-95-07 ⇥ 31 from 90-150F; breakfast 16,50-18F. Closed at weekends in winter; 20 Dec to 4 Jan. Coaches welcome (rest. seats 60). Meals served until 10.30 pm, menus from 48F. Parking, dogs allowed. Sites to visit: medieval Auxerre. English spoken.
♀ ⊗ **CAFÉ DE LA NOUVELLE GARE** (N° RR MAR 25 834) (M. Claude **Halle**) 7, rue Paul-Doumer ☎ 86-46-90-17 Closed Wed. English spoken.
♀ ⊗ **LA PETITE VITESSE** (N° RR OCT 26 697) (M. Frédéric **Gouret**) 44, av de la Puisaye ☎ 86-52-35-29 Closed Sunday. English spoken. See also **VENOY.**

AUXONNE 21130 Côte de Or **RN 5 Map 14-A3**
♀ ⊗ **LE MICADO** N° RR OCT 26 696) (Mme Martine **Seurre**) Rte de Dôle ☎ 80-31-00-45.

AUXY 45340 Loiret **RN 375 Map 9-B1**
♀ ⊗ **AUBERGE DU PUITS** (N° RR JANV 26 419) (Mme Marie-Madeleine **Delteil**) 21, rue Principale ☎ 38-96-70-05 Closed Wed; half of Feb; 8 days in Sept. Restaurant closed Sat, Sun evenings.

AUZITS 12390 Aveyron **RN 140 Map 22-B1**
♀ ⊗ **IGUE DU MOULIN** (N° RR JUIL 26 957) (Mme Brigitte **Felzines**) Rignas ☎ 65-63-90-90.

AVALLON 89200 Yonne **RN 6 Map 13-A2/3**
♀ ⊗ **RELAIS SAINT-CHRISTOPHE** (N° RR OCT 27 053) (M. Rémy Vernier) 13, route de Paris ☎ 86-34-07-17 Closed Sun.

A

AVELIN 59710 Nord **RN 353 Map 5-B1**
♈ ⊗ **A L'EMBUSCADE** (N° RR AOU 14 906) (Mme **Lemoine**) 14, Route de Seclin ☎ 20-32-90-33 Closed Sat, Sun, Fri evening. Meals until 9.30pm.

AVESNES-SUR-HELPE 59440 Nord **RN 2 Map 6-A1**
♈ ⊗ **LE RELAIS MARGUERITE** (N° RR JUL 14 444) (M. Marguerite **Sorriaux**) 22, avenue de la Gare ☎ 20-61-17-88 Closed 1 to 15 Aug.

AVÈZE 72400 Sarthe **Map 8-B3**
♈ ⊗ ⌂ **AUBERGE DU CHEVAL BLANC** (N° RR JUL 24 290) (M. Michel **Beule** - SARL) La Ferté-Bernard ☎ 43-93-17-05 ⊸ 20 Coaches welcome (rest. seats 300).

AVIGNON (84000 Vaucluse) **RN 7 Map 24-A2**
♈ ⊗ ⌂ **2 Stars NN LE RELAIS D'AVIGNON – SARL d'Exploitation** (N° RR NOV 22 100) (M. Henri **Savry**) Montfavet ☎ 90-88-18-06 **Minitel** ⊸ 18 Restaurant – 200 seats. Parking – 9000m^2 – with loudspeaker. Full-board 200–250F per night. Coaches welcome (rest. seats 140/110). Evening meals. English, Spanish spoken.

AVIGNONET DE LAURAGAIS 31290 Hte-Garonne **RN 113 Map 22-A2**
♈ ⊗ ⌂ **LA PERGOLA** (N° RR MAI 22 329) (M. Etienne **Batan**) ☎ 61-81-63-54 **Minitel** ⊸ 6 Closed Sat evening to Sun evening; from 15 Nov to 30 Nov; 15 days in Feb. Coaches welcome (rest. seats 170). Evening meals. Spanish spoken.
⚱ **Total Station Service LE RELAIS DE NAUROUZE** (N° RR JUL 25 060) (Mme Christiane **Fernandez**) Aire du Lauragais ☎ 61-81-68-23 Open 24 hours. English, Spanish spoken.

AVION 62210 P.-de-C. **RN 43 Map 5-B3**
♈ ⊗ **LE PTI-POT** (N° RR FEV 23 655) (M. and Mme Pierre **Milleville**) 276, Bld H.-Martel ☎ 21-43-14-12 Closed Sun afternoon. Coaches welcome (rest. seats 45). Evening meals until 8.30pm.

AVRANCHES 50300 Manche **RN 176 Map 8-A1**
♈ ⊗ **LE RELAIS DES ROUTIERS** (N° RR OCT 26 341) (M. Jean-Pierre **Liberge**) 70, rue de la Constitution ☎ 33-58-01-13 Closed Sun, except Jul, Aug; half of Sept. Coaches welcome (rest. seats 32/35). Evening meals until 8.30pm. English spoken.
♈ ⊗ **LES ROUTIERS Chez Jean-Pierre et Joëlle** (N° RR SEPT 27 030) (M. Jean-Pierre **Lambert**) 107, rue de la Liberté ☎ 33-58-19-30 Closed Sun and 1st to 20th August.

AWOINGT près CAMBRAI 59400 Nord **RN 39 Maps 6-A1 and 5-B3**
♈ ⊗ ⌂ **AU CHANT DES OISEAUX** (N° RR DEC 22 594) (M. **Plouquet**) 3, route du Cateau ☎ 27-81-31-05 **Minitel** ⊸ 14 Closed Sun; 10 to 20 Aug. Full-board 160F per night. Coaches welcome (rest. seats 70). Evening meals.

AYNAC 46120 Lot **RD 940 Map 17-B1**
♈ ⊗ **RELAIS DU QUERCY** (N° RR AVR 26 525) (Mme Nicole **Lacam**) Grande Rue ☎ 65-38-98-91 Coaches welcome (rest. seats 68). English spoken.

AZAY-LE-FERRON 36290 Indre **Map 12-B3**
♈ ⊗ **L'UNION** (N° RR JUL 25 983) (M. Thierry **Audoin**) Place de l'Église ☎ 54-39-20-88 Closed Mon. Filling station near.

AZAY-LE-RIDEAU 37190 I.-et-L. **RN 751 and RD17 Map 12-B2**
♈ ⊗ **LE RELAIS DE LA GARE** (N° RR SEP 22 484) (M. Robert **Bodier**) 59, avenue de la Gare ☎ 47-43-30-60. Closed Sun; Aug. Coaches welcome (rest. seats 120). Evening meals.

AZERAT 24210 Dordogne **RN 89 Map 17-A1**
♈ ⊗ ⌂ **LE RELAIS D'AZERAT** (N° RR SEP 12 424) (Mme **Debord**) ☎ 53-05-21-05 ⊷ 4 Closed end Aug. Full board. Coaches welcome.

BACCARETS (LES) 31550 Hte-Gar. **RN 20 Map 22-A2**
♈ ⊗ ⌂ **LA CHAUMIÈRE** (N° RR JUN 26 933) (M. Daniel **Laroche**) ☎ 61-08-90-70 ⊷ 15 Closed Sun.

BAGNÈRES-DE-LUCHON 31110 Hte-Garonne **Map 21-B3**
♈ ⊗ ⌂ **1 star NN L'ESCAPADE** (N° RR FEV 25 831) (Mme Michèle **Luzent**) 27, av. Jean-Jaurès ☎ 61-79-91-85 ⊷ 11 from 70-90F, breakfast 10–15, 50F Closed low season; Sat, Sun; mid-Dec to mid Jan. Parking, bar, dogs allowed. Sites to visit: Basilique. Some Spanish, English spoken.

BAGNOLS-EN-FORET 83600 Var **Map 25-B2**
♈ ⊗ ⌂ **LE RELAIS DU COMMERCE** (N° RR AVR 24 901) (M. Serge **Ghigo**) Grande Rue ☎ 94-40-60-05 ⊷ 10 Closed Tues low season. Italian Spoken.

BAIGTS-DE-BÉARN 64650 Pyr.-Atl. **RN 117 Map 20-B2/3**
♈ ⊗ ⌂ **LE RELAIS DE BAIGTS** (N° RR MAI 19 349) (Mme **Austruy-Peres**) ☎ 59-69-15-05 ⊷ 7 Full-board 150–180F per night. Coaches welcome (rest. seats 170). Evening meals. English, Spanish spoken.

BAIGTS-EN-CHALOSSE 40380 Landes **RD 2 Map 20-B2**
♈ ⊗ ⌂ **AU CARREFOUR** (N° RR MAR 24 178) (M. Jean **Bonnot**) ☎ 58-98-63-05 ⊷ 4 Closed Mon. Full-board 110F per night. Coaches welcome (rest. seats 100). Evening meals.

B

BAILLEUL 59270 Nord **RN 42 Map 5-A1**
- ♀ ⊗ ⌂ **1 star NN AUBERGE LE SEAU** (N° RR MAI 23 786) (M. Joël **Dequidt**) Le Seau ☎ 20-48-62-00 ⊷ 11 from 110-140F, breakfast to 23F. Full-board 170–190F. Coaches welcome (rest. seats 60). Meals until 10pm. Parking; bar; dogs admitted only to restaurant; pool table; pinball; sites: Museum; Mont de Flandres.
- ♀ ⊗ **CHEZ ANDRÉ** (N° RR MARS 27 222) (M. André **Nooreberghe**) Rte Nle 46771 Rte de Lille RD 933 ☎ 28-49-29-14

BAILLEUL-SUR-THERAIN 60930 Oise **RD 12 and RD 620 Map 3-A2**
- ♀ ⊗ **L'ALOUETTE** (N° RR MAI 26 902) (Mme Mireille **Lemaire**) 4, rue de Villers ☎ 44-07-66-26.

BAILLEULVAL 62123 Pas de Calais **RN 25 Map 5-B3**
- ♀ ⊗ ⌂ **BAC DU SUD** (N° RR JUIL 26 958) (M. Yves **Sanson**) ☎ 21-58-79-12 ⊷ 7 Flemish, Dutch, English spoken.

BAIX 07210 Ardèche **RN 86 Map 24-A1**
- ♀ ⊗ **A MA CAMPAGNE** (N° RR MAI 19 790) (Mme Nara **Arsac**) Quartier des Lilas ☎ 75-85-80-26 Closed Sun evening. Coaches welcome (rest. seats 100). Evening meals.

BALAN-LA-VALBONNE 01120 Ain **Map 2-A2**
- ♀ ⊗ ⌂ **FRONT DE BANDIÈRE SARL** (N° RR JANV 27 136) (M. Henri **Bouvard**) Route de Balan ☎ 78-06-35-61 ⊷ 8 Closed Sat and Sun.

BALARAUC-LE-VIEUX 34770 Hérault) **RN 113 Map 23-B2**
(Voir Issanka)

BALIZAC 33730 Gironde **RD 110 and 111 Map 20-B1**
- ♀ ⊗ **LE RELAIS BASQUE** (N° RR MAI 22 809) (M. **Desclaux**) ☎ 56-25-86-71 Closed Mon; Oct. Coaches welcome (rest. seats 125). Evening meals.

BANNOST 77155 S.-et-M. **RN 4 Map 9-A2**
- ♀ ⊗ **LE RELAIS DE LA GARE** Chez Huguette (N° RR FEV 14 215) (M. Georges **Fontaine**) ☎ 64-01-02-07 Closed Sat, Sun; Aug.

BANYULS DELS ASPRES 66300 Pyr. Orientales **RN 9**
- ♀ ⊗ ⌂ **L'HOSTAL DE CATALUNYA** Sarl (N° RR JUIN 26 909) (M. Robert **Fanon**) Route de Pérthus ☎ 68-21-81-60 ⊷ 11

BAPAUME 62450 P.-de-C. **RN 17 Map 5-B3**
- ♀ ⊗ ⌂ **CHEZ BERNADETTE** (N° RR MAR 24 892) (Mme Bernadette **Molle**) 45, faubourg de Péronne ☎ 21-07-12-78 and 21-07-46-83 ⊷ 7 Closed Sat 8pm to Sun 10pm; Christmas to New Year. Full-board. Coaches welcome (rest. seats 50). Evening meals.

BARAQUEVILLE 12160 Aveyron **RN 88 and 111 Map 22-B1**
- ♀ ⊗ ⌂ **LE RELAIS PALOUS** (N° RR FEV 21 398) (M. Edmond **Palous**) ☎ 65-69-01-89 ⊷ 14 Closed Sun; 24 Dec to 2 Jan. Full-board 125–145F per night. Coaches welcome (rest. seats 110). Evening meals until 12pm.

B

BARATIER 05200 Hautes-Alpes **Map 25-A1**
♈ ⊗ **LES 4 AVENUES** (N° RR JUN 24 598) (M. Christian **Strappazzon**)
Place du Village ☎ 92-43-03-50 Closed Mon evening. English
spoken.

BARBASTE 47230 L.-et-G. **RN 655 Map 21-A2**
♈ ⊗ **LES PALMIERS** (N° RR AVR 21 891) (Société **Gineste et Fils**) ☎
53-65-55-02 Closed Sat in winter, Mon evening; Jan. Coaches
welcome (rest. seats 70). Evening meals. Spanish spoken.

BARBEZIEUX-ST-HILAIRE 16120 Charente **RN 10 Map 15-A2**
♈ ⊗ **LE RELAIS DES ROUTIERS DE LA BILLETTE** (N° RR AOU 22
018) (Mme **Houdusse**) Route Nationale 10, Châteauneuf ☎ 45-78-
57-09 Closed Sun. Open 24 hours. Coaches welcome (rest. seats
200). Evening meals. Menus from 50-70F. Specialities: *confit de
canard, escalope à la charentaise, magret de canard*. Spanish
spoken.

BARJAC 48000 Lozère **Map 23-A1**
♈ ⊗ **PARADIS HOTEL** (N° RR FEV 18 956) (M. **Paradis**) ☎ 66-47-01-
09.

BARNAS 07330 Ardèche **RN 102 Map 24-A1**
♈ ⊗ ⌂ **LE RELAIS DES ROUTIERS** (N° RR AVR 16 028) (Mme
Marthe **Cellier**) ☎ 75-36-40-78 ⊷ 12 Full-board 155F per night.
Coaches welcome (rest.seats 60). Evening meals.

BARNEVILLE-CARTERET 50270 Manche **RN 803 Map 4-B1**
♈ ⊗ ⌂ **HOTEL DES SPORTS** (N° RR AVR 24 196) (M. Pierre **Brien**)
Place du Docteur Aubret ☎ 33-53-84-76 ⊷ 11 Closed Sat
afternoon; Sun 15 Sept to 15 March. Evening meals.

BARQUE (LA) 13970 B.-du-R. **RN 96 and RD 6 Map 24-B3**
♈ ⊗ **LE RELAIS DES QUATRE CHEMINS** (N° RR MAR 26 207)
(Mme Colette **Girardi**) ☎ 42-58-60-03 Closed Sat, Sun low
season. Italian spoken.

BARRE-EN-OUCHE (LA) 27330 Eure **RN 833 Map 8-A3**
♈ ⊗ **CHEZ JACKY ET CORINNE** (N° RR OCT 25 144) (M. and Mme
Jacky **Scipion**) Grande Rue ☎ 32-44-35-28 Coaches welcome (35
seats). Evening meals.

BASSE-INDRE 44160 L.-Atl. **RD 107 Map 11-42**
♈ ⊗ ⌂ **HOTEL BRETON** (N° RR MAI 25 415) (M. Yannick **Jaheny**)
10, Quai Langlois ☎ 40-86-01-65 ⊷ 12 Closed Sat, Sun; Aug.
Meals served at all times.

BASTIDE-L' EVEQUE (LA) 12200 Aveyron **RD 911 Map 22-B1**
♈ ⊗ **RELAIS DE L'HERMET** (N° RR FEV 26 810) (M. Yvon **Bourdon-
cle**) Villefranche-de-Rouergue ☎ 65-65-61-41 Closed Sun, Mon
evenings. Spanish and English spoken.

BAUDRE 50000 Manche
♈ ⊗ **TABAC-ÉPICERIE L'INCOGNITO** (N° RR JUIL 27 317)

B

Baudre continued
(M. Lionel et Mme Monique **Maris-Bret**) Le Bourg ☎ 33-57-89-58
Minitel Closed Sun. English spoken. Evening meals.

BAUME-LES-DAMES 25110 Doubs **RN 83 Maps 10-A3 and 14-B3**
♀ ⊗ ⌂ **3 Stars NN HOTEL ZISS REST LA CREMAILLÈRE** (N° RR
JUL 13 903) (M. Alfred **Ziss**) ☎ 81-84-07-88 **Minitel** Hyèvre-
Paroisse ⌐ 21 3 star rooms, 10 for lorry drivers. Closed Sat; Oct.
Menus from 50-145F. Specialities: *coq au vin, canard à l'orange
porc au madère*. German, English spoken.

BAVANS 25550 Doubs **RN 463 Map 10-A3**
♀ ⊗ ⌂ **LE RELAIS DES MARRONNIERS** (N° RR AOU 15 757) (M.
Louis **Garnier**) Rue des Cerisiers ☎ 81-96-26-54 ⌐ 5 Closed Aug.

BAYEUX 14400 Calv. **RN 13 Map 4-B2**
♀ ⊗ **LA COLOMBE** (N° RR MAR 22 274) (M. **Hardy**) 13, route de
Caen, Saint-Vigor-le-Grand ☎ 31-92-13-65 and 31-21-12-28 **Minitel** ⌐ 3 (furnished) Closed Sat evening, Sun (evening in summer); Jan. Full-board 150F per night. Coaches welcome (rest.
seats 360). Evening meals.

BAZAINVILLE 78123 Yvelines **RN 12 Map 1-B1**
♀ ⊗ **LA PETITE AUBERGE** (N° RR NOV 18 231) (Mme Sonia
Herluison) Place de l'Église ☎ 34-87-61-40.

BAZEILLES 08140 Ardennes **RN 381 Map 6-A2**
♀ ⊗ ⌂ **LA GIVONNE** (N° RR MARS 21 843) (Mme Elisabeth **Huem-
er**) 15, avenue du Général Lebrun ☎ 24-27-05-74 **Minitel** ⌐ 5
Closed Sun; Aug. Full-board 120–150F per night. Coaches welco-
me (rest. seats 120). Evening meals. German, English, Dutch,
Italian spoken.

BAZOCHE-GOUET (LA) 28330 E.-et-L. **RD 927 Map 8-B3**
♀ ⊗ **LA BONNE AUBERGE** (N° RR AVR 22 787) (M. Jean-Paul
Thierry) 54, avenue du Général Leclerc ☎ 37-49-21-61 Closed
fornight in Feb. Evening meals.

BAZOCHES-EN-DUNOIS 28140 E.-et-L. **RN 827 and RD 27 Map 8-B3**
♀ ⊗ **AU BON ACCUEIL - CHEZ MARIE-CLAUDE** (N° RR DEC 21
717) (Mme Marie-Claude **Boucher**) 7, rue de l'Église ☎ 37-22-08-
30. Coaches welcome (rest. seats 50). Evening meals.

BAZOUGES SUR LE LOIR 72200 Sarthe **RN 23 Map 12-A2**
♀ ⊗ **AUBERGE DU SOLEIL LEVANT** (N° RR SEPT 26 996) (M. Denis
Borée) 79, Avenue du Maine ☎ 43-45-33-47. Filling station near.
English spoken.

BEAUCE 35133 Ille-et-Villaine **RN 12 Map 8-B1**
♀ ⊗ **BEC FIN LES ROUTIERS** (N° RR JAN 26 789) (Mme Nicole
Vandevelde), 19, rue de Paris ☎ 99-99-08-00 Closed alternate
Suns; Aug.

B

BEAUCHALOT par SAINT-MARTORY 31360 Hte-Gar. **RN 117 Map 21-B3**
♈ ⊗ ⌂ **AUX BEARNAIS** (N° RR SEP 20 540) (M. René **Frechou**) ☎ 61-90-23-44 ⊷ 5 Closed Mon; 1 to 15 Oct. Full board. Coaches welcome. Evening meals. English, Spanish, German spoken.

BEAUCHAMPS 80770 Somme **RN 16 Bis Map 4-A2**
♈ ⊗ ⌂ **LES ROUTIERS** (N° RR MAI 21 913) (M. Michel **Blot**), 44, Grande Rue ☎ 22-26-13-12 ⊷ 5 Closed Sun; end Dec.

BEAUCROISSANT 38140 Isère **RD 159 Map 24-B1**
♈ ⊗ **LE RELAIS DU CHAMP DE FOIRE** (N° RR MAR 24 889) (Mme Marie-Thérèse **Blain**) Le Bain - Rive-sur-Fure ☎ 76-91-05-17. Closed Sun; fortnight in Aug and fortnight in Sept. Coaches welcome (rest. seats 40).

BEAULIEU 45630 Loiret **RD 926 and 951 Map 13-A2**
♈ ⊗ ⌂ **HOTEL DU LOIRET** (N° RR JAN 22 639) (M. Roland **Goury**) Place du Général-de-Gaulle ☎ 38-35-83-34 ⊷ 7 Closed Sun in winter; 3 weeks in Aug. Full board 145F per night. Evening meals.

BEAUMAIS 14620 Calvados **RD 148 Map 8-A2**
♈ ⊗ **LE RELAIS DES ROUTIERS** (N° RR JUN 21 571) (Mme Bernadette **Saillanfait**) ☎ 31-90-70-88.

BEAUMONT-SUR-VESLE 51400 Marne **RN 44 Map 6-B2 and 9-A3**
♈ ⊗ ⌂ **2 stars NN LA MAISON DU CHAMPAGNE** (N° RR MAR 2 227) (M. Marc **Boulard**) 2, rue du Port ☎ 26-03-92-45 ⊷ 10 from 75-200F, breakfast to 22F. Closed Sun evening, Mon; 2 weeks in Feb; 2 weeks in Oct. German, English, Luxemburg spoken. Coaches welcome (rest. seats 110). Evening meals. Menus from 38-130F. Specialities: *terrines du chef, rognons de veau au ratafia, canard aux griottes.* Sites to visit: Vineyards, 1st World War battlefields.

BEAUNE 21200 Côte-d'Or **RN 74 Map 13-B3**
♈ ⊗ ⌂ **AUBERGE DE LA GARE SARL** (N° RR SEPT 26 655) 11, avenue des Lyonnais ☎ 80-22-11-13 ⊷ 9 Closed Sun, public holidays; Aug.
♈ ⊗ **CAFÉ DE FRANCE** (N° RR NOV 24 023) (M. Jean-Pierre **Le Payen**) 13, Faubourg Bretonnière ☎ 80-22-25-44 Coaches welcome (rest. seats 55).
♈ ⊗ **LE MALMEDY** (N° RR DEC 21 315) (Mme Yvette **Pecout**) 6, rue du Lieutenant-Dupuis ☎ 80-22-14-74 Coaches welcome (rest. seats 90). Evening meals summer only.
♈ **TRUCKSTORE CAFÉ BEAUNE** BP 134 ☎ 80-21-40-78 Télex: 352 105.

BEAUNE-LES-MINES 87830 Haute-Vienne) **RN 20 Map 16-B1**
♈ ⊗ ⌂ **LA TERRASSE** (N° RR MAI 13 721) (Mme Rachel **Barelaud**) ☎ 55-39-90-58 ⊷ 16 Closed Sun and August. English spoken.

85

B

BEAUSSET (LE) 83330 Var **RN 8 Map 24-B3**
☺ ⊗ **TERRASSE OMBRAGÉE SUR L'AÉRODROME** (N° RR NOV 25 207) (Mme Marie-France **Gautier**) RN 8 circuit Paul-Ricard Le Camp du Castellet ☎ 94-90-71-48 Closed Sat; 19 Dec to 5 Jan. Coaches welcome (rest. seats 100). English, Portuguese spoken.

BEAUVOIR-EN-LYONS 76220 Seine-Maritime
☺ ⊗ **RELAIS NORMAND CHEX FRANÇOISE ET JULIEN** (N° RR JUIL 27327) (M. Julien **Jué**) Les Carreaux ☎ 35-90-17-20 **Minitel** Closed Sat, Sun and Bank holidays.

BEAUVOIR-SUR-MER 85230 Vendée **RN 148 Map 11-B2**
☺ ⊗ **AU RELAIS DU GOIS** (N° RR JUN 14 383) (M. Gilles **Grondin**) ☎ 51-68-70-31 Closed 1 to 31 Dec. Coaches welcome (rest. seats 150). Evening meals (Jul, Aug).

BEAUVOIR-SUR-NIORT 79360 Deux-Sèvres **RN 13 Map 15-A1**
☺ ⊗ **L'ETAPE** (N° RR JUL 25 038) (M. Louis **Grignon**) 7, place de l'Hôtel de Ville ☎ 49-09-70-17 Closed Sun afternoon, Mon; end Aug to beginning Sept. Coaches welcome (rest. seats 50). Some English spoken.

BEAUVOIS-EN-CAMBRESIS 59157 Nord **Map 6-A1**
☺ ⊗ **Service Station ELF LE JEUNE BOIS** (N° RR FEV 26 816) (M. Louis **Haesart**) Caudry ☎ 27-85-62-34. English, Dutch, German spoken.

BEDEE 35160 I.-et-V. **RN 12 Map 7-B3**
☺ ⊗ 🏨 **1 Star NN HOTEL DU COMMERCE** (N° RR SEP 13 987) (M. Jean-Louis **Rigoreau**) 14, Place de l'Eglise ☎ 99-07-00-37 and 07-00-76 **Minitel** ⏩ 22 Restaurant closed Sun evening; 1 to 21 Aug. Full board 168-195F per night. Coaches welcome (rest. seats 280). Evening meals. English spoken.

BEFFES 18560 Cher **RN 45 Map 13-B2**
☺ ⊗ 🏨 **LE JACK LONDON** (N° RR JUIL 26 961) (M. Jany **Ombredane**) rue du Château Gaillard ☎ 48-76-54-91 ⏩ 8 English spoken. Filling station near.
☺ ⊗ **AU PAPILLON ROSE** (N° RR AVR 21 865) (Mme **Hautin**) RK route de la Cimenterie ☎ 48-76-50-57 Closed Sat; Oct.

BEIGNON 56300 Morbihan **RN 24 Map 7-B3**
☺ ⊗ 🏨 **LE RELAIS DES ROUTIERS** (N° RR MAR 14 268) (M. Pierre **Labbe**) 40 km from Rennes – 60 km from Vannes ☎ 97-75-74-37 ⏩ 6 Closed Sat afternoon. Coaches welcome (rest. seats 60). Full board 160-180F per night. Evening meals until 9.30pm.

BELLAC 87300 Haute-Vienne **Map 16-B1**
☺ ⊗ **LE RELAIS** (N° RR AVR 25 906) (M. Henri **Cotte**) 3, rue Fernand Fourreau ☎ 55-68-00-22 Closed Sun; Sept. Evening meals.

BELLANCOURT 80100 Somme **RN 35 Map 5-A3**
☺ ⊗ **CHEZ ALINE ET MICHOU** (N° RR JUL 25 477) (M. Jean-Michel **Hoflack**) 2, Rte Nationale ☎ 22-24-35-13 **Minitel** Closed Sun in

winter; 15 days in Sept/15 days Dec. Coaches welcome (rest. seats 60). Evening meals.

BELLEGARDE 01200 Ain **RN 101 Map 18-B2**
Υ ⊗ **LES PLATANES** (N° RR JUL 26 588) (Mme Bruno **Lorenzati**) 5, rue Centrale ☎ 50-48-15-05. Closed Sun; Aug. Italian spoken.

BELLEGARDE 45270 Loiret **RN 60 Maps 9-B1 and 13-A1**
Υ ⊗ ⌂ **1 Star NN LE CAFÉ DU COMMERCE** (N° RR AOU 9 843) (Mme Nelly **Grégoire**) 1, rue de la République ☎ 38-90-10-45 ⊷ 12 (5 with shower) from 85-120F, breakfast from 18-20F. Closed Fri evening, Sat; Dec/Jan. Full-board 150–180F per night. Coaches welcome (rest. 3 rooms 170 seats). Evening meals. Parking; bar; dogs allowed. Sites to visit: Châteaux, Churches.

BELLEGARDE 30127 Gard **RN 113 Map 24-A3**
Υ ⊗ **LE LOU FÉLIBRE** (N° RR DEC 27 119) (Sarl Cabinet Pierre Curie) ☎ 66-01-15-21 Closed Sun (low season) German, English, Spanish and Italian spoken.

BELLE-INUTILE (LA) par CONNERRE 72160 Sarthe **RN 23 Map 8-B2**
Υ ⊗ ⌂ **1 Star NN LA BICHE DOREE** (N° RR JUL 25 595) (Mme Marcelle **Veyreveze**) RN 23 ☎ 43-76-70-45 ⊷ 10 (2 with shower) + 9 not licensed from 90-120F, breakfast from 15-18F. Closed Sat evening, Sun. Coaches welcome (rest. seats 80-100). Full board available. Parking (1 hectare); bar; dogs allowed; TV. Sites to visit: Sarthe and surroundings.

BELLEME 61130 Orne **RN 155 and RD 938 Map 8-B2**
Υ ⊗ ⌂ **SARL LE CHAMP DE FOIRE** (N° RR MARS 27 236) (Mlle **Baire**) 4, place du Gl-Leclerc ☎ 33-73-00-38 ⊷ 6 Closed Sun except 1/5 to 31/8. Spanish and English spoken.
Υ ⊗ **LE GUÉ ROUTIER** (N° RR DEC 26 762) (M. and Mme Bernard **Herouin**) Le Bourg, Le Gué de la Chaine ☎ 33-73-02-66

BELLENGREVILLE 14370 Calv. **RN 13 Map 4-B2**
Υ ⊗ **HOTEL DE LA PLACE** (N° RR MAI 26 253) (M. Désiré **Desmeulles**) 16, rue de Paris ☎ 31-23-61-50 Closed Sat afternoon, Sun. Evening meals.

BELLERIVE 03700 Allier **Map 16-B3**
Υ ⊗ ⌂ **LE BOIS DE BOULOGNE** (N° RR JUIN 26 930) (Mme Edith **Moliner**) 130, avenue de Vichy ☎ 70-32-38-11 ⊷ 6 English and Spanish spoken.

BELLEVILLE 55100 Meuse **Map 6-B3**
Υ ⊗ **CHEZ DÉDÉ** (N° RR MAI 25 417) (M. **Buffelo**) 164, av. du Gl-de-Gaulle ☎ 29-84-57-85 Verdun Italian spoken. Closed Sun and two weeks in SEPT. Coaches welcome (Rest. seats 40).

BELLEVUE-COETQUIDAN 56380 Morbihan **Map 7-B3**
Υ ⊗ ⌂ **L'UNION** (N° RR MARS 20 131) 3, avenue de Brocéliande ☎ 97-75-71-46 ⊷ 5 Closed Sun; Aug. Showers, shared bathroom.

B

BELLEVUE-LA-MONTAGNE 43350 Hte-Loire **RD 906 Map 17-A3**
Y ⊗ ⌂ **HOTEL DES VOYAGEURS** (N° RR MARS 26 217) (Mme
Odette **Chapon**) ☎ 71-00-50-15 ⊷ 12. Full board available.
Coaches welcome (rest. seats 110).

BELLEVUE-par-MORNANT 69440 Rhône **RD 42 Map 2-B1**
Y ⊗ **LE RELAIS DE BELLEVUE** (N° RR MAR 18 045) (M. Georges
Guyot) ☎ 78-81-22-26 Closed Sun; 2 weeks in Aug. Coaches
welcome (rest. seats 70). Meals served until 11pm.

BELLEY 01300 Ain **RN 504 Map 2-A3**
Y ⊗ **REST DE LA GARE** (N° RR AOUT 25 614) (Mme Elisabeth
Bavu) Avenue de la Gare ☎ 79-81-06-60. Full board 130-140F per
night. Coaches welcome (rest. 2 rooms of 80 seats). Meals served
until 10pm.

BELLIGNAT 01810 Ain **RN 840 Map 19-A1**
Y ⊗ **A LA BONNE AUBERGE** (N° RR DEC 18 911) (M. Michel
Detouillon) 11, avenue Oyonnax ☎ 74-77-24-18 ⊷ 3 Closed Aug.

BENESSE-MARENNE 40690 Landes **RN 10 Map 20-A2**
Y ⊗ ⌂ **HOTEL DES PINS** (N° RR JUN 25 023) (M. Jean-Claude
Bernettes) ☎ 58-72-56-41 ⊷ 5 Closed Sun; 20 Sept to 10 Oct.
Coaches welcome (3 dining rooms of 120 places). Meals served
until 9.30pm.

BERCK-SUR-MER 62600 Pas-de-Calais **Map 5-A2/A3**
Y ⊗ **RELAIS D'ARTOIS** (N° RR MARS 26 826) (M. Raoul **Postell**) 20,
rue Alfred-Lambert ☎ 21-09-29-35 ⊷ 14.

BERNES-SUR-OISE 95340 Val d'Oise **Map 3-B3**
Y ⊗ **CHEZ CLAUDINE** (N° RR DEC 27 124) (Mme Claudine **Diehl**)
1, rue de Creil ☎ 34-70-04-00 ⊷ 4. Closed Sat, Sun and August.

BERSON 33390 Gironde **RN 137 Map 15-A3**
Y ⊗ **LA REIGNIERE** (N° RR MAR 18 035) (M. Liliane **Demel**) ☎ 57-
64-35-36 Closed Sat, Sun; Aug or Oct. Coaches welcome (rest.
seats 60). Evening meals.

BERRE 13130 Bouches-du-Rhône **Map 24-B3**
Y ⊗ **CHEZ MIMI ET DONAT REST DE L'ENTENTE** (N° RR DEC 24
801) (M. Donat **Le Guennec**) Rte du Moulin Vieux ☎ 42-85-37-44
Closed Sat, Sun; Aug. German, English spoken.

BERTHOLENE-par-LAISSAC 12310 Aveyron **RN 88 Map 23-A1**
Y ⊗ ⌂ **1 Star NN HOTEL BANCAREL** (N° RR AVR 21 480) (M. Jean
Brun) Situated on outskirts of Palanges forest ☎ 65-69-62-10
Minitel ⊷ 13 from 100-140F, breakfast to 18F. Closed 1st 2
weeks Oct. Full-board 160–180F per night. Coaches welcome
(rest. seats 150). Evening meals. Parking (individual lockable
garages); bar; dogs allowed; Grand Terrasse. Menus 34-100F.
Specialities: *Feuilleté Roquefort, Confit de canard à l'ancienne,
Tripoux du Rouergue.* Sites: Trou de Bozouls, Gorges du Lot.

BESSAY-SUR-ALLIER 03340 Allier **RN 7 Map 16-A3**
♈ ⊗ **LE BAR DE LA ROUTE BLEUE** (N° RR JAN 20 633) (Mme Rolande **Ponta**) rue Charles-Louis-Philippe ☎ 70-43-01-59 Closed Mon; Aug. Coaches welcome (rest. seats 80). Evening meals.

BESSE-SUR-BRAYE 72310 Sarthe **RN 821 Map 12-A3**
♈ ⊗ ⌂ **1 Star NN LE RELAIS DE LA GARE** (N° RR OCT 13 181) (Mme Marguerite **Lenoir**) 19, avenue de la Gare ☎ 43-35-30-22 ⊸ 15. Meals served in evening.

BESSIÈRES 31660 Haute-Garonne **Map 22-A2**
♈ ⊗ ⌂ **1 Star NN LE BESSIÉRAIN** (N° RR NOV 27 101) (M. Philippe **Turmo**) avenue de Montauban ☎ 61-84-00-95 Rest. closed August.

BEURLAY 17250 Chte-Mme **RN 137 Map 11-B1**
♈ ⊗ **LE RELAIS D'ARY** (N° RR SEPT 26 631) (M. Yves **Mariaud**) L'Olivière- Saint-Porchaire ☎ 46-95-01-39 Coaches welcome (rest. 3 rooms of 75 places). Meals served until midnight. Spanish spoken.

BEUVRY-LES-BETHUNE 62660 P.-de-C. **RN 43 Map 5-A1**
♈ ⊗ **AU BON ACCUEIL** (N° RR MAR 26 883) (Mme Madiana **Thurlure**) 32, route Nationale ☎ 21-65-15-60.

BEUZEVILLE 27210 Eure **RN 175 and CD 22 Map 4-B2**
♈ ⊗ **CAFÉ DE L'ESPÉRANCE** (N° RR DEC 27 125) (Mme Denise **Deguine**) 4, rue Pasteur ☎ 32-57-70-60 Closed Sun pm and 2 weeks of August. English spoken.

BEYNAC-EN-PÉRIGORD 24220 Dordogne **RD 703 Map 15-B2**
♈ ⊗ ⌂ **2 Stars NN SARL HOSTELLERIE MALEVILLE** (N° RR FEV 25 804) (M. Jacques **Maleville**) ☎ 53-29-50-06 ⊸ 20 Closed Mon from Oct to Easter. English spoken. Full board 195 to 250F. Coaches welcome (Rest. seats 150) evening meals served until 11.30pm.

BEZENET 03170 Allier **RN 145 Map 16-A2**
♈ ⊗ **RESTAURANT DU MIDI** (N° RR MAR 23 154) (M. Michel **Destainville**) Route Nationale ☎ 70-07-72-15 ⊸ 4 Closed Sat; 1 week May, 1 week Oct or Nov. English, Spanish, Italian spoken.

BEZIERS 34500 Hérault **RN 113 Map 23-A2**
♈ ⊗ ⌂ **LE RELAIS DE LA GRANDE VITESSE** (N° RR MAI 19 050) (Mme Anne-Marie **Prome**) 23, boulevard de Verdun ☎ 67-76-26-30 Closed Wed. Coaches welcome (rest. seats 40). Evening meals.

BIARS-SUR-CERE 46290 Lot **RN 140 Map 17-B1**
♈ ⊗ ⌂ **CHEZ ALAIN RELAIS ROUTIERS** (N° RR AVR 23776) (M. Alain **Cavalhac**) 16, av. de la République ☎ 65-38-42-30 ⊸ 4 Closed Sun; Aug. Coaches welcome (rest. seats 110). Evening meals.

B

BIGAROUX-SAINT-SULPICE-DE-FALEYRENS 33300 Gironde **RN 670 Map 15-A3**
♈ ⊗ ⌂ **LE RELAIS CHEZ LA PUCE** (N° RR SEP 10 992) (Mme Renée **Forillière**) ☎ 51-24-71-18 ⊷ 5 Closed Sat, Sun. Coaches welcome (rest. seats 70).

BINAS 41240 L.-et-C. **RN 157 Map 12-A3**
♈ ⊗ **LE SAINT CHRISTOPHE** (N° RR AVR 24 930) (M. Philippe **Duvernet**) 17, place St-Maurice ☎ 54-82-40-26 Closed Sun. Full-board 160–180F per night. Evening meals.

BITSCHWILLER-LES-THANN 68620 Ht-Rhin **RN 66 Map 10-B3**
♈ ⊗ ⌂ **LE RELAIS DE LA VILLE DE THANN** (N° RR JAN 10 268) (M. Alain **Bannwarth**) 12, rue du Rhin ☎ 89-37-02-64 ⊷ 5 Closed Sat; Sept. German, English spoken.

BIVILLE-LA-BAIGNADE 76890 S.Mme **RN 27 Map 3-A1**
♈ ⊗ **LA CUILLERE EN BOIS** (N° RR NOV 24 021) (Mme Yvette **Guerillon**) ☎ 35-32-88-81 Closed Wed. Evening meals.

BLACY 51300 Marne **RN 4 Map 9-A3**
⛽ **Esso Service Station LES INDES** (N° RR OCT 550000093) (M. Gilles **Hurel**) ☎ 26-74-16-36 Closed Sun. English spoken.

BLAGNY 08110 Ardennes **RN 381 Map 6-A3**
♈ ⊗ **LE RELAIS DES CITES** (N° RR FEV 17 463) (M. Gérard **Lemaître**) 37, Rte Nationale ☎ 24-22-00-23 Closed Sat; Aug. Evening meals.

BLAMONT 54450 Meurthe-et-Moselle **Map 10-A2**
⛽ **Total Service Station RELAIS D'OGEVILLER** (N° RR FEV 24 862) (M. Christian **Perrette**) Rte Nle 4 ☎ 83-72-27-82 Closed Sun. German spoken.

BLANC-MESNIL (LE) 93150 Seine-St-Denis **RN 2 Map 1-A3**
♈ ⊗ **LA TRAVERSEE DE L'ATLANTIQUE** (N° RR JAN 9 225) (M. Auguste **Lemore**) 178, rue de Flandre ☎ 48-66-89-24 Closed Sun.
♈ ⊗ **LE BON ACCUEIL** (N° RR SEP 26 663) (M. André **Seban**) 58, avenue du 8-Mai-1945 ☎ 48-67-19-88. Open 8am–2am daily. Coaches welcome (rest. seats 123 in 3 rooms). English spoken.

BLANZY 71450 Saône-et-Loire **Map 18-A1**
♈ ⊗ **BAR RESTAURANT DE LA GARE** (N° RR OCT 27 043) (M. Bernard **Borowski**) 16, rue de la Gare ☎ 85-68-03-05 English spoken.

BLAUSASC 06440 Alpes-Maritimes
♈ ⊗ **LE RELAIS CAMPAGNARD** (N° RR JUIL 27 323) (Mme Marie **Negri**) Pointe de Blausasc ☎ 93-91-13-14 English spoken. Evening meals served until 9pm.

BLAYE-LES-MINES 81400 Tarn **RN 88 Map 22-B1**
♈ ⊗ ⌂ **RELAIS SAINTE MARIE** (N° RR MARS 26 847) (M. Jacky **Lacroix**) 53, Bois Redon, Carmaux ☎ 63-76-53-81. ⊷ 7 Closed Sat, Sun.

BLENOD-LES-PONT-A-MOUSSON 54700 M.-et-M. **RN 57 Map 14-B1**
Ⓨ ⓧ **CHEZ FERNANDE** (N° RR DEC 23 056) (SARL Chez Fernande) 88, avenue Victor-Claude ☎ 83-81-03-54 Closed Sun; Aug. Evening meals.

BLERE 37150 I.-et-L. **RN 76 Map 12-B3**
Ⓨ ⓧ **LE RELAIS** (N° RR DEC 17 964) (Mme Paulette **Rossignol**) 48, route de Tours ☎ 47-57-92-31 **Minitel** Closed Sat evening; Sept. Coaches welcome (rest. seats 130). Evening meals.

BLOIS 41000 L.-et-C. **RD 951 Map 12-A3**
Ⓨ ⓧ **BAR DE LA CITÉ** (N° RR MARS 26 862) (M. Didier **Moreau**) 55, avenue de Vendôme ☎ 54-43-48-54 Closed Sat and Sun. Coaches welcome (Rest. seats 60). Evening meals.
Ⓨ ⓧ **CAFÉ-ROUTE** (M. Jean-Louis **Pignot**) Autoroute A10 ☎ 54-46-84-73 Self-service café open 6am to 11pm.

BLYES 01150 Ain **Autoroute A42 Map 2-A2**
Ⓨ ⓧ 🏠 **AUBERGE DE BLYES** (N° RR DEC 25 237) (M. Georges **Durand**) Lagnieu ☎ 74-61-50-15 ⊷ 4 Closed Sun. Full-board 150–180F per night. Coaches welcome (rest. seats 180). Evening meals until midnight.

BOEN-SUR-LIGNON 42130 Loire **RN 89 Map 18-A2**
Ⓨ ⓧ **BAR RELAIS ROUTIERS** (N° RR JUN 26 921) (Mme Laurence **Carton**) 83, rue de Lyon ☎ 77-24-44-76. Closed Sun.

BOGNY-SUR-MEUSE 08120 Ardennes **Map 6-A2**
Ⓨ ⓧ **LE RELAIS DE LA GARE CHEZ COCO** (N° RR JUL 24 619) (M. Enrique **Herraiz**) 1, rue de la Vallée ☎ 24-32-03-51 Closed Sun; Aug.

BOISNEY 27300 Eure **RN 13 Map 4-B3**
Ⓨ ⓧ 🏠 **CHEZ MARC** (N° RR SEP 25 099) (M. Jean-Pierre **Thomas**) Rte Nle 13 ☎ 32-43-23-43 ⊷ 7.

BOIS D'OINGT (LE) 69620 Rhône **Map 2-A1**
Ⓨ ⓧ **LE RELAIS DU LAC** (N° RR AVR 24 917) (Mme Christiane **Sibourg**) Les Petits Ponts ☎ 74-71-60-01 Closed Tue afternoon. Evening meals.

BOIS-PARIS see MAINVILLIERS

BOISSY-SOUS-ST YON 91780 Essonne **RN 20 Map 9-B1**
Ⓨ ⓧ **LA RELAIS DE TORFOU** (N° RR FEV 27 181) (M. Mohamed **Toufahi**) RN 20 30, av. de Paris ☎ 64-91-30-50 English, German and Spanish spoken.

BOLLENE 84500 Vaucluse **RN 7 Map 24-A2**
Ⓨ ⓧ 🏠 **1 Star NN LE RELAIS DE LA CROISIERE** (N° RR MAI 19 792) (M. Paul **Laugier**) ☎ 90-30-20-05 ⊷ 17 from 80-195F, access for disabled. Open 6 am to 11 pm. Closed Sats 1 Oct to 1 Jun. Evening meals. Parking; bar; dogs allowed.

B

BONCHAMP-LES-LAVAL 53210 Mayenne **RN 157 Map 8-B1**
♀ ⊗ ⌂ **LE RELAIS DE LA CORBINIERE** (N° RR JAN 17 733) (M.
Roger **Dessaint**) ☎ 43-90-36-04 ⚊ 7 Closed Sat evening, Sun
from end March to beginning Nov. Coaches welcome (rest. seats
60). Evening meals until 10pm.

BONLOC 64240 Pyrénées-Atlantiques **RN 21 Map 20-A3**
♀ ⊗ **LILI PEAN** (N° RR NOV 25 190) (M. Gaston **Fouché**) **Hasparren**
☎ 59-29-51-48 **Minitel** Closed Sat; 15 Dec to 15 Jan. Coaches
welcome (rest. seats 150). Evening meals. English spoken.

BONNEVILLE-SUR-ITON (LA) 27190 Eure **RD 129 and RN 830 Map
3-B1 and 8-A3**
♀ ⊗ **CAFÉ DES SPORTS** (N° RR NOV 8 068) (M. Roland **Fontaine**) 45,
rue Jean-Maréchal ☎ 32-37-10-16 ⚊ 4 Closed Christmas, New
Year. Evening meals.
CAFÉ DE L'ÉGLISE (N° RR SEP 26 999) (M. and Mme Sylvain
Dareau and Olida **Vasseur**) 23, rue Jean-Maréchal ☎ 32-37-11-90
⚊ 3 Filling station near.

BONSECOURS 12560 Aveyron **Map 23-A1**
♀ ⊗ **LES ROUTIERS** (N° RR AOU 25 072) (Mme Thérèse **Vayssie**)
Campagnac ☎ 65-47-64-77 Closed Sat.

BONSON 42160 Loire **RD 82 Map 18-A2**
♀ ⊗ ⌂ **1 Star NN LE RELAIS DES SPORTS** (N° RR FEV 23 679)
(Mme Arlette **Pasca**) 14, avenue de la Gare ☎ 77-55-20-12 ⚊ 7
Full-board 130–140F per night. Coaches welcome (rest. seats 45).
Evening meals until 8.30pm. German, Italian spoken.

BORDEAUX 33000 Gironde **RN 10 Maps 15-A3, 20-B1 and 21-A1**
♀ ⊗ **LE RELAIS DU BON COIN – Chez Georgette** (N° RR JAN 24
081) (Mme Georgette **Betbeder**) 142, rue Lucien-Faure ☎ 56-39-
40-13 1 shower. Closed Sat, Sun; Aug.
♀ ⊗ **RESTAURANT DE L'UNION** (N° RR AVR 27 255) (M. Dominique
Depeyris) 116, rue Lucien-Faure ☎ 56-50-05-77 Closed Sat pm,
Sun and August. English spoken.
♀ ⊗ ⌂ **LE PORTO** (N° RR DEC 24 771) (Mme Rosa-Maria **Pereira**)
202 bis, quai de Brazza ☎ 56-86-15-93 ⚊ 6 Closed Sat, Sun; Aug.
Evening meals. Portuguese, Spanish spoken.
♀ ⊗ **CHEZ PIERRETTE** (N° RR AOU 26 973) (M. Alain **Debot**) 186, av
de Labarde ☎ 56-39-66-70 Closed Sat, Sun; last week Jun, first
fortnight in Jul. Some English, German spoken. Filling stations
near.

BORDS 17430 Chte-Mme
♀ ⊗ **CAFÉ DU CENTRE** (N° RR OCT 26 361) (M. Martial **Per-
rocheau**) ☎ 46-83-84-31 Evening meals served until 9pm. German spoken.

LA BORIE see RIBERAC 24600 Dordogne

BORT-LES-ORGUES 19110 Corrèze **RN 122 Map 17-A2**
♀ ⊗ ⌂ **LE RELAIS DES ROUTIERS – CHEZ ANTOINETTE** (N° RR

B

SEP 14 954) (Mme Antoinette **Cheriex**) 9 place du Champ-de-Foire ☎ 55-72-00-42 ⊷ 5.

BOSGUÉRARD DE MARCOUVILLE 27520 Eure **RN 138 Map 4-B3**
♀ ⊗ ⌂ **1 Star LA TÊTE D'OR** (N° RR MARS 26 844) (M. Gérard **Anquetin**) Route de Lisieux ☎ 35-87-60-24 ⊷ 14. Rooms 103 to 135F. Breakfast 16 to 23F. Wheelchair access. Closed at end of January. Dogs allowed. Horse riding and forest walking close by.

BOUC-BEL-AIR 13320 B.-du-R. **RN 8 Map 24-B3**
♀ ⊗ **LE RELAIS DE LA MALLE** (N° RR JUL 24 276) (M. Jean-Louis **Zanon**) ☎ 42-22-08-84 Closed Sat, Sun. Evening meals served until 8pm.

BOUDOU 82200 T.-et-G. **RN 113 Map 22-A2**
♀ ⊗ **LE MAQUISARD** (N° RR AOUT 25 619) (Mme Flora **Leghima**) RN 113 Moissac ☎ 63-39-66-38 Spanish, German spoken.

BOUESSAY 53290 Mayenne **RN 159 Map 12-A2**
♀ ⊗ ⌂ **LE RELAIS DES ROUTIERS** (N° RR JUN 19 824) (M. **Brilliet**) Rte de Sablé ☎ 43-70-82-05 ⊷ 13 Closed Sat afternoon, Sun. Evening meals.

BOUGUENAIS 44340 L.-Atl. **RN 751 Map 11-A3**
♀ ⊗ **A LA FERME** (N° RR JANV 25 786) (M. Yvon **Burlot**) 65, rue de la Pierre face Zl de Chevire ☎ 40-65-23-58 Closed Sat, Sun.

BOUJAN SUR LIBRON 34760 Hérault **RN 113 Map 23-A2**
♀ ⊗ ⌂ **LE CARRY** (N° RR SEP 27000) (Mme Patricia **Michavila**) ☎ 67-31-63-48 ⊷ 10 Closed Sun. English spoken. Filling station 2 kms distant.

BOULAY-LES-BARRES 45140 Loiret **RN 155 Map 13-A1**
♀ ⊗ ⌂ **L'AUBERGE DE LA ROUTE** (N° RR JUN 22 389) (M. and Mme Jacky **Gasnot**) 21, rte d'Orléans ☎ 38-75-34-90 ⊷ 7 Closed Sat; Aug. Evening meals until 10pm.

BOULIGNY 55240 Meuse **Map 6-B3**
♀ ⊗ **AU LION D'OR** (N° RR SEP 26 640) (M. Abdelkrime **Benzidour**) 72, rue de la Libération ☎ 29-87-93-34 Arabic spoken.

BOULOGNE SUR GESSE 31350 Haute Garonne **Map 21-B3**
Snack Bar LA GUINGUETTE (N° RR MAI 19 356) (M. Pierre **Favre**) Route de Blojan ☎ 61-88-11-64. Open 24 hrs. Italian, Spanish, Portuguese, English spoken. Near to filling station.

BOULOGNE-SUR-MER 62200 P.-de-C. **RN 1 Map 5-A2**
♀ ⊗ ⌂ **LE RELAIS DES DEUX GARAGES** (N° RR OCT 25 673) (M. Maurice **Lachère**) 54, avenue John-Kennedy ☎ 21-91-12-96 ⊷ 14 Closed Sat afternoon, Sun. Full-board 107–137F per night. Evening meals. English spoken.

BOULOIRE 72440 Sarthe **RN 157 Map 8-B3**
♀ ⊗ **LE P'TIT MARCHE** (N° RR JUN 26 573) (M. Francis **Hemonnet**), 82, rue Nationale ☎ 43-35-40-04 Closed Thur.

93

B

BOUQUEMAISON 80600 Somme **RN 16 Map 5-A3**
♀ ⊗ **LE RELAIS DES ROUTIERS – Chez Josette** Tobacconist (N° RR SEP 14 943) (Mme Josette **Doal**) 60, rue Saint-Pol ☎ 22-77-02-18 Closed 10 to 31 Aug.

BOURBON-LANCY 71140 S.-et-L. **RN 73 Map 16-A3**
♀ ⊗ ⌂ **HOTEL DE L'UNION** (N° RR SEPT 26 056) (M. Michel **Fleury**) Le Fourneau ☎ 85-89-15-07 ▬ 6 Closed end Dec. Full-board 120-130F per night. Coaches welcome (rest. seats 40). Evening meals.

BOURG-EN BRESSE 01250 Ain **RN 75 Map 18-B1**
♀ ⊗ **LE PUB** (N° RR JAN 26 796) (Mme. Paulette **Sueur**) Noirefontaine ☎ 74-23-05-40 Italian spoken.

BOURG-ET-COMIN 02160 Aisne **RD 967/925 Map 6-B1**
♀ ⊗ **L'ESCALE** (N° RR MARS 27 203) (M. Jacques **Pate**) 1, rue de Laon ☎ 23-24-40-44 Closed Mon pm.

BOURG-DE-PÉAGE 26300 Drôme **RD 532 Maps 18-B3 and 24-A1**
♀ ⊗ **LE RELAIS DU VERCORS** (N° RR FEV 23 646) (M. Raphaël **Sanchez**) L'Écancière ☎ 75-48-83-44 Grill Pizzeria Wedding receptions, banquets. Coaches welcome (rest. seats 90). Evening meals. English spoken.

BOURGANEUF 23400 Creuse **RN 140, 141 and RD 8 Map 16-B1**
♀ ⊗ **LE RELAIS DE LA COUPOLE** (N° RR FEV 16 891) (M. Gérard **Paquet**) 17, avenue Turgot ☎ 55-64-08-99 ▬ 13 Closed Sat; 25 Nov to 20 Dec. English spoken.
♀ ⊗ ⌂ **AU RENDEZ-VOUS DES CHASSEURS** (N° RR FEV 22 656) (Mme Monique **Feisthammel**) lieu-dit Puy-La-Croix – Saint-Pardoux-Morterolles ☎ 55-64-12-42 ▬ 16 Closed Sun.

BOURGES 18000 Cher **RN 151 Map 13-B1**
♀ ⊗ ⌂ **LES AILES** Sarl (N° RR OCT 27 038) 147, avenue Marcel Haegelen ☎ 48-21-57-86 ▬ 16 Closed Sun. English and German spoken.

BOURGNEUF-EN-MAUGES 49290 M.-et-L. **RN 762 Maps 12-A1 and, 11-A3**
♀ ⊗ ⌂ **LE RELAIS DES ROUTIERS** (N° RR AOU 16 174) (M. Étienne **Albert**) 6, rue Notre-Dame ☎ 41-78-03-61 ▬ 5 Closed Sun. Coaches welcome (rest. seats 90). Evening meals.

BOURGOIN-JALLIEU 38920 Isère **RN 85 Map 2-B2**
♀ ⊗ **SARL LA MAISON BLANCHE** (N° RR AVR 26 493) (M. Andre **Piloz**) RN 85 Nivolas-Vermelle ☎ 74-27-92-86 Closed Sat, Sun; Aug (3 weeks). Coaches welcome (rest. seats 90).

BOURNAN-BAGNEUX 49210 M.-et-L. **RN 160 Map 12-B2**
♀ ⊗ **LE RELAIS DE COTE DE BOURNAN-BAGNEUX** (N° RR JUN 16 601) (M. Claude **Sauzay**) 288, rue du Pont-Fouchard ☎ 41-50-18-02 Closed Sun. Coaches welcome (rest. seats 48).

BOURRAS 16200 Charente **RN 141 Map 15-A2**
♈ ⊗ **LE RELAIS DES VIGNES** (N° RR FEV 25 801) (Mme Monique **Delavoie**) RN 141 Commune de Mérignac ☎ 45-35-83-16 or 45-35-81-62 **Minitel** Closed Sun; Sept. Evening meals until 10pm.

BOUSSAIS 79600 Deux-Sèvres **RD 725 Map 12-B2**
♈ ⊗ **LE VERRE A SOI Tobacconist** (N° RR SEP 25 656) (M. Loïc **Boisselet**) **Airvault** ☎ 49-69-71-69 Closed Wed afternoon; 15 to 30 Aug.

BOUSSES 47420 Lot-et-Garonne **RD 665 Map 21-A2**
♈ ⊗ **AUBERGE DES RELAIS – Chez Nicole** (N° RR JUL 21 592) (Mme Nicole **Guillygormar'ch**) Au Bourg ☎ 53-89-11-62 Coaches welcome (rest. seats 60). Evening meals.

BOUSSOULET 43260 Haute-Loire **RD 15 Map 18-A3**
♈ ⊗ ⌂ **1 Star NN AUBERGE DU MEYGAL** (N° RR FEV 24 840) (M. René **Chapuis**) **St Julien Chapteuil** ☎ 71-08-71-03 ⊷ 12 (5 with own WC) from 70-85F. Full-board 120F per night. Coaches welcome (rest. seats 120/130). Evening meals. Parking; bar; dogs allowed. Lakes and forests to visit.

BOUVILLE 28800 E.-et-L. **RN 10 Map 8-B3**
♈ ⊗ **LE RELAIS DU BOIS DE FEUGERES** (N° RR JAN 15 914) (M. **Coatrieux**) ☎ 37-47-23-01 Closed Sat evening.

BOUVRON 44130 L. Atl. **RN 771 and D 16 Map 11-A2**
♈ ⊗ **LE BRETAGNE** (N° RR MARS 26 209) (M. Christian **Biard**) 1, Rue Louis Guihot, Blain ☎ 40-56-31-05 Closed Sun afternoon. Coaches welcome (rest. seats 170). Evening meals. English spoken.

BOUXWILLER 67330 Bas-Rhin **RD 6 and 7 Map 10-B1**
♈ ⊗ ⌂ **2 Stars NN LE RELAIS DU SOLEIL PMU** (N° RR AOU 15 750) (M. Charles **Jaeger**) 71, Grand'Rue ☎ 88-70-70-06 ⊷ 15 Closed Wed, Sun evening, beginning July to end school holidays; February '89. Full-board 140–170F per night. Coaches welcome (rest. 3 rooms with 120 seats). Evening meals. German, English spoken.

BOUY-LUXEMBOURG 10220 Aube **Map 9-B3**
♈ ⊗ **CHEZ RAYMONDE** (N° RR OCT 25 143) (Mme Raymonde **Bouvron**) **Tobacconist** ☎ 25-46-33-80 Closed Tue.

BOUZONVILLE 57320 Moselle **RN 418 Map 10-A1**
see CHEMERY-LES-DEUX

BOVES 80440 Somme **RN 334 Motorway Amiens-Roye Map 5-B3**
♈ ⊗ **LA GRENOUILLÈRE** (N° RR MAI 25 939) (M. Bouhou **Ouannoune**) La Grenouillère ☎ 22-09-31-26 **Minitel** Closed Sun (except for banquets); 3 weeks Aug. Coaches welcome (rest. seats 50). Evening meals. English, Algerian spoken.

B

BRAM 11150 Aude **RN 113 Map 22-B2**
♀ ⊗ 🏠 **AUBERGE MONTPLAISIR – Chez Alain** (N° RR DEC 21 332) (M. Alain **Albecq**) ☎ 68-76-12-75 ⊷ 6 Closed Sat, Sun; 1 to 31 Aug; 24 Dec to 1 Jan. Evening meals.

BRANSLES 77620 S.-et-M. **RN 219 Map 9-B2**
♀ ⊗ 🏠 **LE LION D'OR** (N° RR OCT 25 156) (M. Philippe **Vercruyssen**) 2, av. du Gâtinais ☎ 64-29-55-05 ⊷ 7 Closed Tue.
♀ ⊗ 🏠 **LE RELAIS DE L'UNION** (N° RR MAR 25 342) (Mme Christine **Soares**) 2, place A.-Briand ☎ 64-29-59-14 ⊷ 6 Closed Wed and 14 Jul-15 Aug. Evening meals. English spoken.

BRAS-SUR-MEUSE 55100 Meuse **RD 964 Map 6-B3**
♀ ⊗ **LE RELAIS DE LA PAIX** Petrol, tobacconist (N° RR JUN 25 976) (Mme Anny **Renard**) 8, rue Raymond-Poincaré ☎ 29-83-90-13 Closed Tue. Coaches welcome (rest. seats 55). Evening meals.

BRASSAC-LES-MINES 63570 P.-de-D.) **RD 34 Map 17-A3**
♀ ⊗ **LE BRASSAC** (N° RR FEV 27 175) (M. Édouard **Kaluza**) 6, av. du Château ☎ 73-54-29-23 Closed Tues pm and Sun pm.

BRAY 27170 Eure **D 133 Map 4-B3**
♀ ⊗ **AUX AMIS** (N° RR DEC 26 765) (Mme Margaret **Herils**) Beaumont-Le-Roger ☎ 32-35-05-26 Closed Sun.

BRÈCE 53120 Mayenne **Map 8-B1**
♀ ⊗ **LE DOMINO** (N° RR JAN 26 428) (M. **Carlin**) Le Bourg ☎ 43-08-62-72 Evening meals served.

BRESSUIRE 79300 Deux-Sèvres **RN 748 Maps 11-B3, 12-B1 and 15-A1**
♀ ⊗ **LE FOCH** (N° RR FEV 25 822) (M. Marcel **Chailloux**) 51, bd du Ml-Foch ☎ 49-65-01-69 Closed Sat evening, Sun.

BRETHENAY 52000 Hte-Marne **RN 67 Map 14-A2**
♀ ⊗ 🏠 **BELLEVUE** (N° RR AOUT 7903) (Mme Micheline **Bourgoin**) Chaumont ☎ 25-32-51-02 Closed Sun and September.

BRETONCELLES 61110 Orne
♀ ⊗ 🏠 **HOTEL DE LA GARE** (N° RR OCT 26 335) (M. **Alloteau**) 17, rue Ernest Sagot ☎ 37-37-20-13 ⊷ 6 Closed Sun. Full-board 135F per night. Evening meals.

BRETTEVILLE-L'ORGUEILLEUSE 14740 Calvados **RN13 Map 4-B2**
♀ ⊗ 🏠 **AU GRAND MONARQUE** (N° RR OCT 10 066) (Mme Madeleine **Laurent**) 37, Rte de Caen ☎ 31-80-70-35 ⊷ 5 Closed Sat afternoon, Sun afternoon; Sept. Evening meals served except on Sat, Sun.

BRIANÇON 05100 Htes-Alpes **Map 19-B3**
♀ ⊗ **LA LANTERNE** (N° RR NOV 24 424) (M. René **Parisot**) (2 km from Sud Briançon RN 80) Chamandrin ☎ 92-21-12-33 Closed Sun. Coaches welcome (rest. seats 100). Evening meals. English, Spanish spoken.

B

BRIARE 45250 Loiret **RN 7 Map 13-A1/2**
Y ⊗ 🏠 **SARL LE RELAIS** (N° RR OCT 26 685) (M. Eric **Bourgouin**)
Gare de Chatillon-sur-Loire ☎ 38-31-44-42 ⇀ 8 Closed Sat
afternoon, Sun. German and English spoken.

BRIENNE 71290 Saône-et-Loire **Map 18-B1**
Y ⊗ **AUX AMIS DE LA ROUTE** (N° RR OCT 27 041) (Mme Elsa
Busca) Bas de Brienne ☎ 85-40-04-18 Closed Mon and August.
Italian and English spoken.

BRIENON-SUR-ARMANÇON 89210 Yonne **Map 13-A2**
Y ⊗ 🏠 **LES ROUTIERS** (N° RR MARS 27 239) (M. Christian **Dussart**)
21, rte de Joigny ☎ 86-43-00-63 Polish, Russian and English
spoken.

BRIGNOLES 83170 Var **RN 7 and RD 554 Map 25-A2**
Y   **LA MAMMA AUBERGE LA REINETTE** (N° RR NOV 28 081)
(Mlle Santina **Sepilesu**) RN 7 ☎ 94-59-07-46. Closed Sun and
August. German, Italian, Spanish and English spoken.

BRIIS-SOUS-FORGES 91640 Essonne **Autoroute A 10 Map 1-A2**
Y   **CAFÉ ROUTE** Motorway A10 (M. Yannick **Foucault**) Limours-
Janvry ☎ 64-90-77-18 Open 6am to 10.30pm.

BRIONNE 27800 Eure **RN Map 4-B3**
Y ⊗ 🏠 **HOTEL DU HAVRE** (N° RR MARS 26 484) (M. **Kopacz**) Place
Fremont-des-Essarts ☎ 32-44-80-28 **Minitel** ⇀ 16 English, Polish,
German spoken. Full board available. Coaches welcome (rest.
seats 240). Evening meals served.

BRIOUDE 43100 Haute-Loire **RN 102 Map 17-A3**
Y ⊗ **LE RELAIS DES SPORTS** (N° RR AVR 16 506) (M. Roger
Devins) Route de Clermont ☎ 71-50-14-39 ⇀ 4 (for drivers only).
Closed Sun; 15 Aug to 1 Sept. Coaches welcome (rest. seats 52).
Evening meals.

BRIOUX-sur-BOUTONNE 79170 Deux-Sèvres **RN 150 Map 15-A1/2**
Y ⊗ **AUBERGE DU CHEVAL BLANC** (N° RR AVR 25 915) (M. Henri
Nicole) Place du Champ-de-Foire ☎ 49-07-50-52. Closed Mon
evening. Coaches welcome (rest. seats 200). Evening meals.

BRIOUZE 61220 Orne **RN 24 Bis Map 8-A2**
Y ⊗ 🏠 **LE RELAIS DE LA POSTE** (N° RR FEV 3 369) (Mme
Maupas) ☎ 33-66-03-16 ⇀ 10 Evening meals until midnight.

BRIVE 19100 Corrèze **RN 89 and D Map 17-A1**
Y ⊗ 🏠 **NOUVEL HOTEL** (N° RR JAN 26 159) (M. Patrick **Lomey**) 2,
Rue Desgenettes ☎ 55-86-01-66 **Minitel** ⇀ 6 Closed Sat after-
noon, Sun; Aug.

BRIVE-LA-GAILLARDE 19100 Corrèze **RN 89 Map 17-A1**
Y ⊗ 🏠 **CHEZ MONIQUE** (N° RR MAR 23 187) (Mme Monique
Richard) Varetz ☎ 55-85-02-07 ⇀ 8.

B

BRIVE-CHARENSAC 43700 Hte-Loire **RN 88 and 535 Map 17-A3**
♇ ⊗ ⌂ **LE RELAIS DU COMMERCE** (N° RR DEC 23 561) (MM.
Ferret-Masson) 2, route de Lyon (on the banks of the Loire) ☎
71-09-16-16 ⊸ 10 Closed Sat. Full-board 160–170F per night.
Coaches welcome (rest. seats 40/50). Evening meals.

BROGLIE 27270 Eure **RN 138 Map 8-A2**
♇ ⊗ ⌂ **LES TOURISTES ET LES ROUTIERS – RELAIS DE BROG-
LIE** (N° RR JUN 17 824) (Mme Julienne **Vannier**) Côté de Bernay
à Broglie, rue Augustin-Fresnel ☎ 32-44-60-38 ⊸ 5 Closed 10
days in Feb. Coaches welcome (rest. seats 42). Evening meals.

BROMONT-LAMOTHE 63230 P.-de-D. **RD 941 Map 16-B2**
⊗   **LE RELAIS DE BOISSY** (N° RR FEV 14 203) (Mme **Boissy**) ☎ 73-
88-71-04.

BROU 28160 Eure-et-Loire **RN 155 Map 8-B3**
♇ ⊗ ⌂ **LE RELAIS DE LA GARE – LE RELAIS DE L'ARC-EN-
CIEL** (N° RR MAR 16 915) (M. Alain **Duparc**) 76, avenue du Gl-
de-Gaulle ☎ 37-47-00-81 ⊸ 11 Closed Sun; Aug. Coaches
welcome (rest. seats 72). Evening meals.

BROUT-VERNET 03110 Allier **Map 16-B3**
♇ ⊗ ⌂ **CENTRE ROUTIERS – SARL** (N° RR JANV 24 475) (Mme
Roux) Rte Nle 9, ☎ 70-58-24-61 **Minitel** ⊸ 14. Closed Sun. Full
board 150F per night. Coaches welcome (rest. seats 70). Evening
meals.
♇ ⊗ ⌂ **LES 3 CANARDS SARL** (N° RR JUL 26 589) (M. Patrice
Peltier) RN 9 Escurolles ☎ 70-58-20-88 Closed Sun. English,
Spanish spoken.

BRUAILLES 71500 S. et L. **RD 972/986 Map 18-B1**
♇ ⊗ ⌂ **REST. DES 4 CHEMINS** (N° RR JUL 26 589) (M. Jean-Pierre
Petitjean) Louhans ☎ 85-75-15-81 ⊸ 6 Closed Tue evening.
Open 24 hours.

BRUAY-EN-ARTOIS 62700 Pas-de-Calais near Nle 41 **Map 5-A1**
♇ ⊗ ⌂ **1 Star NN LA LOUETTE (formerly CHEZ MICHEL) Sarl
Cali** (N° RR MARS 26 635) (M. Serge **Domart**) 114, rue Raoul
Briquet, Place de la Gare ☎ 21-53-42-07 ⊸ 15 from 75-135F;
breakfast 10-18F; TV (optional). Parking; bar; dogs allowed.
Amusements: pin ball, darts, pool. Sites: Base d'Olhain, Colinne
de l'Artois, châteaux.

BUCEY-LES-GY 70700 Haute-Savoie **RD 474 Map 14-B3**
♇ ⊗ **CAFÉ DE LA GARE** (N° RR MAI 25 921) (Mme Yvette **Bole-
Besancon**) Pizzeria Rue de la Gare ☎ 84-32-92-02 Coaches
welcome (rest. seats 48/58). Evening meals until midnight.

BUIGNY-ST-MACLOU 80100 Somme **RN 1 Map 5-A3**
♇ ⊗ ⌂ **LE RELAIS DES ROUTIERS** (N° RR JUN 16 117) (M. Marc
Caron) ☎ 22-24-20-47 ⊸ 5 Closed Sat afternoon.

B

BUISSE (LA) 38500 Isère
Ⴢ ⊗ **RELAIS DES ROUTIERS CHEZ ANNIE** (N° RR MARS 27 219)
(Mme Annie **Revigliono**) Le Village Voiron ☎ 76-55-00-67 Italian
spoken.

BUNCEY 21400 Côte d'Or **RN 71 Map 13-A3**
Ⴢ ⊗ **LE CHARIOT** (N° RR JUN 26 555) (Paulette and Nadine **Lacroix**)
Chatillon/Seine ☎ 80-91-09-82 Night bell. Closed Sunday afternoon; 15-24 July. Coaches welcome (rest. seats 60). English
spoken.

BUSLOUP 41160 Seine-et-Marne **RN 33 Map 9-A2**
Ⴢ ⊗ **CAFÉ DU COMMERCE** (N° RR JUIN 26 927) (M. Gérard
Lefevre) Morée ☎ 54-23-43-41 Closed 8-30 Aug; 24 Dec-5 Jan.

BUSSIÈRES 77750 Seine-et-Marne **RN 33 Map 9-A2**
Ⴢ ⊗ **LE RELAIS AU SANS-GENE** (N° RR SEP 19 941) (M. Raymond
Tixier) 32, Rte de la Ferté-sous-Jouarre ☎ 60-22-50-18 Closed
Tue in Feb, Jul. Coaches welcome (rest. seats 80). Evening
⌂ meals. German, Polish spoken. Menus from 55-120F. Specialities:
*Andouillette au champagne, Filet de canard à l'orange ou aux
pruneaux.*

BUZANÇAIS 36500 Indre **RN 143 Map 12-B3**
Ⴢ ⊗ ⌂ **LE RELAIS DES ROUTIERS** (N° RR NOV 17 676) (M. Serge
Imbert) 15, route de Tours ☎ 54-84-07-37 ⊷ 8.
Ⴢ ⊗ **LES ROUTIERS** (N° RR JANV 26 133) (M. Bernard **Souadet**) 48,
rue des Hervaux ☎ 54-84-05-16 Closed Mon afternoon. Evening
meals.

C

CABOURG 14390 Calvados **RN 813 Map 4-B2**
Ⴢ ⊗ ⌂ **HOTEL DE LA MER** (N° RR AOUT 26 023) (Mme Suzanne
Cottineau) 2, av. René Coty Le Home Varaville ☎ 31-91-27-77 ⊷
10 Closed Sun; 1 Oct to 1 May; 15 Dec to 15 Jan. Full-board 160F
per night. Coaches welcome (rest. 2 rooms, 54, 12 seats).
Evening meals.
Ⴢ ⊗ **LE COLOMBIER** (N° RR NOV 26 103) (M. Gérard **Baudel**)
Route de Cabourg, Petiville ☎ 31-78-00-67 Closed Sun; Sept.
Evening meals.

CAEN 14000 Calvados **RN 13 Map 4-B2 and 8-A1**
Ⴢ ⊗ ⌂ **1 Star NN LA RENAISSANCE** (N° RR FEV 20 652) (M.
Lehericey) **Saint-Martin-des-Besaces** ☎ 31-68-72-65 ⊷ 8 Clo-
sed Mon, except in Summer; Jan. English spoken.

C

CAEN VENOIX 14000 Calvados **RN 175 Map 4-B2**
♀ ⊗ 🏠 **LE VELODROME** (N° RR MARS 26 195) (M. Daniel **Levi-goureux**) 9, av. Henri Cheron ☎ 31-74-40-71 ⊷ 5 Closed Sat, Sun; Aug. Evening meals.

CAGNY 14630 Calvados **RN 13 Map 4-B2**
♀ ⊗ 🏠 **1 Star NN HOTEL DES ROUTIERS Chez Jean-Louis et Monique** (N° RR FEV 25 806) (M. Louis **Charpentier**) 22, Rte de Paris ☎ 31-23-41-27 ⊷ 9 Closed Sun; Aug. Full board 150F per night; half board 115F per night. Evening meals. English spoken.
♀ ⊗ 🏠 **HOTEL DE LA POSTE** (N° RR JUL 26 602) (M. Dominique **Klaczak**) 32, Rte de Paris ☎ 31-23-41-26 ⊷ 5. Full board 140F per night. Coaches welcome (rest. seats 50). Evening meals.

CAHORS 46000 Lot **RN 20 Map 22-A1**
♀ ⊗ 🏠 **LE RELAIS DE LA BOURSE** (N° RR MAR 23 721) (M. Jean-Henri **Lebouvier**) 7, place Rousseau ☎ 65-35-17-78 ⊷ 12 Closed Sun; Aug. Full board 130–145F per night. Coaches welcome (rest. seats 90). Evening meals.

CAHUZAC-SUR-ADOUR 32400 Gers **RD 935 Map 21-A2**
♀ ⊗ 🏠 **LE RELAIS DES PYRÉNÉES** (N° RR OCT 14 016) (M. **Pozzobon**) ☎ 62-69-73-03 ⊷ 7 Closed Sat; Oct. Full-board 150F per night. Coaches welcome (rest. seats 50).

CAISSARGUES 30132 Gard **RN 113 – Nîmes St-Gilles Map 24-A3**
♀ ⊗ **LE MIRMAN** (N° RR FEV 26 446) (SNC Denis **Amigo**) Rte de Saint-Gilles Les Portes de Mirman ☎ 66-29-54-87. Closed Sat evening, Sun.

CALLAC 22160 C. du N **RN 787 Map 7-A2**
♀ ⊗ 🏠 **LES ROUTIERS** (N° RR OCT 26 064) (Mme Marie Yvonne **Richard**) 21, Rue de la Gare ☎ 96-45-51-10 ⊷ 7 Closed Sun. Full board 140F per night. Coaches welcome (rest. seats 95). Evening meals until 10.30pm.

CALLENGEVILLE 76270 Seine-Maritime **Map 4-A3**
♀ ⊗ 🏠 **AUBERGE NORMANDE** (N° RR NOV 24 750) (Mme Françoise **Foulny**) Rte Nle 28 Neufchâtel ☎ 35-93-74-07 ⊷ 6. Closed Sat. Full board 150–200F per night. Coaches welcome (2 rooms, 70 places). Evening meals until 11pm.

CAMBRAI 59400 Nord **RN 17 Maps 5-B3, 6-A1 and A3**
♀ ⊗ 🏠 **LE RELAIS DES ROUTIERS** (N° RR MAI 7 690) (M. Roger **Guisgand**) 1084, av. du Cateau ☎ 27-81-35-82 ⊷ 4 Closed Sun; Aug. or July. Full-board 135F. Evening meals.
♀ ⊗ **LA GARGOTE - Chez Jean** (N° RR MAI 25 401) (M. Claude **Bedu**) 136, bld Jean-Bart ☎ 27-81-07-18 Closed Sun. Coaches welcome (3 rooms – 140 seats).
♀ ⊗ 🏠 **CHEZ ROGER** (N° RR MARS 27 204) (M. Roger **Leprince**) 10, rue des Docks ☎ 27-83-26-05 ⊷ 6 Closed Sat pm, Sun and August.

CAMBRAI 59400 Nord **see AWOINGT**

C

CAMBRES 76570 S. Mme **Map 3-A1**
♀ ⊗ **LES AMIS DE LA ROUTE** (N° RR FEV 26 182) (Mme Denise **Ponthieux**) RN 27, Pavilly ☎ 35-32-51-98 Closed Sat, Sun. Coaches welcome (rest. seats 120). Evening meals before 8.30pm. English spoken.

CAMP DU CASTELLET (LE) 83330 Var **RN 8 Map 24-B3**
♀ ⊗ **LE RELAIS CHEZ MIMI** (N° RR AVR 25 890) (Mme Francine **Ponche**) ☎ 94-90-70-53 Closed Sat, Sun. Coaches welcome (rest. seats 120 and terrace). Evening meals. Sat. English, Italian spoken.

CAMPSEGRET 24140 Dordogne **Nle 21 Map 15-B3**
♀ ⊗ **LE TAMARIS** (N° RR JUN 26 370) (M. Claude **Boetsh**) Lacroix/Villamblard ☎ 53-24-21-75. Coaches welcome (rest. seats 60 + terrace). Evening meals.

CANNES-LA-BOCCA 06150 Alpes-Mmes **Map 25-B2**
♀ ⊗ **PARIS-PROVENCE** (N° AVR 25 903) (M. Joaquim **Roldan**) 68, rue Francis Tonner ☎ 93-47-10-48 ⊷ 48 Closed Sun (low season) Spanish spoken.
♀ ⊗ CAVE DE LA ROUBINE (N° RR SEPT 26 313) (Mme **Pelletier**) 40, avenue de la Roubine ☎ 93-47-77-10 Closed Sun. Italian spoken.

CANNET-DES-MAURES (LE) 83340 Var **RN 7**
♀ ⊗ **AUX QUATRE VENTS** (N° RR JUIN 26 273) (M. Daniel **Lemaire**) Quartier La Forge ☎ 94-60-73-05 Closed Fri eve, all day Sat. Evening meals. English, German spoken.

CAP-DE-PIN par ESCOURCE 40210 Landes **RN 10 Map 20-B2**
♀ ⊗ ⌂ **AU ROUTIER** (N° RR MAR 9 439) (M. Jean-Pierre **Fortinon**) ☎ 58-07-20-54 ⊷ 15 Closed Sat (except high season); Christmas; Feb. Full board 150–180F per night. Menus from 50–190F. Specialities: *Salade de foie de canard frais, Ris de veau Madère, Magret grillé*. Coaches welcome (rest. seats 100). Evening meals.

CAPENDU 11700 Aude **RN 113 Map 22-B2**
♀ ⊗ **LA CAVE DES ARTS** (N° RR JANV 26 431) (M. Yves **Peyramayou**) RN 113 ☎ 68-79-09-30 Closed Tue, Wed evenings in winter (1 Nov to 1 May). English, Spanish spoken.

CAPPELLE-EN-PEVELE 59242 Nord **RN 393 Map 5-B1**
♀ ⊗ **L'AS VEGAS** (N° RR SEP 26 666) (Mme. Eliane **Duquesnoy**) 13, rue de l'Obeau ☎ 20-61-83-10 Closed Sun. Aug.

CARCASSONNE 11000 Aude **RN 113 Map 22-B2**
♀ ⊗ ⌂ **LE RELAIS DE L'AVENIR** (N° RR MAR 1 824) (Mme Madeleine **Pesez**) 93, avenue Francklin-Roosevelt ☎ 68-25-09-39 ⊷ 12 Closed Sun; public holidays.
♀ ⊗ ⌂ **2 étoiles NN AIR MOTEL SALVAZA** (N° RR NOV 27 096) (Mme ina **Pfeiffer**) **Aéroport de Salvaza Route de Montréal** ☎ 68-71-64-64 (hôtel) 68-72-52-89 (restaurant) ⊷ 24 Closed Mon. Restaurant closed Christmas week. German and English spoken.

C

CARENTAN 50500 Manche **RN 13 Map 4-B1**
♀ ⊗ **LE DERBY** (N° RR SEPT 26 993) (Maurice **Le Guélinet**) 21, rue de la 101 Airborne ☎ 33-42-04-77 Closed Sat afternoon, Sun and public holidays. Meals served until 9pm. Filling station near.

CARHAIX 29270 Finistère **RN 164 Map 7-A/B2**
♀ ⊗ ⌂ **AU CHEVAL BRETON** (N° RR SEP 16 715) (M. Louis **Le Mignon**) 2, boulevard de la République ☎ 98-93-01-38 ⇥ 10 at l'Hôtel du Cheval Breton + 15 at l'Hôtel Le Paradis. Closed Sun; Aug.

CARIGNAN 08110 Ardennes **Map 6-A3**
♀ ⊗ **LE RELAIS** (N° RR AVR 26 500) (M. Fabrice **Fossani**) 33, rte de Sedan ☎ 24-22-08-78 ⇥ 6 Coaches welcome (rest. seats 60). Evening meals.

CARNOULES 83600 Var **Map 25-A2**
♀ ⊗ ⌂ **CHEZ DOUDOU** (N° RR JUN 25 025) (M. Adrien **Piasco**) 20, rue Pierre-Sémard ☎ 94-28-33-15 ⇥ 4 Closed Sat low season, 15 days Sept. Full-board 160F per night. Coaches welcome (rest. seats 150). Evening meals until 9pm. Italian spoken.

CARPENTRAS 84200 Vaucluse **RN 538 Map 24-A2**
♀ ⊗ **BAR DU MARCHE GARE** (N° RR AVR 24 922) (M. Bernard **Gil**) Marché Gare ☎ 90-63-19-00 Closed Sun. Coaches welcome (rest. seats 200). Spanish spoken.

CARPIQUET 14650 Calvados
♀ ⊗ **LE POURQUOI PAS?** (N° RR JUIN 27 312) (M. Didier **Prempain**), 33, route de Bayeux Bellevue ☎ 31-73-84-84 Closed Sat evening, Sun and August.

CARSIX 27300 Eure **RN13 Map 4-B3**
♀ ⊗ ⌂ **L'ESCALE** (N° RR OCT 26 711) (M. Michel **Silliau**) Carre four de Malbrouck ☎ 32-44-79-99 ⇥ 4 Closed Sat afternoon, Sun.

CARTELEGUE 33390 Gironde **RN 137 Map 15-A3**
⊗ ⌂ **1 Star NN CHEZ OLGA - LE RELAIS DE L'ESCALE** (N° RR AOU 9 840) (M. and Mme Alban **Durand**) Le Bel Ormeau ☎ 56-42-71-18 Closed Sat; 15 Dec to 15 Jan. English, German, Spanish spoken.

CARVIN 62220 P.-de-C. **RN 25 Map 5-A/B1**
♀ ⊗ ⌂ **A L'ARRET DES ROUTIERS - AUX COPAINS** (N° RR JUN 18 427) (Mme Micheline **Dujardin**) 31, rue d'Arras ☎ 21-37-00-35 ⇥ 6 Closed Sun. Evening meals.

CAST 29150 Finistère **RD 7 and 107 Map 7-B1**
♀ ⊗ ⌂ **1 Star NN LE RELAIS SAINT-GILDAS** (N° RR MAR 22 727) (Mme Marie **Philippe** for l'Hôtel and M. Patrice **Philippe** for restaurant) 11 and 13, rue du Kreisker ☎ 98-73-54-76 or 73-55-43 ⇥ 15 from 90–180F, breakfast 15–18F. Closed Sat; end Dec. Full-board 140–185F per night. Coaches welcome (rest. seats 80/20). Evening meals until 9pm. Parking; bar; dogs allowed; private

garden. Menus 40–170F. Specialities: seafood platter, homemade couscous. Places to visit: chapels, crucifixes. English spoken.

CASTELNAU-RIVIÈRE-BASSE 65700 Htes-Pyrénées **Map 21-A2**
♟ ⊗ **LE MILLEPATTE** (N° RR MAI 27 285) (M. André **Zanardo**) Route de Bordeaux ☎ 62-31-97-99 **Minitel**

CASTELSARRASIN 82100 T.-&-G.) **RN 113 Map 22-A1**
♟ ⊗ ⌂ **1 étoille NN CHEZ MAURICE** (N° RR JANV 27 152) (M. Jean-Pierre **Boissier**) 35, rte de Toulouse ☎ 63-32-30-83 ⊷ 15 Closed Sat. pm, Sun; 1st to 22nd August. Specialities: Cassoulet, Duck Breasts and Preserved Duck.

CASTETS-DES-LANDES 40260 Landes **RN 10 Map 20-A2**
♟ ⊗ **LE STUC** (N° RR SEPT 18 528) (Mme **Calleja**) ☎ 58-89-40-62 Closed 15 to 30 Oct. Evening meals. Spanish spoken.
♟ ⊗ **LE CARRIOU DE CHANCHON** (N° RR DEC 25 766) (M. Jean **Castets**) RN 10 ☎ 58-89-40-63 Closed Mon in winter; Oct.

CASTRES 81100 Tarn **RN 622 Map 22-B2**
♟ ⊗ **AUX AMIS DE LA ROUTE** (N° RR OCT 17 391) (M. Michel **Labessouille**) av. Charles-de-Gaulle ☎ 63-35-54-38 ⊷ 5 Coaches welcome (rest. seats 70). Evening meals.

CATEAU (LE) 59360 Nord **RN 39 Map 6-A1**
♟ ⊗ **CHEZ NADINE** (N° RR JUN 25 954) (Mme **Gladieux-Legrand**) 41, rue Charles-Seydoux ☎ 27-84-08-72 Coaches welcome (rest. seats 50). Evening meals. English spoken.

CAUDAN 56850 Morbihan **RD 81 (ZA de Kergoussel) Map 7-B2**
⊗ **LE BOUTON D'OR** (N° RR FEV 27179) (Mme Joëlle **Le Bail**) ☎ 97-81-16-01 Closed Sat, Sun; English spoken.

CAUDEBEC-LES-ELBEUF 76320 S.-Maritime **RN 321 Map 3-B1**
♟ ⊗ **LE RELAIS TIVOLI** (N° RR AVR 25 908) (M. André **Jean**) 43, rue Félix-Faure ☎ 35-77-16-94 Closed Sat, Sun; public holidays.

CAULNES 22350 C.-du-N.) **Map 7-B3)**
♟ ⊗ **LES ROUTIERS** (N° RR MARS 22726) (Mme. **GAUDREL**) 40, rue de la Gare ☎ 00-00-00-00.

CAUNEILLE 40300 Landes **RN 117 Map 20-A2**
♟ ⊗ **AU HAOU** (N° RR MARS 26 836) (Mme Henriette **Lalanne**) ☎ 58-73-04-60 Closed 20 Dec–5 Jan.

CAUSSADE 82300 Tarn-et-Garonne **RN 20 Map 22-A1**
♟ ⊗ ⌂ **Restaurant (rattaché de tourisme) RELAIS D'AUVERGNE** (N° RR JUIL 25 040) (M. Antoine **Noualhac**) Zl de Meaux ☎ 63-93-03-89 ⊷ 14 Closed Sun. Full board 165 to 193F. Coaches welcome (rest seats 120). Evening meals.

CAUVERVILLE-EN-ROUMOIS 27350 Eure **RN 175 Map 4-B3**
♟ ⊗ **AUX AMIS DE LA ROUTE** (N° RR AVR 22 777) (M. Michel **Carré**) ☎ 32-57-01-55 Closed Sat, Sun; Aug. Evening meals.

C

CAVAILLON 84300 Vaucluse **RN 538/573 Map 24-A3**
♀ ⊗ **LE RELAIS SAINT-JACQUES** (N° RR NOV 24 024) (Mme
Jeannine **Raoux**) 649, avenue de la Libération ☎ 90-71-42-02
Closed Sat evening, Sun; Christmas to New Year. Italian, some
English spoken.

CAVALERIE (LA) 12230 Aveyrôn **RN 9 Map 23-A1**
♀ ⊗ ⌂ **RELAIS DES INFRUTS** (N° RR SEPT 27 034) (M. Jeannot
Lazabonne) Commune La Couvertoirada ☎ 65-62-70-82 ⇥ 7
Spanish spoken.

CAZAN 13116 B. du R. **RN 7 Map 24-B3**
⊗ **L'ESCALIER CHEZ ALEXANDRE** (N° RR JUL 25 473) (M.
Alexandre **Ghigo**) RN 7 Vernègues ☎ 90-59-13-15 Closed Sun.

CELLE-SAINT-AVANT (LA) 37610 Indre-et-Loire **Map 12-B2**
♀ ⊗ ⌂ **LA CARAVANE** (N° RR DEC 24 440) (M. Fernand **Jules**) ⇥ 8.
Meals served until 1 am.

CELON 36200 Indre **RN 20 Map 16-A1**
♀ ⊗ **LA BROUETTE** (N° RR NOV 22 991) (Mme Yvette **Dufour**) ☎ 54-
25-32-08 Closed Sun; 15 Aug to end of Sept.

CENAC-SAINT-JULIEN 24250 Dordogne **RN 703 Map 17-B1**
♀ ⊗ **LA PROMENADE** (N° RR OCT 25 153) (M. Pascal **Thomas**) RN
703 ☎ 53-28-36-87 ⇥ 4.

CERE 400900 Landes **Map 20-B2**
♀ ⊗ **RELAIS DE L'ECUREUIL** (N° RR SEPT 26 674) (Mme Martine
Belmonte) Au Bourg ☎ 58-51-49-33 Closed Wed. Some English,
Portuguese, Spanish spoken.

CESTAS 33610 Gironde **RN 10 Maps 15-A3 and 20-B1**
♀ ⊗ **LE TAHITI** (N° RR JUN 25 024) (Mme Marie-France **Debacker**)
Rte de Bayonne ☎ 56-78-27-25 Closed Sat afternoon to Sun;
public holidays (unless reserved for group/coach); Christmas to
New Year. Coaches welcome. Evening meals.

CHAGNY 71150 Saône-et-Loire **RN 74 Maps 13-B3 and 18-A/B1**
♀ ⊗ ⌂ **LE RELAIS TERMINUS** (N° RR JUL 21 575) (M. Jean-Louis
Potsimeck) 1, avenue de la Gare ☎ 85-87-18-13 ⇥ 15 Closed
Sun; Dec. Full-board 160–180F per night. Coaches welcome
(rest. seats 55). Evening meals. English, Polish spoken.

CHAIGNES 27120 Eure **Map 3-B1**
♀ ⊗ ⌂ **MA NORMANDIE** (N° RR AVR 25 920) (M. Gérard **Ducoat**)
Rte Nle 13 ☎ 32-36-95-52 ⇥ 14 Closed Sat evening, Sun. English
spoken.

CHAINGY 45161 Loiret **RN 152 Map 13-A1**
♀ ⊗ **RELAIS DE FOURNEAUX** (N° RR MAI 26 548) (M. Carlos **De
Sousa**) Rte Nle 152 ☎ 38-80-69-12 Closed Sun. English spoken.

C

CHAINTRIX 51130 Marne **RN 33 Map 9-A3**
♀ ⊗ **LE RELAIS DE LA SOUDE** (N° RR DEC 26 113) (SARL La SEFID-Mme Josette **Jacquart**) RN 33, Vertus ☎ 26-66-43-80 Evening meals until mid-night. German spoken.

CHALAIS (ou CHALEIX) 24800 Dordogne **RN 21 Map 17-A1**
Voir THIVIERS

CHALETTE-SUR-LOING 45120 Loiret **Map 9-B1**
♀ ⊗ ⌂ **CAFÉ DE L'OUEST** (N° RR NOV 26 737) (Mme Lucette **Pfeiffer**) 82, rue de la Fontaine ☎ 38-93-19-33 ⇥ 2

CHALLANS 85300 Vendée **RN 148 Map 11-B2**
♀ ⊗ **LE RELAIS DE LA NOUE** (N° RR AVR 24 209) (Mme Monique **Menez**) Place Victor-Charbonnel ☎ 51-93-20-20 Closed Sun.

CHALLUY 58000 Nièvre **RN 7 Map 13-B2**
♀ ⊗ **LE RELAIS DU PONT CARREAU** (N° RR AVR 22 283) (Mme Fernande **Taillemitte**) ☎ 86-21-00-02 ⇥ 4.

CHALONS-SUR-MARNE 51000 Marne **RN 3 and 33 Maps 6-B2 and 9-A3**
⊗ **AU MONT SAINT-MICHEL** (N° RR JUN 15 689) (SNC-**Queige, Mazeau et Cie**) 31, route de Troyes RN 77 ☎ 26-68-05-08 Closed Sun evening. Coaches welcome (rest. seats 160). Evening meals. English, Spanish spoken. 3 parking areas.
♀ ⊗ ⌂ **LE DELKO** (N° RR SEP 25 101) (M. Christian **Sinot**) rue de Douanes **La Veuve** ☎ 26-67-30-68 **Minitel** ⇥ 8 Closed Sun.

CHALON-SUR-SAONE SUD 71240 S.-et-L. **Map 18-B1**
⚲ **Total Service Station LE RELAIS DE SEVREY** (N° RR FEV 24 090) (M. Hervé **Bouvier**) RN 6 ☎ 85-48-30-24 Closed Sat 10.30pm to Sun 8.00am. Open 24 hours.

CHAMALIERES-SUR-LOIRE 43800 Haute-Loire **Map 18-A3**
♀ ⊗ ⌂ **LES ROUTIERS** (N° RR MARS 26 289) (Mme Françoise **Gentes**) Vorey ☎ 71-03-42-10 ⇥ 4. Filling station 4.5 kms.

CHAMANDRIN 05100 Htes-Alpes **RN 94 Map 19-A3 see BRIANÇON**

CHAMARANDE 91730 Essonne **RN 20 Map 9-B1**
⊗ ⌂ **1 Star NN SARL LE RELAIS DE MONTFORT** (N° RR FEV 17 740) (M. Roland **Cottin**) Rte Nle 20 ☎ 60-82-20-80 ⇥ 31 Closed Sat afternoon, Sun; Aug; last month in Dec. Coaches welcome (rest. seats 120). Evening meals until 10.30pm. English spoken.

CHAMBERY 73000 Savoie **RN 6 Map 19-A2**
♀ ⊗ **LE RELAIS DES ABATTOIRS – Clara et Chantal** (N° RR FEV 26 456) (Mmes **Vallifuoco-Véronèse**) Place Pierre-de-Coubertin ☎ 79-69-03-97 Closed Sat afternoon, Sun; Jul. Italian, Spanish spoken.

CHAMBILLY 71100 Saône-et-Loire **Map 18-A1**
♀ ⊗ ⌂ **LE RELAIS DU COMMERCE ET DES SPORTS** (N° RR MAI

C

Chambilly continued

20 727) (M. Paul and Monique **Prioris**) rue du Gl-de-Gaulle ☎ 85-25-03-62 ⇥ 6 Closed Sat afternoon. Italian spoken. Shaded terrace, 'boule' played.

CHAMBLY 60230 Oise **Map 3-B2**

♟ ⊗ ⌂ **LE RELAIS DE CHAMBLY** (N° RR DEC 26 130) (Mme Françoise **Violette**) 660 av. A.-Briand ☎ 34-70-50-37 ⇥ 14 Closed Sat, Sun; 20 Dec–20 Jan. Full-board 150–190F per night. Evening meals. Filling station near.

CHAMBORET 87140 Haute-Vienne **RN 147 Map 16-B1**

♟ ⊗ **LA BERGERIE** (N° RR SEP 24 344) (M. Roger **Hilaire**) **Nantiat** ☎ 55-75-78-21. Coaches welcome (rest. seats 70). Evening meals.

CHAMBOULIVE 19450 Corrèze **D 940 Map 17-A1**

♟ ⊗ ⌂ **RELAIS DU GOZEE** (N° RR JAN 26 793) (Mme Lina **Mazurier**) Route de Tulle ☎ 55-21-60-90 ⇥ 5 Closed 24 Aug–8 Sep. Portuguese spoken.

CHAMBOURCY 78240 Yvelines **RN 13 Map 1-A2**

♟ ⊗ **LES ROUTIERS** (N° RR MAI 22 814) (Mme Denise **Pettinotti**) 63, route de Mantes ☎ 39-65-43-19 Closed Sun; Aug. Spanish spoken.

CHAMP-SUR-DRAC 38560 Isère **RN 85 Map 19-A3 see JARRIE**

CHAMPAGNE 72470 Sarthe **RN 157 Map 8-B2**

♟ ⊗ **LE RELAIS DES FOUGERES** (N° RR JUL 26 594) (M. Hubert **Gehan**) RN 157 ☎ 48-89-50-96 Closed Sun. Coaches welcome (rest. seats 50). Meals served until 10pm.

CHAMPAGNE-MOUTON 16350 Charente **RN 740 Map 15-B2**

♟ ⊗ ⌂ **1 Star NN LE RELAIS DE PLAISANCE** (N° RR SEP 15 354) (Mme Denise **Delhoume**) ☎ 45-31-80-52 and 45-31-98-19 ⇥ 15 Closed Mon. Full-board 180–200F per night. Coaches welcome (rest. seats 100). Evening meals served until 10pm.

CHAMPAGNEUX 73240 Savoie **RN 516 Map 19-A2**

♟ ⊗ ⌸ **RELAIS DES TROIS PROVINCES - CHEZ NICOLE** (N° RR FEV 26 459) (Mme Nicole **Curtillat**) ☎ 76-31-83-22 Closed Aug.

CHAMPAGNOLE 39300 Jura

♟ ⊗ **LES ROUTIERS** (N° RR AVR 25 873) (M. Georges **Chagre**) La Billaude ☎ 84-52-07-95 Closed Sun. Evening meals.

CHAMPIGNEULLES 54520 M.-et-M **RN 4 Maps 10-A2 and 14-B1**

♟ ⊗ **AUBERGE FLEURIE** (N° RR MAR 24 891) (Mme Nathalie **Cheikh**) FONDS DE TOUL Les Baraques Nancy Ouest ☎ 83-98-27-30 Closed Sat, Sun; 15 days in Feb; Jul. English, German spoken.

CHAMPLOST 89210 Yonne **Map 9-B2**

♟ ⊗ **CHEZ MARIE-CLAUDE** (N° RR OCT 26 356) (Mme Marie-

Claude **Lauvin**) 23 Rte de Paris ☎ 86-43-14-71 Closed Wed. Coaches welcome (rest. seats 70). Evening meals.

CHAMPREPUS 50800 Manche **Map 8-A1**
♀ ⊗ 🏠 **LE RELAIS DE CHAMPREPUS** (N° RR JUL 26 579) (Mlle. Marie-Françoise **Menard**) Le Bourg Villedieu-les-Poêles ☎ 33-51-42-32 Closed Wed; Sept or Feb. Coaches welcome (rest. seats 48).

CHAMPROND-EN-GATINE 28240 E.-et -L. **RN 23 Map 8-B3**
♀ ⊗ **LE RELAIS DE CHAMPROND** (N° RR OCT 23 997) (M. Michel **Jonnier**) 5, Grande-Rue ☎ 37-49-82-18 Closed Sun; 15 to 30 Aug.

CHAMPROND-EN-PERCHET 28400 Eure-et-Loir **see NOGENT-LE-ROTROU**

CHAMPS-SUR YONNE 89290 Yonne **Autoroute A 6 Sens Paris-Lyon Map 13-A2**
♀ ⊗ **LE RELAIS VENOY** (M. Philippe **Tonic**) Autoroute A 6 ☎ 86-52-35-53 Self-service restaurant.

CHAMPSAC-JOUVEAU 87230 Hte-Vienne **Map 15-B2**
♀ ⊗ **LE RELAIS DU TILLEUL** (N° RR OCT 24 710) (Mme Renée **Astier**) ☎ 55-78-44-06.

CHAMPTOCE-SUR-LOIRE 49170 Maine-et-Loire **Maps 11-A3 and 12-A1**
♀ ⊗ **HOTEL DE LA GARE** (N° RR NOV 26 373) (Mme Agnès **Chêne**) Rte de Montjean ☎ 41-39-91-75 **Minitel** ⊷ 4 Closed Sat, Sun; 1 Aug to 17 Aug. Coaches welcome (rest. seats 35). English, Spanish spoken.

CHANGÉ 53810 Mayenne **Map 8-A1**
♀ ⊗ **LE RELAIS DE NIAFLES** (N° RR FEV 27 187) (M. Pierre **Dabet**) Niafles ☎ 43-53-76-15 Closed Sat, Sun, July and August.

CHANIERS 17610 Charente-Maritime **Map 15-A2**
♀ ⊗ **AUBERGE DE LA BOISERIE** (N° RR MAI 27 294) (M. Jean-Pierre **Lorillon**) Le Maine Alain ☎ 46-91-11-78 Evening meals.

CHANTENAY-SAINT-IMBERT 58240 Nièvre **RN 7 Map 16-A3**
♀ ⊗ **AU BON ACCUEIL** (N° RR DEC 9 101) (Mme Lucette **Vacher**) RN 7 St-Pierre-le-Moutier ☎ 86-38-61-95 Closed Sat midday, Sun; 15 Aug to 8 Sept. Evening meals.
♀ ⊗ **RELAIS SAINT-IMBERT** (N° RR JANV 27150) (Mlle **Fressie**) **St-Pierre-le-Moutier** ☎ 86-36-61-55 Closed Sun. German spoken. Specialities Sauerkraut and Potee (veg cooked with meat and beans).

CHAPELAUDE 03530 Allier **RN 143 Map 16-A2**
♀ ⊗ **LE RELAIS DES TARTASSES** (N° RR MAR 24 873) (Mme Colette **Boutillon**) Huriel ☎ 70-06-45-06 ⊷ 4 Coaches welcome (rest. seats 50). Evening meals.

C

CHAPELLE (LA) 73220 Savoie **RN 6 Map 19-A2**
♀ ⊗ **RESTOROUTE LA CHAPELLE** (N° RR OCT 26 353) (M. Gilbert **Martoia**) Aiguebelle ☎ 79-36-17-09 German, English, Italian spoken.

CHAPELLE (LA) 18380 Cher **CD 940**
♀ ⊗ **LES ROUTIERS** (N° RR JAN 26 782) (M. Jean-Marc **Joyeux**) 22, rue Alain-Fournier ☎ 48-73-94-18.

CHAPELLE-CARO (LA) 56460 Morbihan **RN 166 Map 7-B3**
♀ ⊗ ⌂ **LE RELAIS DES ROUTIERS** (N° RR MAR 23 725) (Mme Marie-Claire **Boulvais**) La Gare ☎ 97-74-93-63 **Minitel** ⊷ 4 Coaches welcome (rest. seats 90). Evening meals until 11pm.

CHAPELLE D'AUREC (LA) 43120 Haute-Loire **Map 18-A3**
♀ ⊗ ⌂ **RELAIS DE LA CHAPELLE** (N° RR JUIN 27 295) (M. Gabriel **Colombet**) La Mioulaterre ☎ 71-66-53-55 ⊷ 4 Closed Sun pm. Evening meals.

CHAPELLE DU BOIS (LA) 72400 Sarthe **Map 8-B2 Axe Alençon – Mamers – St Cosmes – La Ferté – Bernard – Aut A11 – RD2**
♀ ⊗ **LA CROIX BLANCHE** (N° RR MAI 26 886) (Mme Annich **Boudet**) Le Bourg ☎ 43-93-18-01 Closed Aug.

CHAPELLE-DU-NOYER (LA) 28200 E.-et-L **RN 10 Map 8-B3**
♀ ⊗ **RELAIS DE LA FRINGALE** (N° RR JUN 26 575) (M. Gérard **Hamard**) 4, rue de Beauvoir ☎ 37-96-84-97.

CHAPELLE-GUILLAUME (LA) 28330 E. et L. **Map 8-B3**
♀ ⊗ **REST DE L'UNION** (N° RR AOUT 22 436) (M. Michel **Galu- peau**) Place de l'Église ☎ 37-49-20-88 Closed Mon afternoon.

CHAPELLE-LA-REINE (LA) 77760 S.-et-M. **RN 51 Map 9-B1/2**
♀ ⊗ **LE RELAIS DE LA SALAMANDRE** (N° RR AVR 6 476) (M. J. **Guyon**) 5, rue du Docteur Battesti ☎ 64-24-30-03 ⊷ 6 Open 24 hours. Closed Sat.
⇥ Sun. Aug. Coaches welcome (rest. seats 44). Evening meals.

CHAPELLE-SAINT-LAURENT (LA) 79430 Deux Sèvres **RN 748 Map 15-A1**
♀ ⊗ **RELAIS DES SPORTS** (N° RR AVR 26 231) (Mme Louisette **Guérin**) 6 Route de Bressuire ☎ 49-72-05-64 Coaches welcome (rest. seats 110). Evening meals.

CHAPELLE-SAINT-SEPULCRE (LA) 45210 Loiret **RN 60 Map 9-B2**
♀ ⊗ **LA POTENCE** (N° RR FEV 25 825) (Mme Liliane **Visier**) RN 60 ☎ 38-92-03-10 **Minitel** Closed Sat.

CHAPPELE-ST-URSIN (LA) 18570 Cher **RN 151 Map 13-B1**
♀ ⊗ **RELAIS 151** (N° RR JANV 27 148) (Mme Claudine **Maslarde**) Le Subdray Les Tailles Heurtault ☎ 48-55-12-47 Closed Sun, open 5.30 to 12.30am. English spoken.

C

LA CHAPELLE SOUS DUN 71800 Saône-et-Loire **Map 18-A2**
🍷 ⊗ **BAR RESTAURANT DE LA MINE** (N° RR SEPT 26 660) (Mme Ariette **Champiaux**) ☎ 74-89-55-30.

CHAPELLE-SUR-LOIRE (LA) 37140 Indre-et-Loire **RN 152 Map 12-B2**
🍷 ⊗ 🏠 **LE RELAIS DE LA MAIRIE** (N° RR AVR 21 509) (M. Jacques **Joyeau**) Place Albert Ruelle ☎ 47-97-34-07 ⊷ 12 Full-board 160–180F per night. Coaches welcome (rest. seats 60). Evening meals.

CHARENTON 94220 Val-de-Marne Porte de Charenton **Map 1-B3**
🍷 ⊗ **Aux Armes de Normandie et d'Auvergne – L'ALLIANCE** (N° RR AOU 19 120) (M. Albert **Series**) 121, rue de Paris ☎ 43-68-03-71 Closed Wed; Aug. Meals served until 9pm.
🍷 ⊗ **PARIS-LISBONNE** (N° RR MAI 24 229) (SARL **Le Paris-Lisbonne/Durarte**) 195, rue de Paris ☎ 46-68-32-29 Closed Aug. Evening meals until 10pm. Portuguese, Spanish spoken.

CHARENTON-SUR-CHER 18210 Cher **RN 151 Bis Maps 13-B2 and 16-A2**
⊗ **A LA BONNE TABLE** (N° RR NOV 18 554) (Mme Antoinette **Frège**) ☎ 48-60-72-73. Closed Aug.

CHARMES-SUR-L'HERBASSE 26260 Drôme **Map 18-B3**
🍷 ⊗ **LE CABARET NEUF** (N° RR AVR 27 253) (M. Michel **Deveton**) ☎ 75-45-65-65 Closed Tues and 15th Sept. to 1st Oct.

CHARROUX 86250 Vienne **CD 148 Map 15-B1/2**
🍷 ⊗ 🏠 **LE RELAIS DE LA CROIX-BLANCHE** Sarl (N° RR OCT 27 072) (M. Philippe **Jansen**) Place Saint-Pierre ☎ 49-87-50-41 ⊷ 7 Closed Sat and Sun.

CHARSONVILLE 45130 Loiret **RN 157 Map 12-A3**
🍷 ⊗ **Tobacconist LE RELAIS DES ROUTIERS** (N° RR NOV 21 705) (M. Jacques **Rouilly**) 15, rue de la Libératon ☎ 38-74-23-00 **Minitel** Closed Sun, Mon evening; 3 weeks in Aug; 2 weeks in winter. Coaches welcome (rest. seats 55).

CHARTRES 28000 Eure-et-Loire **RN 10 Map 8-B3**
🍷 ⊗ 🏠 **2 Stars NN LE RELAIS BEAUCERON** (N° RR AVR 19 743) (M. **Lichet**) Mignières. This hotel, in the centre of Beauce, is 200m from the Thivars exit of Autoroute Océane A11, and near Nationale No 10: 10 km from Chartres, 100km from Paris. ☎ 37-26-46-21 ⊷ 30 from 165–196F, breakfast 19–28F, bath, shower, own WC, colour TV. Open 5am to mid-night. Restaurant Closed Sun. Coaches welcome (rest. seats 60). Evening meals. English, Spanish spoken. Menus from 46–98F. Specialities: *Andouille de Boilleau aux flageolets, Sauté de veau orléannis Pâté en croûte maison.* Parking, bar, dogs allowed. Sites to visit: Valleys of the Eure and Loire, windmills of Beauce.

🍷 ⊗ **LE RELAIS DES BEAUMONTS** (N° RR MAI 25 392) (M. Jean-Claude **Esnault**) Rocade Sud de Chartres Av. François Arago ☎

C

Chartres continued
37-28-22-00 Closed Sat, Sun; Aug. Evening meals until mid-night.

CHARTRES 28000 Eure-et-Loire **RN10 Map 8-B3**
♀ ⊗ **RESTAURANT LE PALMIER** (N° RR FEV 26 803) (M. Boussad **Naar**) 20, the Saint-Maurice ☎ 37-21-13-89.

CHARTRES 28300 GASVILLE-MAINVILLIERS – Eure-et-Loir **Autoroute A-11 Océane Map 8-B3 Sens Paris-Province**
♀ ⊗ **Café-Route** (N° RR RA-1) Aire de Service de la Fosse Blanche ☎ 37-31-62-42 Routier menus in self-service restaurant in winter 7.00am to 10.30pm; summer 6.30am to 11.30pm. Shop.
♀ ⊗ **CAFÉ ROUTE** Sens Province/Paris Autoroute A11 ☎ 37-31-62-41 Self-service restaurant open in winter 7.00am to 10.30pm; summer 6.30am to 11.00pm. English, German, Spanish spoken. Shop.

CHARVIEU 38230 Isère **RD 98 Map 2-A2**
♀ ⊗ **CHEZ MICHEL** (N° RR AVR 26 494) (M. Michael **Mandran**) Rte de Lyon – La Léchère – Pont de Cheruy ☎ 78-32-23-27 Closed Sun. Coaches welcome (rest. seats 30).

CHASSENEUIL 16260 Charente **RN 141 Map 15-B2**
♀ ⊗ ⌂ **LE RELAIS DES TILLEULS** (N° RR MAR 18 063) (Mme **Bonneau**) 20, rue du Temple ☎ 45-39-57-90 ⊷ 7 Full-board 140–200F per night. Coaches welcome (rest. seats 120). Evening meals served until 12.15am.

CHASSE-SUR-RHONE 37670 Isère **CD 12 Map 2-B1**
♀ ⊗ **CENTRAL BAR CHEZ MEDA** (N° RR AOU 20 804) (M. Jean-Luc **Merandat**) 5, rue Pasteur ☎ 72-24-00-88 Closed Sun evening. Coaches welcome (rest. seats 200). Spanish, English spoken.

CHASSILLE 72910 Sarthe **RN 157 Map 8-B2**
♀ ⊗ ⌂ **LE PETIT ROBINSON** (N° RR NOV 26 740) (M. **Fournigault**) ☎ 43-88-92-01 ⊷ 4 Closed Sat.

CHATAIGNERAIE (LA) 85120 Vendée **RD 949 Map 11-B3**
♀ ⊗ ⌂ **HOTEL DU CHEVAL BLANC** (N° RR JUIL 26 940) (M. Ramond **Retailleau**) Le Bourg Breuil-Barret ☎ 51-69-67-64 ⊷ 7 Closed Mon.

CHATEAUBERNARD Map 15-A2
♀ ⊗ **PENSION DU CAMP** (N° RR NOV 25 726) (M. Jean-Louis **Bruno**) Rte de Barbezieux La Pointe A Rullaud ☎ 45-82-09-47 ⊷ 5 Closed Fri evening, Sat, Sun (can open for pre booked groups). Full-board 170F per night. Coaches welcome (rest. seats 89 in 3 rooms). Evening meals. Spanish spoken.

CHATEAUBRIANT 44110 L.-Atl. **RN 775 Maps 11-A3 and 12-A1**
♀ ⊗ ⌂ **1 Star NN LE RELAIS PARIS-OCEAN** (N° RR SEP 20 280) (Mme Madeleine **Dubois**) 25-27-29, rue d'Ancenis ☎ 40-81-21-79 **Minitel** ⊷ 7 Restaurant closed Sun; 20 Dec to 10 Jan. Evening meals.

C

CHATEAUDUN 28000 Eure-et-Loir **RD 995 Map 8-B3**
♈ ⊗ **LE SAINT JEAN** (N° RR FEV 24 117) (Mme Monique **Brin**) 1,
route de Brou ☎ 37-45-56-75 Closed Sun. Coaches welcome (rest.
seats 32/24/10). Evening meals until 9pm.

CHATEAU-GAILLARD-SANTILLY 28310 Eure-et-Loir **RN 20 Map 9-B1**
♈ ⊗ **RELAIS 20** (N° RR JANV 25 789) (M. Abaerrahman **Boubekeur**)
RN 20 ☎ 37-90-07-33 **Minitel** Closed Sat evening, Sun. Coaches
welcome. Evening meals. English, German, Arabic spoken.
♈ ⊗ **AU ROUTIER GAILLARD – Chez Lili** (N° RR DEC 21 750)
(Mme Liliane **Kieffer**) ☎ 37-90-07-03 Closed Sat afternoon to Sun
morning.

CHATEAU-GONTIER 53200 Mayenne **Map 12-A1**
♈ ⊗ **L'ÉTOILE** (N° RR JUN 26 569) (M. Emmanuel **Gohier**) 43, rue
Garnier ☎ 43-07-20-80 Closed 3 weeks in Aug.

CHATEAU-L'HERMITAGE 72510 Sarthe **RD 307 Map 12-A2**
♈ ⊗ **LA BELLE CROIX** (N° RR NOV 26 742) (M. Bruno **David**)
Beauregard-Mansigné ☎ 43-79-11-89. Closed Sun afternoon.

CHATEAU-THEBAUD 44690 L.-Atl. **RN 137 Map 11-B3**
♈ ⊗ ⌂ **LA SAUCISSE VOLANTE** (N° RR FEV 25 820) (M. Serge
Violeau) Le Butay Rte de La Rochelle ☎ 40-06-63-55 ⇌ 5 Closed
Sat evening, Sun; May or Jun. Evening meals.

CHATEAUNEUF see GERMIGNY-DES-PRES 45110 Loiret

CHATEAUNEUF 35430 I.-et-V. **RN 137 Map 7-A3**
♈ ⊗ ⌂ **LION D'OR** (N° RR NOV 25 167) (Mme Ginette **Brodbecker**)
137, rue Principale ☎ 99-58-40-11 **Minitel** ⇌ 10 Closed Mon
2pm–5pm. Full-board 160–200F per night. Coaches welcome
(rest. seats 80). Evening meals. Restaurant + grill, 28 seats, with
terrace. English spoken.

CHATEAUNEF-DE-FAOU 29119 Finistère **RN 787 Map 7-B1**
♈ ⊗ **CHEZ MARIANNE** (N° RR DEC 15 473) (Mlle Marie **Taridec**) 8,
rue Jean-Dorval ☎ 98-81-73-67.

CHATEAUNEUF-DE-GALAURE 26330 Drôme **Map 18-B3**
♈ ⊗ ⌂ **BAR HOTEL RESTAURANT DE LA MAIRIE** (N° RR JUIN 26
932) (M. Alain **Daveau**) Le Village ☎ 75-68-61-72 ⇌ 5 English
and a little German spoken.

CHATEAUNEUF-LE-ROUGE 13790 B.-du-R. **RN 7 Map 24-B3**
♈ ⊗ **LA CARDELINE** (N° RR MAI 25 425) (M. Michel **Bernard**) RN 7
☎ 42-58-62-30 Closed first fortnight in Jan. Evening meals until
11pm. English, German spoken.

CHATEAUNEUF-LES-MARTIGUES 13220 B.-du-R. **RN 568 Map 24-B3**
♈ ⊗ **L'OASIS** (N° RR FEV 26 461) (M. Jacques **Ribero**) Route de

111

C

Chateauneuf-les-Martigues continued
Marseille ☎ 42-79-88-35 Closed all day Sat, Sun; Aug. Coaches welcome (rest. seats 80). English, Spanish spoken.

CHATEAURENARD 13160 B.-du-R. **RN 57 Map 24-A3**
♈ ⊗ **LE PANORAMIQUE** (N° RR FEV 26 448) (M. Alain **Mourier**) Centre nautique ☎ 90-94-76-40 Coaches welcome (rest. seats 50). Showers, swimming pool in summer. English spoken.

CHÂTEAUROUX 05360 Hautes-Alpes **RN 94 Map 25-A1**
♈ ⊗ ⌂ **1 star NN HÔTEL DAUPHINOIS L'ASSIETTE GOUR-MANDE** (N° RR JANV 27 141) (M. Michel **Pouypoudat**) rue Centrale ☎ 92-43-22-01 ⤙ 10 English spoken.

CHATEAUROUX 36000 Indre **RN 20 Maps 12-B3, 13-B1 and 16-A1**
♈ ⊗ **BAR DE L'AVENUE** (N° RR OCT 25 147) (M. Laurent **Guillot**) 1, avenue de la Manufacture ☎ 54-34-09-27 Closed Sun. English spoken.
♈ ⊗ **SARL L'ETAPE** (N° RR FEV 23 681) (Gérant M.D. **Noiret**) Déols ☎ 54-22-03-77 **Minitel** Open 24 hours a day. Coaches welcome (rest. seats 300).
♈ ⊗ ⌂ **1 Star NN LE RALLYE** (N° RR JANV 26 433) (Mme Françoise **Jasmin**) 9, rue Bourdillon ☎ 54-34-37-41 ⤙ 8 from 59–100F, breakfast from 12.50–16F. Closed Sun; Feb. Bar, small dogs allowed.

CHÂTEAUROUX-LUANT 36300 Indre **RN 20 Map 16-A1 voir à VELLES**

CHATELET-SUR-CHUISNES (LES) par COURVILLE 28270 Eure-et-Loir **RN 23 Map 8-B3 see CHUISNES**

CHATELUS 03120 Allier **Map 16-B3**
♈ ⊗ **LES CHEVREAUX** (N° RR MARS 27209) (M. Joseph **Bernard**) RN 7 Arfeuilles ☎ 70-55-00-79 Spanish and English spoken.

CHATELUS-MALVALEIX 23270 Creuse **RN 690 Map 16-A2**
♈ ⊗ ⌂ **LE RELAIS DES VOYAGEURS** (N° RR AOU 23 409) (M. Claude **Brunet**) Route de La Châtre ☎ 55-80-78-11 ⤙ 5 Closed Wed evening; Oct. English spoken.

CHATELLERAULT 86100 Vienne
♈ ⊗ **L'ARCHE DU POITOU** Autoroute A-10 (M. Lionel **Violette**) Aire d'Antran ☎ 49-02-72-04 Self service restaurant.

CHATENOY 45260 Loiret **RD 948 Map 13-A1**
♈ ⊗ **AUBERGE DE L'ETANG** (N° RR DEC 26 124) (M. Alain **Fornale**) Le Bourg ☎ 38-59-47-50 Coaches welcome (rest. seats 42/30). Evening meals by reservation only. English, Spanish spoken.

CHATILLON-EN-BAZOIS 58110 Nièvre **RD 978 Map 13-B2**
♈ ⊗ ⌂ **HOTEL DU RELAIS** (N° RR MAR 22 737) (M. Jean-Jacques **Charprenet**) ☎ 86-84-13-79 ⤙ 7 Closed Sun; public holidays.

C

CHATILLON-LE-ROI 45540 Loiret **RD 927 Map 9-B1**
♀ ⊗ **LE RELAIS DES FINS GOURMETS** (N° RR FEV 26 812) (M. and
    Mme Joël and Jeanne **Lenglet**) 41, rue du Château ☎ 38-39-97-12
    Closed Sun (except in hunting season); Jun.

CHATILLON-SUR-INDRE 36700 Indre **RN 143 Map 12-B3**
♀ ⊗ 🏠 **LE RELAIS DU MAIL** (N° RR OCT 22 980) (M. **Duluard**)
    Boulevard du Général-Leclerc ☎ 54-38-71-21 and 38-80-25 ⊷ 11
    Closed Sun; 29 Dec to 1 Jan 89. Full-board 145F per night.
    Coaches welcome (rest. seats 50). Evening meals.

CHATRE (LA) 36400 Indre **RN 143 Map 16-A2**
♀ ⊗ 🏠 **2 Stars NN SARL DU LION D'ARGENT** (N° RR OCT 3 251)
    (M. Pierre-Marie **Audebert**) 2, avenue du Lion d'Argent ☎ 54-48-
⊷ 11-69 and 48-15-67 ⊷ 26 English spoken.

CHATRES-SUR-CHER 41320 L.-et-C. **RN 76 Map 13-B1**
♀ ⊗ **LES ROUTIERS** (N° RR MARS 25 857) (M. Gérard **Coutaud**) 60,
    rue du 11-Novembre ☎ 54-98-01-93 Closed Sun. Coaches welco-
    me (rest. seats 40). Evening meals in July/Aug.

CHATTE 38160 Isère **RN 92 Map 18-B3**
♀ ⊗ **LE SIROCCO** (N° RR AVR 26 227) (M. Maurice **Moyroud**)
    Quartier St Ferreol ☎ 76-64-43-41 Closed Sat afternoon, Sun; 1–15
    Aug. Evening meals.

CHAUFFOUR-LES-BONNIERES 78270 Yvelines **RN 13 Maps 3-B1
and 8-A3**
♀ ⊗ 🏠 **AU BON ACCUEIL** (N° RR DEC 6 601) (M. Gérard **Magne**) ☎
    34-76-11-29 **Minitel** ⊷ 20 Closed Sat; 14 Jul–14 Aug. Coaches
    welcome (rest. seats 100). Evening meals.

CHAUMERGY 39230 Jura **RD 468 et 33**
Voir LONS-LE-SAUNIER

CHAUMONT 52000 Haute-Marne **RN 19 Map 14-A2**
♀ ⊗ **CHEZ JEAN** (N° RR MAI 14 804) (M. Jean **Corroy**) 29, avenue
    Carnot ☎ 25-03-06-57.
♀ ⊗ 🏠 **AUBERGE DES ROUTIERS** (N° RR OCT 22 964) (M. Said
    Maames) 53, av. de la République ☎ 25-03-08-60 ⊷ 7 Closed
    Wed. English, Italian, German, Arabic spoken.

CHAUMONT-SUR-AIRE 55260 Meuse **RN 35 Map 14-A1**
♀ ⊗ 🏠 **LE RELAIS DE LA RENAISSANCE** (N° RR AVR 20 428) (M.
    André **Nucci**) ☎ 29-70-66-60 ⊷ 8 Closed Sun; Feb. Italian
    spoken. Parking for heavy loads.

CHAUNY 02300 Aisne **Map 6-A/B1**
♀ ⊗ 🏠 **LE CASAMANCE** (N° RR DEC 27 114 (M. Gilles **Claisse**) 92,
    rue de la Chaussée ☎ 23-52-16-33 Closed Sun. English spoken.

CHAUSSEE-DE-DAMERY (LA) 51200 Marne **RN 3 Map 9-A3**
♀ ⊗ 🏠 **1 Star NN AUBERGE DE LA CHAUSSEE** (N° RR OCT 11 069)
    (M. **Lagarde**) 5, avenue de Paris 5 km from Épernay ☎ 26-58-40-

C

Chaussee-de-Damery continued
 66 ▨ 9 Closed Mon evening; 22 Aug to 15 Sept. Coaches welcome (rest. seats 50). Evening meals.

CHAUSSIN 39120 Jura **RN 73 Map 18-B1**
☿ ⓧ ⌂ **CAFÉ DE LA GARE** (N° RR OCT 26 707) (Mme. Nicole **Julien**) RN 73 Peseux ☎ 84-70-14-23 ▨ 20 Closed midday Sat to Mon 6am.

CHAUVIGNY 86300 Vienne **RN 151 Map 15-B1**
☿ ⓧ **LE RELAIS DU MARCHE** (N° RR JUL 25 048) (M. Joël **Torsat**) 8, place du Marché ☎ 49-46-32-34 Closed Thur; 15 Sept to 15 Oct. Coaches welcome (rest. seats 70). Evening meals until 9pm.

CHAUX-BALMONT 74770 Haute-Savoie **RN 201 Map 19-A2**
☿ ⓧ ⌂ **1 Star NN L'AUBERGE** (N° RR SEP 26 310) (M. Louis **Cantagrel**-Monique **Bodin**) ☎ 50-46-71-02 **Minitel** ▨ 10 from 90–145F breakfast to 19F. Full-board available. Coaches welcome (for breakfast only). Evening meals. Parking, bar, dogs allowed, amusements, terrace. Sites to visit: old town at Annecy, bridge at Alby, gorges of Fier.

CHAZEUIL 03500 Allier **CD 146 Map 16-A3**
☿ ⓧ **LE RELAIS DU PONT DE CHAZEUIL** (N° RR NOV 26 094) (M. Maurice **Chaduc**) Au Pont Chazeuil – Paray Sous Briailles ☎ 70-45-08-11 Coaches welcome (rest. seats 55). Meals until 10.30pm.

CHELLES 77500 Seine-et-Marne **RN 34 Map 1-A3**
☿ ⓧ ⌂ **HOTEL DE LA PETITE VITESSE** (N° RR AVR 26 875) (M. Michel **Chea**) 32, avenue du Marais ☎ 64-21-09-47 ▨ 7 Closed Sun.

CHELSEY 21430 Cote-d'Or **RN 6 Map 13-B3**
☿ ⓧ **LE RELAIS DES ROUTIERS** (N° RR JAN 23 630) (M. Bernard **Sentein**) Liernais ☎ 80-84-40-42 Closed Sun; 15 to 25 Aug. Coaches welcome (rest. seats 100/50/45). Meals served until 1am. German spoken.

CHEMAUDIN 25320 Doubs **RN 73 Map 14-B3**
☿ ⓧ **LE RELAIS DES ROUTIERS – Chez Cocotte** (N° RR FEV 20 663) (Mme **Grosperrin**) La Cocotte ☎ 81-59-51-92.

CHEMERY-LES-DEUX-BOUZONVILLE 57320 Moselle **RD 918 Map 10-A1**
☿ ⓧ ⌂ **RELAIS MATHIS** (N° RR DEC 19 601) (Mme Marie **Koch**) ☎ 87-78-30-79 ▨ 6 Closed 15 Aug to 30 Sept. German spoken.

CHENEVIERES 54120 M.-et-M. **RN 59 Maps 10-A2 and 14-B1**
☿ ⓧ **LE RELAIS DES ROUTIERS – Chez Jean-Lou et Agnès** (N° RR JAN 23 629) (M. Jean-Louis **Rémy**) 10, route Nationale ☎ 83-72-62-75 Closed Sun; Sept. Coaches (50 seats on reservation).

CHENOVE 21300 Cote-d-Or **RN 74 Map 14-A3**
☿ ⓧ ⌂ **1 Star AU BON COIN** (N° RR OCT 23 957) (M. Marcel **Marin**)

54, route de Dijon ☎ 80-52-58-17 ⚊ 13 Closed Sat, Sun; Aug.

CHERBOURG 50100 Manche **RN 13 Map 4-A1**

☖ ⊗ ⌂ **LES ROUTIERS** (N° RR JUN 26 258) (Mme Viviane **Couvrie**) 10, rue de l'Onglet ☎ 33-53-08-15 ⚊ 11 Closed Fri evening, Sun evening. English, Spanish spoken.

☖ ⊗ **CAFETERIA TRUCK-STOP** (N° RR MAR 23 181) (**Société de Catering**) quai de Normandie ☎ 33-44-21-72 and 33-44-18-69 Coaches welcome (rest. seats 100). Evening meals until 11.00pm. English, German spoken.

☖ ⊗ ⌂ **A L'HORIZON** (N° RR MAI 24 969) (MM. Yves-Richard **Prunier** Frères) 24, rue Surcouf ☎ 33-93-85-85 ⚊ 8 Closed Sun. English spoken.

CHERES (LES) 69380 Rhone **Map 2-A1**

⛽ **Total Service Station LE RELAIS DU GRAVEYRON** (**Sté Rhodis** M. Claude **Mur**) Autoroute A6 ☎ 78-47-60-36 Open 24 hours. English, German spoken.

CHERRE 72400 Sarthe **Map 8-B2/3**

☖ ⊗ **LE MONACO** (N° RR OCT 25 163) (Mme Jacqueline **Manzo**) 193, rue Princesse Alice de Monaco **La Ferté-Bernard** ☎ 43-93-16-03 Tobacco – Magazines – Closed Sun afternoon. Italian, German spoken.

CHESNAY 27160 Eure **Map 8-A3**

☖ ⊗ **CHEZ CLAUDE** (N° RR MAI 26 244) (M. Claude **Blanfune**) Condé sur Iton ☎ 32-29-89-27 Closed Sun; mid-Jul to mid-Aug. Evening meals.

CHEVILLY-LARUE 94150 Val-de-Marne **RN 7 Map 1-B2**

☖ ⊗ **LE RELAIS D'AUVERGNE** (N° RR JAN 17 729) (M. **Carayol**) 4, place de la Libération ☎ 46-86-55-32 Closed Sat, Sun; Aug. Coaches welcome (rest. seats 120).

CHICHE 79350 Deux-Sevres **RN 149 Bis Map 12-B2**

☖ ⊗ **LE RELAIS CHEZ JACQUES** (N° RR DEC 24 434) (M. Jacques **Vincent**) 27, place St-Martin ☎ 49-72-40-51 **Minitel** Closed Wed evening; Christmas to 1 Jan. Coaches welcome (rest. seats 55). Evening meals.

CHIERZAC par BEDENAC 17210 Chte-Mme **RN 10 Map 15-A3**

☖ ⊗ **AU RENDEZ-VOUS DES ROUTIERS** (N° RR JUN 1922) (M. Robert **Laville**) ☎ 46-04-44-24 Closed Sat evening, Sun evening. Evening meals until 11pm.

CHOISY-LE-ROI 94600 Val-de-Marne **RN 186 Map 1-B3**

☖ ⊗ ⌂ **LE STADE** (N° RR DEC 26 750) (M. J-Claude **Villechenoux**) 134, avenue de Villeneuve-Saint-Georges ☎ 48-90-90-55 ⚊ 7 Closed Sun; Aug.

☖ ⊗ ⌂ **LE RELAIS DES MILLE PATTES** (N° RR JAN 24 838) (Mme Geneviève **Chenevier**) 98, av. Victor-Hugo ☎ 48-90-93-31 ⚊ 10 Closed Sun. Arabic, English spoken.

☖ ⊗ **IL PALADINO** (N° RR OCT 26 709) (M. Rocco **Fuina**) 92, av.

C

Choisy-le-Roi continued
Victor Hugo ☎ 48-90-94-17. Closed Sun; Aug. Italian, Spanish spoken.

CHOLET 49300 M.-et-L. **RN 160 Maps 11-B3 and 12-B1**
♀ ⊗ ⌂ **LE RELAIS DES ROUTIERS** (N° RR JUL 12 347) (M. Michel **Dubillot**) 13, place de la République ☎ 41-62-11-09 ⊷ 19 Closed Sun; Jul. Evening meals.
♀ ⊗ **CHEZ DÉDÉ** (N° RR FEVR 258090) (M. André **Bourgey**) 66, bld de Strasbourg ☎ 41-62-27-79 **Minitel** ⊷ 5 Closed Sat, Sun; Aug. (Meals at weekends for booked Routiers.) Meals served until 9.30pm approx.
♀ ⊗ **LE RELAIS DES PRAIRIES** (N° RR SEPT 26 318) (Mme **Albert**) Parc des Prairies, bd du Pont de Pierre ☎ 41-58-09-39 Coaches welcome (rest. seats 120). Meals served in evening. English, German spoken.

CHONAS-L'AMBALLAN 38121 Isere **RN 7 Map 2-B1**
♀ ⊗ **L'ETAPE** (N° RR OCT 26 359) (M. Guy **Ailloud**) Grand-Champ ☎ 74-58-87-50 Closed Sun.

CHORGES 05230 Hautes-Alpes **RN 94 Map 25-A1**
♀ ⊗ ⌂ **1 Star NN HOTEL DES ALPES** (N° RR NOV 19 996) (M. Roger **Mauduech**) Route Nationale 94 ☎ 92-50-60-08 ⊷ 25 from 90–190F, breakfast from 18–28F. Closed 5 Oct to 10 Nov. Full-board 180–190F per night. Coaches welcome (rest. seats 80). Evening meals.

CHOUAIN 14250 Calvados **RD 6 Map 4-B2**
♀ ⊗ **AUX TROIS ÉCUS** (N° RR AVR 26 870) (Mme Marie-France **Gras**) English and Spanish spoken.

CHUISNES 28190 Courville-sur-Eure – Eure-et-Loir) **RN 23 Map 8-B3**
♀ ⊗ **SARL LES CHATELETS L'ESCALE ROUTIÈRE** (N° RR JUIN 27 305) (M. Gerard **Brulé**) lieu-dit Les Chatelets ☎ 37-23-21-75 Closed Sun. Coaches welcome (rest. seats 60). Evening meals.

CIEURAC-LALBENQUE 46230 Lot **RN 20 Map 22-A1**
♀ ⊗ **RESTO AIR** (N° RR AVR 26 520) (Mme Françoise **Lavigne**) RN 20 Puit-d'Enteste ☎ 65-21-05-62 Closed Wed. Spanish spoken.

CIOTAT (LA) 13600 B.-du-R. **Map 24-B3**
⊗ **LOU PITCHOUNET** (N° RR MAR 26 202) (M. Thierry **Guinet**) 8, rue Fougasse ☎ 42-08-28-99 Closed Wed; Feb. Coaches welcome (rest. seats 75). Evening meals.

CIVRAY 86400 Vienne **Map 15-B1/2**
♀ ⊗ **RELAIS DES USINES** (N° RR DEC 27 129) (M. Patric **Martel**) 19, route, de Saint-Pierre ☎ 49-87-04-33 Closed Sat 2pm until Sun 8pm and Bank Holidays.

CLAIRVAUX-LES-LACS 39130 Jura **RN 78 et 83 Map 19-A1**
♀ ⊗ **LES ROUTIERS** (N° RR SEPT 27 024) (M. Denis **Perrin**) 4, route de Lons ☎ 84-25-85-57 ⊷ 10 From 88.50F to 108F, breakfast 20F.

Closed Sun evening. English and Italian spoken. Heated swimming pool. Dogs allowed. Visit the lakes, grotto and dam.

ℙ ⊗ ⌂ **2 star NN HÔTEL DE L'HORLOGE** (N° RR SEPT 27 038) (M. André **Chiron**), 15, Grande-Rue ☎ 84-48-30-09 ⊷ 10 Closed Tues all year, Tues and Wed low season. English spoken. Heated swimming pool.

CLAIX 38640 Isère **RN 75 Map 19-A3**
ℙ ⊗ **LE GALION** (N° RR FEV 24 130) (Mme Marcelle **Tronchet**) Cours de la Libération ☎ 76-98-44-26.

CLAMART 92140 Hauts-de-Seine **Porte de Chatillon Map 1-B2**
ℙ ⊗ **LE RELAIS DU SOLEIL COUCHANT** (N° RR MAR 10 405) (M. Marc **Trameçon**) 151, avenue du Gal de Gaulle ☎ 46-32-05-94 Closed Sun; Aug.

CLAVIERES Commune d'ARDENTES 36120 Indre **RN 143 Map 16-A1**
ℙ ⊗ **LES ROUTIERS DE CLAVIERES** (N° RR SEP 16 224) (M. Daniel **Touchon**) Route de Châteauroux- Montluçon ☎ 54-26-98-46 ⊷ 4 Closed 20 Dec to 20 Jan. Evening meals.

CLAYE-SOUILLY 77410 S.-et-M. **CD 212 Map 1-A3**
ℙ ⊗ **LE RELAIS DE LA ROSEE** (N° RR AVR 25 367) (M. Pierre **Blom**) ☎ 60-26-17-74 **Minitel** ⛽ **Service Station with HGV garage** Closed Sun. Evening meals.

CLELLES 38930 Isère **Map 24-B1**
ℙ ⊗ ⌂ **HOSTELLERIE DU TRIÈVES** (N° RR JANV 27 139) (Mme Odlie **Chrétien**) place de la Gare ☎ 76-34-45-40 ⊷ 7

CLERAC 17270 Charente-Maritime **CD 158/134 Map 15-A3**
ℙ ⊗ ⌂ **1 Star NN AUBERGES DES BANANIERS –** (N° RR SEP 26 651) (Mme Danielle **Arcay**) Montguyon ☎ 46-04-13-17 ⊷ 5. Filling station near.

CLEREY SUD 10390 Aube **RN 71 Map 9-B3**
ℙ ⊗ **LE RELAIS ROUTIER FRANCO-BELGE** (N° RR AVR 26 504) (M. Bernard **Durville**) RN 71 1, avenue de Bourgogne ☎ 25-46-01-50 Closed Sat afternoon, Sun; public holidays; 15 days at end of year. Parking area 2000 sq.m.

CLERMONT-FERRAND 63000 Puy-de-Dôme **RN 9 Map 16-B3**
ℙ ⊗ ⌂ **1 Star NN AUVERGNE PYRÉNÉES - LES ROUTIERS** (N° RR AVR 22 778) (Mme **Laborde**) 12 bis, place Carme ☎ 73-92-35-73 ⊷ 14 from 93,60–216F, breakfast to 18F, telephone in room. Full-board 170–220F per night. Coaches welcome (rest. seats 80). Evening meals. English, Spanish spoken. Parking; bar; dogs allowed; sports centre nearby.
ℙ ⊗ **LE ROUTIER** (N° RR AVR 27 254) (Mme Jocelyne **Sauret**) 12, rue d,'Estaing ☎ 73-90-15-24 Closed Sat and 15/8 to 15/9.

C

CLÉRY-EN-VEXIN 95420 Val-d'Oise **Map 3-B2**
♀ ⊗ **AUBERGE DE CLÉRY-EN-VEXIN** (N° RR FEV 27 174) (M. Jean-Guy **Degoul**) RN 14 n°4 ☎ 34-67-44-14 Closed Sun.

CLICHY 92100 Hauts-de-Seine **Porte de Clichy et Porte d'Asnières Map 1-A2**
♀ ⊗ **AU SOLEIL** (N° RR SEP 26 989) (M. Roger **Queyraud**) 105, bld Victor Hugo ☎ 47-37-15-45. Closed Sun.

CLION-SUR INDRE 36700 Indre **Map 12-B3**
♀ ⊗ **AUBERGE DU PIE DE BOURGES** (N° RR AOU 24 652) (Mme Nicole **Chamton**) 31, Rue Nationale ☎ 54-38-60-90. ⊷ 7 Coaches welcome (rest. seats 48). Evening meals.

CLIOUSCAT 266 30 Drôme **RN7 Map 24-A1 See SAULCE**

CLUIS 36340 Indre **RN 990 and RD 38 Map 16-A1**
♀ ⊗ **LE RELAIS DES ROUTIERS** (N° RR JAN 15 090) (Mme **Mireau**) Rue du Champ-de-Foire ☎ 54-31-23-02. Coaches welcome (rest. seats 80). Evening meals until 9pm.

CLUNY 71250 S.-et-L. **RN 80 Map 18-A1**
♀ ⊗ **AUBERGE DU CHEVAL BLANC** (N° RR FEV 21 785) (SARL **Bouillin/Papion**) 1, rue Porte-de-Mâcon ☎ 85-59-01-13 Closed Sat; 20 Dec to 5 Jan. Coaches welcome (rest. seats 120). Evening meals.

CLUSE (LA) 01460 Ain **RN 84 Map 19-A2**
♀ ⊗ **AU PETIT BAR** (N° RR JUL 17 022) (M. Jean **Dufour**) Place de la Cluse ☎ 74-76-03-57 Closed Sun; Aug.

CLUSES 74300 Haute-Savoie **Map 19-B2**
♀ ⊗ **LE REFUGE** (N° RR AVR 27 257) (M. Serge **Rousseau**) Arraches Cheflieu ☎ 50-90-33-99 English and German spoken.

COEMONT-VOUVRAY 72500 Sarthe **RN 158 Map 12-A2**
♀ ⊗ **LE BON COIN** (N° RR SEP 19 886) (Mme **Jouanneau**) ☎ 43-44-04-17.

COETMIEUX 22400 C.-du-N. **Map 7-A23**
⚒ **Service Station RELAIS MANCHE ATLANTIQUE** (N° RR AOU 55 000002) (SARL Jean-Louis **Merdrignac**) RN Bel-Air **Lamballe** Sens Lamballe/St-Brieuc ☎ 96-34-31-23 Bar; buffet; HGV car park; car wash; Service Station; Shop.

COGOLIN 83310 Var **RN 98 Map 25-A3**
♀ ⊗ **AUBERGE DU GISCLET** (N° RR JUL 26 954) (M. Robert **Vialenc**) ☎ 94-56-40-39 Closed Sun out of season. Italian, Spanish, English spoken.

COLEMBERT 62142 Pas-de-Calais **RN 42 Map 5-A2**
♀ ⊗ ⌂ **CAFÉ DU COMMERCE** (N° RR JUL 26 966) (M. and Mme

C

Gourdin-Duhautoy) Route Nationale ☎ 21-33-31-11 Closed Sun. Filling station near.

COLLONGES-LES-PREMIERES 21110 Côte-d'Or **RN 5 and RD 116 Map 14-A3**
♀ ⊗ **LA BONNE AUBERGE** (N° RR AVR 26 521) (M. Pierre **Colot**) 8, avenue de la Gare ☎ 80-31-32-01. Open 7 days a week 6am–11pm.

COLLONGES-SOUS-SALEVE 74610 Hte-Savoie **RN 206 and 201 Map 19-A2**
♀ ⊗ **LE RELAIS DU COMMERCE** (N° RR AVR 25 377) (M. Bernard and Mme Francine **Denis**) Bas de Collonges St-Julien-en-Genevois ☎ 50-43-60-29 ⊷ 3 Closed Mon; Aug. English, some German spoken.

COLMAR 68000 Haut-Rhin **RN 83 Map 10-B2**
♀ ⊗ **GARE DES MERCHANDISES** (N° RR DEC 26 770) (Mme Pascale **Debenath**) 53, route de Roufflach ☎ 89-41-39-95 Closed Sun. German, English spoken.
⚑ **BP Service Station AIR ROUTE** (N° RR JUL 550000099) (M. Daniel **Binder**) 45, route de Strasbourg (double station) ☎ 89-41-07-55 **Minitel** (main station) 89-23-88-19 (2nd station) Open 24 hours. Shop.

COLOMBELLES 14460 Calvados **RD 513 Map 4-B2**
♀ ⊗ ⌂ **REST PERRIOU** (N° RR AVR 26 221) (M. Jean-Claude **Musson**) 3, route de Cabourg ☎ 31-72-18-89 ⊷ 27 Closed Sun. Full-board 120F per night. Coaches welcome (rest. seats 80). Evening meals.

COLOMBES 92700 Hauts-de-Seine **Porte Maillot Map 1-A2**
♀ ⊗ **BERRY** (N° RR JAN 16 853) (M. **LEROY**) 134, boulevard de Valmy ☎ 42-42-02-08.

COLOMBEY-LES-BELLES 54170 M.-et-M. **RN 74 Map 14-B1**
♀ ⊗ **AUBERGE LORRAINE** (N° RR AVR 26 234) (M. Claude **Arnould**) 71, rue Carnot ☎ 83-52-00-23 Coaches welcome (rest. seats 70). Evening meals.

COLOMBY 50700 Manche **RD 2 (Valognes/Avranche) Map 4-B1**
♀ ⊗ **CHEZ MÉMÈNE** (N° RR JUN 26 572) (Mme Germaine **Delacotte**) Le Bourg-Valognes ☎ 33-40-10-59 Closed Mon; 2nd fortnight Aug. Snacks in the evenings.

COLPO 56390 Morbihan **Map 7-B2**
♀ ⊗ **CHEZ DOMINIQUE** (N° RR AVR 26 230) (M. Daniel-André **Brequel**) 20, rue Nationale ☎ 97-66-84-43 Some English.
♀ ⊗ ⌂ **AUX DÉLICES DE L'OCÉAN** (N° RR AVR 25 385) (M. Jean-Claude **Le Guillan**) 1, avenue de la Princesse ☎ 97-66-82-21 ⊷ 13 Closed 15 June to 8 Jul. Full-board 135–140F per night. Coaches welcome (rest. seats 180). Evening meals.

C

COMBEAUVERT 23250 Creuse **RD 940 Map 16-B1**
♀ ⊗ **LE RELAIS DES SAPINS** (N° RR JUN 23 305) (Mme **Szerve**) **Thauron** ☎ 55-64-02-65 ⇥ 4 Closed Sat; 1st 2 weeks Sept. Full-board available. Coaches welcome (rest. seats 70). Meals served until 11pm.

COMBLANCHIEN 21700 Côte-d'Or **RN 74 Map 14-A3**
♀ ⊗ ⌂ **AUBERGE DU GUIDON** (N° RR FEV 24 121) M. André **Vauchez**) Rte Nle 74 ☎ 80-62-94-39 ⇥ 8 Closed Sat, Sun; Aug. Meals served until 11pm.

COMBRES 28480 E.-et-L. **Map 8-B3**
♀ ⊗ **HOTEL DE LA CROIX BLANCHE** (N° RR OCT 24 305) Mme Danielle **Verrien**) Place de l'Église ☎ 37-49-43-54.

COMBRESSOL 19250 Corrèze **RN 89 Map 17-A2**
♀ ⊗ **2 stars NN LE CHATEL** (N° RR JUL 26 959) (Mme. Yolande **Audier**) La Chapelle ☎ 55-94-22-04 **Minitel** ⇥ 11 Closed Fri in winter; 15 Dec–15 Jan. Filling station near.

COMBRONDE 63460 Puy-de-Dôme **RN 144 et CD 223 Map 15-B3**
♀ ⊗ ⌂ **RELAIS DE L'HERMITAGE** (N° RR NOV 27 107) (Mme Chantal **Duprat**), 5, Belle-Allée ☎ 73-97-10-57.

COMBROUZE 12240 Aveyron **D 911 Map 22-B1**
♀ ⊗ ⌂ **LE RELAIS BONNET** (N° RR JUL 19 107 (Mme Rolande **Bonnet**) ☎ 65-69-93-01 ⇥ 14 Closed Sun. Coaches welcome (rest. seats 70). Evening meals.

COMINES 59560 Nord **Map 5-B1**
♀ ⊗ **AUX AMIS DE LA ROUTE** (N° RR SEPT 27 015) (Mme Christiane **Verbeke**) 6, rue de Pont ☎ 20-39-04-67 Closed Tues pm. Dutch spoken.

COMMODITE (LA) par SOLTERRE 45700 Loiret **RN 7 Map 13-A1/2**
♀ ⊗ **AUBERGE DE LA ROUTE BLEUE** (N° RR MAR 2 687) (SNC **Rocco**) ☎ 38-94-90-04 Closed Tue evening, Wed; 3 to 27 Aug. Coaches welcome (60/32 seats). Evening meals. Some
🍴 Spanish spoken.

COMPIÈGNE 60200 Oise **RN 31-32-35 Map 3-A3**
♀ ⊗ **BAR DE LA MARINE** (N° RR JUL 25 993) (M. Bernard **Piat**) 17, rue de l'Estacade ☎ 44-40-15-14 Closed Sat afternoon, Sun; Aug. Coaches welcome (rest. seats 44). Evening meals until 9.30pm.

CONCOURSON-SUR-LAYON 49700 M.-et-L. **RN 960 Map 12-B2**
♀ ⊗ **AUBERGE DU HAUT LAYON** (N° RR DEC 26 746) (M. Bernard **Battais**) Rte Nationale ☎ 41-59-27-60 Closed Sun evening (winter). English spoken.

CONDÉ-SUR-NOIREAU 14110 Calvados **RN 162 Map 8-A1/2**
♀ ⊗ **LE RELAIS DES PROMENADES** (N° RR JAN 18 594) (M. Michel **Jomat**) 2, rue Motte-de-Lutre Angle rue St-Martin ☎ 31-69-03-36

C

Minitel ⌐ 4 Closed Sun; Aug. Full-board 150–200F per night. Evening meals.

CONDÉ-SUR-VIRE 50890 Manche **Map 4-B1**
♀ ⊗ ⌂ **HOTEL DES ROCHES** (N° RR MAI 26 546) (M. Achour **Mohabeddine**) 12, rue Alfred Duros ☎ 33-55-20-82 ⌐ 8 Closed Sun. English spoken.

CONNANTRE 51230 Marne **RN 4 Map 9-A3**
♀ ⊗ **LA GRAPPE D'OR** (N° RR MARS 26 472) (M. Claude **Longatte**) 1, rue del a Gare ☎ 26-81-04-62 **Minitel** ⌐ 6 Closed Sun; Jan.

CONNERRE 72160 Sarthe **RN 23 Map 8-B2/3**
♀ ⊗ **LE RELAIS DU COMMERCE** (N° RR AVR 11 404) (M. Daniel **Charpentier**) 14, rue de Paris ☎ 43-89-00-55 Closed Sun; Aug. Coaches welcome (rest. seats 120).

CONQUEREUIL (LA) 44290 Loire-Atlantique **RD 124 Map 11-A2**
♀ ⊗ **LE RELAIS DES ROUTIERS – LE BON ACCUEIL** (N° RR NOV 16 350) (Mme Eugénie **Louis**) ☎ 40-87-36-04. Coaches welcome (100 seats reservable). Evening meals.

CONSENVOYE 55110 Meuse **RD 964 Map 8-B3**
♀ ⊗ ⌂ **AUBERGE LORRAINE** (N° RR MAR 26) (Mme Denise **Poussant**) Grand Rue ☎ 29-85-80-19 ⌐ 6 Closed Sat; 2nd fortnight Feb. English spoken.

CONTREXÉVILLE 88140 Vosges **RN 64 Map 14-B2**
♀ ⊗ **LE BELFORT** (N° RR JUIN 25 957) (M. André **Sundhauser**) 587, av. Division Leclerc ☎ 29-08-04-22 Closed Sun. Evening meals on Sat.

CORAY 29145 Finistère **CD 15 et 36 Map 7-B1**
♀ ⊗ **LE BREIZH RELAIS** (N° RR NOV 27 089) (M. Albin **Le Roux**) Place de l'Église ☎ 98-59-36-26 Closed Monday pm and Tuesday pm.

CORBEIL-ESSONNES 91100 Essonne **RN 7 Map 1-B3**
♀ ⊗ ⌂ **1 Star NN L'ERMITAGE** (N° RR JUL 18 796) (M. and Mme Jacques **Teboul**) 137, boulevard de Fontainebleau ☎ 64-96-29-42 ⌐ 20 Closed Sun afternoon (hotel open). English spoken.
♀ ⊗ **LA NACELLE** (N° RR OCT 24 701) (Mme Patricia **Sonnet**) 31, rue de la Papeterie ☎ 64-96-21-17 Closed Sun afternoon.
♀ ⊗ **L'ESCALE** (N° RR JUL 18 461) (M. Marcel-André **Gatefait**) 10, rue de Seine ☎ 64-96-26-58 Closed Sun; Sept.
⚑ **Total Service Station LE RELAIS DE VILLABE** (N° RR DEC 25 230) Autoroute A6 ☎ 60-86-28-17 Cards GR – DKV open 24 hours. **See also VILLABE** and **LISSES**

CORBIGNY 58800 Nièvre **Map 13-B2**
♀ ⊗ **LES AMIS DES ROUTIERS** (N° RR DEC 24 777) (Mme Colette **Perini**) Rte de Clamecy ☎ 86-20-19-77 Closed Sun; 13 Sep–10 Oct. Coaches welcome (rest. seats 30). Evening meals.

C

CORMEILLES-EN-VEXIN 95830 Val-d'Oise **Map 3-B2**
♀ ⊗ **LE MONTMARTRE** (N° RR JANV 26 427) (M. Jean-Claude **Lorre**) SNC Le Relaxe 4, rue Jean Jaurès ☎ 34-66-61-18 **Minitel** Closed Mon. Coaches welcome (rest. seats 40) Evening meals.

CORMERY 37320 Indre-et-Loire **RN 143 Map 12-B3**
♀ ⊗ ⌂ **LA CHAUMIERE** (N° RR OCT 22 984) (Mme **Colle**) La Croix-d'Avon ☎ 47-50-20-26 ↤ 6 Closed Fri evening.

CORMORANCHE-SUR-SAONE 01290 Ain **Map 18-B1**
♀ ⊗ ⌂ **1 Star NN AUBERGE CHEZ LA MÈRE MARTINET** (N° RR JUL 23 864) (Mme Geneviève **Martinet**) ☎ 85-36-20-40 **Minitel** ↤ 7 Closed Wed; 15 Aug to 10 Sept. Full-board 195F to 250F per ⊷ night. Coaches welcome (rest. seats 35). Evening meals.

CORNE 49250 M.-et-L. **RN 147 Map 12-A2**
♀ ⊗ **LE RELAIS DE LA CROIX BLANCHE** (N° RR JUL 25 479) (M. Jean-Noël **Pignard**) La Croix Blanche RN 147 ☎ 41-45-01-82 Closed Sat evening; Sun; Christmas to New Year. Evening meals.

CORNEVILLE-SUR-RISLE 27500 Eure **RN 180 Map 4-B3 see PONT-AUDEMER**

CORON 49690 Maine-et-Loire **RD 960 Map 12-B1**
♀ ⊗ ⌂ **LA BOULE D'OR** (N° RR MARS 26 851) (Mme Marie-Claire **Merlet**) 56, rue Joachim du Bellay ☎ 41-55-81-84 ↤ 11 Closed Wed from 3.30pm. English spoken.

CORPS 38970 Isère **RN 85 Map 19-A3**
♀ ⊗ **LE RELAIS DU TILLEUL** (N° RR JUL 25 979) (M. Claude **Jourdan**) Rue des Fossés ☎ 76-30-00-43 ↤ 10 Closed Nov, 1st 2 weeks Dec. Full-board 200F per night. Coaches welcome (rest. ⊷ seats 60). Evening meals. English, German spoken.

CORPS-NUDS 35150 Ille-et-Vilaine **RN 163 Map 7-B3**
♀ ⊗ **LES ROUTIERS** (N° RR FEV 22 676) (Mme Solange **Piel**) Place de l'Eglise ☎ 99-44-00-25 Closed Sat; Aug.

COSNE 58200 Nièvre **RN 7 Map 13-A/B2**
♀ ⊗ ⌂ **1 Star NN LE RELAIS DES TROIS COULEURS** (N° RR MAR 6 751) (MM. Jean and Pierre **Morfaux**) 21, rue St-Agnan ☎ 86-28-23-50 ↤ 25 Closed last week Dec to 2nd week Jan. Full-board ⊷ 130–150F per night. Coaches welcome (rest. seats 120). Evening meals. Menus from 42–83F. Specialities: *coq au vin,* frogs' legs à la provençale.

COSNE D'ALLIER 03430 Allier **Map 16-A2**
♀ ⊗ **LA PISCINE LES ROUTIERS** (N° RR MAI 265380) (M. Patrick **Thévenot**) 4, rue de la République ☎ 70-07-52-99.
♀ ⊗ **LE LION D'OR** (N° RR MARS 27 207) (M. Jean-Yves **Bernardeau**) 7, place de la Liberté ☎ 70-07-12-20.

COSTAROS 43490 Hte-Loire **RN 88 Map 17-B3**
♀ ⊗ ⌂ **RELAIS ROUTIERS** (N° RR JUN 21 957) (Mme Marie-Thérèse

Rossello) Rue Principale ☎ 71-57-16-04 ⊷ 17 Closed Sat afternoon in winter. Coaches welcome (rest. seats 60). Spanish spoken.

COUCOURDE (LA) 26740 Drôme **RN 7 Map 24-A1/2**
♀ ⊗ ⌂ **RELAIS DES MARRONNIERS** (N° RR AOUT 26 022) (M. **Léorat**) Derbière ☎ 75-51-06-25

COULLONS 45500 Loiret **RD 51 Map 13-A1**
♀ ⊗ ⌂ **LE ROUSSILLON** (N° RR SEP 25 640) (M. Eric **Vialatte**) 45, rue du Sergent-Lelièvre ☎ 38-36-10-49 ⊷ 11 Closed Sun afternoon. Full-board 145F per night. Coaches welcome (rest. seats 240). Evening meals.

COULMIER-LE-SEC 21400 Côte-d'Or **RD 980 Map 13-A3**
♀ ⊗ **LE RELAIS DES ROUTIERS** (N° RR JUL 24 267) (M. Jeran-Maurice **Terillon**) ☎ 80-93-13-09 Closed Sun; 1st fortnight in Aug; Christmas to New Year. Coaches welcome (rest. seats 30). Evening meals until midnight.

COULOMBIERS 86600 Vienne **RN 11 Map 15-B1**
♀ ⊗ **LE RELAIS DE LA PAZIOTERIE** (N° RR JUL 25 050) (Mme Yvonne **Barrusseau**) Lusignan ☎ 49-60-90-59 Coaches welcome (rest. seats 67).

COULOUTRE 58220 Nièvre **RD 1 Map 13-A/B2**
♀ ⊗ **AUBERGE DU NIVERNAIS** (N° RR DEC 24 443) (M. Jean-Bernard **Michel**) Rue Principale ☎ 86-39-32-17 Closed Mon.

COURBAN 21520 Côte d'Or **RD 965 Map 13-A3**
♀ ⊗ ⌂ **LES ROUTIERS – Chez Jaquotte** (N° RR JUN 25 965) (Mme Jacqueline **Aubry**) Montigny-sur-Aube ☎ 80-91-72-81 ⊷ 5 Closed Sun afternoon (unless by previous arrangement). Full-board 130–150F per night. Coaches welcome (rest. seats 80). Evening meals.

COURCELLES-LES-GISORS 60240 Oise **RD 981 Map 3-B2**
♀ ⊗ **AUBERGE DU CARREFOUR** (N° RR DEC 21 716) (M. Daniel **Hillion**) ☎ 32-55-03-16 Closed Sat evening to Sun evening. 1 to 15 Sept. Coaches welcome (rest. seats 60). Evening meals.

COURNEUVE (LA) 93120 Seine-St-Denis **Porte de la Villette Map 1-A2/3**
♀ ⊗ ⌂ **L'ESCALE DES ROUTIERS** (N° RR JAN 26 786) (M. and Mme **Khaled**) 27, avenue Jean-Jaurès ☎ 48-36-43-78 Arabic, English, Italian spoken.
♀ ⊗ ⌂ **CAFE DE L'AVENIR** (N° RR SEP 26 662) (M. Sadid **Hadj-Arab**) 98, ave. P.-V. Couturier ☎ 48-36-37-53 Closed Sun afternoon.

COURTENAY 45320 Loiret **RN 60 Map 9-B2**
♀ ⊗ ⌂ **LE RELAIS DES SPORTS** (N° RR MAI 7 681) (M. Armand **Martin**) 38, rue de Villeneuve ☎ 38-97-32-37 ⊷ 9 Closed Sun; 15

C

Courtenay continued
to 30 Mar; 15 to 30 Aug. Coaches welcome (rest. seats 60). Evening meals.

COURTHEZON 84350 Vaucluse **RN 7 Map 24-A2**
⊗ **LE RELAIS DU SOLEIL** (N° RR MAI 25 423) (M. Jean **Pacome**) RN 7 ☎ 90-70-74-36 Closed Sat, Sun. Italian, German spoken.

COURTISOLS 51460 Marne **RN 3 Maps 6B2 and 9-A3**
♀ ⊗ **LE RELAIS DES TOURISTES** (N° RR NOV 18 551) (M. Gérard **Gaubert**) 57, route Nationale ☎ 26-69-61-42 ⊷ 4 Closed 15 Aug for 3 weeks. Coaches welcome (rest. seats 120). Evening meals.

COUSSAC-BONNEVAL 87500 Haute-Vienne **RN 701 Map 17-A1**
♀ ⊗ 🏠 **LE RELAIS DU GAI COUSSAC** (N° RR DEC 20 051) (Mme Marcelle **Dorion**) Rue du 11 Novembre ☎ 55-75-21-59 Closed Sept. Full-board 130F per night. Coaches welcome (rest. seats 100). Evening meals.

COUSTELLET 84220 Vaucluse **RN 100 Map 24-B2**
♀ ⊗ **LE SARRET** (N° RR MAR 25 336) (M. André **Simonin**) RN 100 **Cabrières d'Avignon** (Gordes) ☎ 90-71-85-58 ⊷ 7 Closed Sun; Feb.

COUTANCES 50200 Manche **RN 171 Map 8-A1**
♀ ⊗ 🏠 **1 Star NN LE RELAIS DU VIADUC** (N° RR JUN 16 098) (Mme
⊷ **Hossin**) 25, avenue de Verdun ☎ 33-45-02-68 **Minitel** ⊷ 10 from 70–150F, breakfast 17–20 F; telephone in room. Closed Fri evening, Sun evening out of season; Sep. Full-board 180–240F per night. Coaches welcome (rest. seats 70/40). Evening meals. English, German spoken. Menus from 38–230F. Specialities: *Langouste gratinée, Tripes maison, Gigot d'agneau.* Sites to visit: cathedral.

COUX (LE) 24220 Dordogne **RD 703 et 710 Map 17-B1**
♀ ⊗ **LA COTTE DE MAILLES** (N° RR NOV 27 078) (Mme Michelle **Mandler**) Place de l'Église ☎ 53-31-61-04 Closed 15/12 to 15/1. English and German spoken.

COZES 17120 Chte-Mme **Map 15-A2**
⛽ **Shell Service Station BEL AIR** (N° RR AVR 550 000 08) (M. Jacques **Gadiou**) Rte de Royan ☎ 46-90-84-12 Grezac.

CRAVANT 89460 Yonne **RN 6 Map 13-A2**
♀ ⊗ 🏠 **LE RELAIS DES DEUX PONTS** (N° RR JAN 17 724) (Mme Isabelle **Nogueria**) 17, route de Paris ☎ 86-42-24-01 ⊷ 10 Portuguese spoken.

CREIL 60109 Oise **RN 16 Map 3-B3**
♀ ⊗ 🏠 **CHEZ PIERROT** (N° RR JUL 25 489) (M. Jacques **Bouchart**) 36, rue des Usines ☎ 44-25-37-22 ⊷ 9 Closed Sat, Sun; Aug.

C

CREMIEU 38460 Isère **RN 157 Map 2-A2**
♀ ⊗ **LE RELAIS DE L'HOTEL DE VILLE** (N° RR MAI 24 579) (M. Jean **L'Hopital**) 1, place de la Nation ☎ 74-94-76-09.

CREMIEU 38460 Isère **see SABLONNIÈRES**

CRENEY 10150 Aube **RD 960 Map 9-B3**
♀ ⊗ **LE RELAIS DU CENTRE** (N° RR DEC 26 128) (M. Jacques **Jeandon**) 29, route de Brienne ☎ 25-81-39-79 Evening meals.

CRESPIERES 78121 Yvelines **RN 307 Map 1-A1**
♀ ⊗ **AUBERGE DES ROUTIERS** (N° RR DEC 9 124) (Mme Magdeleine **Glatigny**) ☎ 30-54-44-28 Closed Mon; Aug. Evening meals.

CREST 26400 Drome **Map 24-A1**
♀ ⊗ **LE CHAMPS DE MARS** (N° RR AVR 27 259) (M. Bernard **Genthon**) 8, place de la Liberté ☎ 75-40-61-06 Closed Mon. German spoken.

CREUSOT (LE) 71200 S.-et-L. **RN 80 Map 18-A1**
♀ ⊗ ⌂ **LE RELAIS DES ROUTIERS** (N° RR SEP 22 041) (M. **Beauclair**) 26, rue de l'Yser ☎ 85-55-04-34 ⊨ 14 Closed Sat afternoon. Full-board 142F per night. Coaches welcome (rest. seats 50). Evening meals.

CREUZIER-LE-VIEUX 03300 Allier) **Map 16-B3**
♀ ⊗ ⌂ **CHEZ LA MÈRE RIBOULIN** (N° RR AVR 27 247) (SARL Marcel **Joly**) 10, rue des Ailes ☎ 70-98-44-88 ⊨ 14 Repas servi le soir.

CREVANT-MONTIERCHAUME 36130 Indre **Map 13-B1**
♀ ⊗ **LE RELAIS DES ROUTIERS** (N° RR DEC 11 180) (Mme **Belouin-Ferre**) ☎ 54-36-00-19 Closed Sun.

CREVECŒUR LE GRAND 60360 Oise **RN 30 and RD 932 Map 3-A2**
♀ ⊗ **LE RELAX** (N° RR JUIL 26 969) (M. Michel **Dubois**) 12, rue de Breteuil ☎ 44-46-87-65 Closed Sun; Filling station near.

CROISEE-ROUVRAY (LA) 21530 Côte d'Or **RN 6 Map 13-B3**
♀ ⊗ **RESTAUGRILL DE LA CROISÉE** (N° RR SEPT 26 036) (Mme Nicole **Sozzi**) ☎ 80-64-70-44 Closed Sat; Sun. Full-board 90–120F per night. Coaches welcome (rest. seats 150). Evening meals until 11pm.

CROISIÈRE (LA) 23300 Creuse **RN 145 and 20 Map 16-B1**
♀ ⊗ ⌂ **LES ROUTIERS** (N° RR JUL 26 596) (M. Raymond **Boutet**) La Croisière St-Maurice ☎ 55-63-77-55 ⊨ 11 Closed 24 Dec–2 Jan. Full-board 140–150F per night. Coaches welcome (rest. seats 50). Evening meals.

CROISY-SUR-ANDELLE 76780 S.-Marit **RN 31 Map 3-A1**
♀ ⊗ **LE RELAIS DU COMMERCE** (N° RR OCT 23 975) (Mme Colette **Belière**) RN 31 ☎ 35-23-61-82 Closed Sun; 15 Dec to 10 Jan. Coaches welcome (rest. seats 80). Evening meals.

C

CROIX 59170 Nord **RD 14 Map 5-B1**
♀ ⊗ **LE RELAIS DE L'HOTEL DE VILLE** (N° RR MAR 21 837) (Mme Lucette **Streleki**) 211, rue Jean-Jaurès ☎ 20-70-50-92 Closed Mon afternoon; Jul.

♀ ⊗ ⌂ **LE RELAIS CHEZ HENRI** (N° RR DEC 24 051) (Mme **Vandesompele**) 53, avenue Georges-Hannart, 188, rue Gustave Dubled ☎ 20-72-59-08 **Minitel** ◄ 9 Closed Sun; Aug. Full-board 180–220F per night. Coaches welcome (rest. seats 60). Evening meals until 9pm. Flemish spoken.

CROIX-BLANCHE-SOLOGNY (LA) 71960 S.-et-L. **RN 79 Map 18-A1**
Voir BERZÉ-LA-VILLE

CROIX-CALUYAU-BOUSIES 59222 Nord **RD 932 Map 6-A3**
♀ ⊗ **LE RELAIS DES ROUTIERS** (N° RR JUL 21 991) (Mme Josette **Verriez**) Le Gué-Fené ☎ 27-84-15-99.

CROIX-CHAPEAU 17220 Chte-Mme **Map 11-B1**
♀ ⊗ **RELAIS DE PARIS** (N° RR DEC 26 412) (M. Jean-Paul **Thabault**) 60, avenue de la Libération ☎ 46-35-81-20 Closed Wed.

CROIX-VALMER (LA) 83420 Var **RN 559 Map 25-A3**
♀ ⊗ ⌂ **LA CIGALE** (N° RR MAI 24 966) (M. Eric **Korhel**) Rte Nle 559 ☎ 94-79-60-41 ◄ 7.

CROLLES 38190 Isère **RN 90 Map 19-A3**
♀ ⊗ ⌂ **1 Star NN HOTEL DU PETIT PONT** (N° RR JUN 25 946) (M. André **Legallais**) RN 90 ☎ 76-08-03-92 Montfort ◄ 13 from 85–230F Closed Mon; Nov. Full-board 160–280F per night, Coaches welcome (rest. seats 60). Evening meals from 7pm to 8.30pm. Parking; bar; dogs allowed; 'boule' played; ski runs near. Some German spoken.

CRUAS 07350 Ardeche **RN 86 Map 24-A1/2**
♀ ⊗ **AUX AMIS DES ROUTIERS** (N° RR JUL 17 322) (Mme Jeannette **Pistoresi**) ☎ 75-51-41-12 Coaches welcome (rest. seats 120). Evening meals until 11pm.

CRUET-MONTMELIAN 73820 Savoie **RN 6 Map 19-A2**
♀ ⊗ ⌂ **CHEZ MARCEL** (N° RR DEC 26 747) (M. Jean-Noël **Padel**) La Gare ☎ 79-84-28-68 ◄ 9 English, German spoken.

CUIGY-EN-BRAY 60850 Oise **RN 3 Map 3-A2**
♀ ⊗ **RELAIS DE ST-LEU** (N° RR NOV 26 365) (M. Jacques **Delaruelle**) ☎ 44-82-53-17 **Minitel** Closed Sun. Coaches welcome (rest. seats 100). Evening meals.

CUISE-LA-MOTTE 60350 Oise **RN 31 Map 6-B1**
♀ ⊗ **AUX AS DU VOLANT** (N° RR MAI 26 547) (M. Dominique **Bignet**) 23, rue du Dr Moussaud ☎ 44-85-70-51 ◄ 4 Closed Sat, Sun; 24 Dec to 2 Jan. Coaches welcome (rest. seats 74). English spoken.

C

CUISEAUX 71480 Saône-et-Loir **Map 18-B1**
♈ ⊗ **RELAIS FRANC COMTOIS** (N° RR FEV 26 441) (M. Gilles **Donguy**) Joudes ☎ 85-72-79-79 Closed Sat afternoon; Sun; 15 days in Aug; 15 days at Christmas/New Year. Evening meals.

CUISERY 71290 S.-&-L. **RD 971 Map 18-B1**
♈ ⊗ **SARL LE JARDIN DE LA COQUELLE** (N° RR JANV 27 157) (M. Jean-Paul **Fallet**) Zone artisanale du Bois Bernoux ☎ 85-40-06-90 Closed Mon. English spoken. Specialities: regional products (Chickens, Snails etc) Monkfish in Sauce Armoricaine 39.50F, Perch Fillet in Chardonnay 41F.

CULAN 18270 Cher **RD 943 Map 16-A2**
♈ ⊗ ⌂ **1 Star NN HOTEL DU BERRY** (N° RR MAR 23 155) (Mme **Perrot**) Route de Châteaumeillant ☎ 48-56-65-93 ⊷ 7 from 80–120F Closed Sun; 15 Dec to 1 Jan. Full-board 150F per night. Coaches welcome (rest. seats 50/60). Evening meals until midnight. Parking; bar; dogs allowed. Sites to visit: château, church, museum, dam at Sidiailles.

CUON 49150 M.-et-L. **Map 12-A2**
♈ ⊗ **LA POMM'DE PIN** (N° RR AVR 25 904) (Mme Yvette **Pécot**) RN 938 Le Bourg ☎ 41-82-75-74 ⊷ 4 Closed Mon afternoon; Aug. Coaches welcome (rest. seats 60). Evening meals until 10pm.

CUQ-TOULZA 81470 Tarn **RD 621 Map 22-A2**
♈ ⊗ ⌂ **1 Star NN LE RELAIS CHEZ ALAIN – La Bombardière** (N° RR MAR 22 271) (M. Alain **Pratviel**) ☎ 63-75-70-36 ⊷ 10 at 160F, breakfast from 20 to 25F. Full-board 170–185 F per night. Coaches welcome (rest. seats 400). Evening meals. Parking; bar; dogs allowed; TV room; walks. Sites to visit: Lake Saint Ferréol, Cordes, Sidobre. English spoken.

CUSSAC 87150 Hte-Vienne **RD 699 Map 15-B2**
♈ ⊗ **LES BRUYÈRES** (N° RR JAN 25 787) (M. **Morichon**) Place de l'Église ⊷ 4 English spoken.
♈ ⊗ ⌂ **LA BARRIÈRE** (N° RR AVR 27 240) (Mme Denise **Barrière**) ☎ 55-70-94-84 ⊷ 9

CUSSET 03300 Allier **Map 16-B3**
♈ ⊗ ⌂ **HOTEL DE LA GARE LES ROUTIERS** (N° RR JAN 26 421) (M. Jean **Laroque**) 1, route de Paris ☎ 70-98-26-10 ⊷ 3 Closed Sun; Aug.
♈ ⊗ **LES MONTAGNARDS** (N° RR JUN 26 922) (M. Roger **Pol**) 20, rue Général Raynal ☎ 70-98-38-60 Closed Sun; 15 days July. Filling station near.

CUSSY-LES-FORGES 89200 Yonne **RN 6 Map 13-A3**
♈ ⊗ **LE RELAIS 6** (N° RR FEV 26 805) (M. Hamid **Adjaoud**) ☎ 86-33-10-14 Closed Mon.

CUVILLY 60490 Oise **RN17 Map 3-A3**
♈ ⊗ ⌂ **LA CAMPAGNARDE** (N° RR JUN 26 922) (M. Daniel **Hillion**) 5, route de Flandres ☎ 44-85-00-30 ⊷ 9 Closed Sun; 1–15 Sept.

C

CUZIEU 42330 Loire **RN 82 Map 18-A2**
⚑ ⊗ ⌂ **REST DE LA MAIRIE** (N° RR AVR 26 225) (Mme Janine **Dard**) RN 82, Le Bourg ☎ 77-54-88-21 ⇥ 12 Closed Sun; 15 days at Christmas; 3 weeks in Aug.

D

DAGNEUX 01120 Ain **RN 84 Map 2-A2**
⚑ ⊗ **RELAIS DE LA PLACE** (N° RR OCT 26 336) (Mme **Aliu** and M. **Colin**) 96, rte de Genève ☎ 78-06-43-70 Spanish, Italian spoken. Evening meals until mid-night.

DAMBACH-LA-VILLE 67650 Bas-Rhin **RD 210 1 km from Nle 422 Map 10-B1**
⚑ ⊗ **AUBERGE DE LA GARE** (N° RR SEPT 26 054) (Mme Christine **Sutter**) 1, rue de la Gare ☎ 88-92-47-11 Closed Wed; end Aug; Christmas; end Feb. Coaches welcome (rest. seats 30). German, some English spoken.

DAMVILLE 27240 Eure **Map 8-A3**
⚑ ⊗ **BAR DE L'AVENIR** (N° RR AOUT 26 978) (Mme Chantal **Noël**) 5, rue de Verdun ☎ 32-34-50-24 English, Italian, Portuguese, Spanish spoken.

DANGERS 28190 Eure-et-Loir **CD 939 Map 8-A/B3**
⚑ ⊗ **LE RELAIS** (N° RR DEC 27 134) (M. Patrick **Ollier**) rue de Chartres ☎ 37-22-90-30 Closed Sun and two weeks in August.

DANGÉ-ST-ROMAIN 86220 Vienne **Map 12-B2**
⚑ ⊗ ⌂ **LE NATIONAL CHEZ ARLETTE** (N° RR AVR 25 374) (Mme Arlette **Turquais**) 120, RN 10 ☎ 49-86-40-14 ⇥ 6 Closed Sun. Evening meals. Coaches welcome. HGV parking.

DANNEMOINE 89700 Yonne **RD 905 Map 13-A3**
⚑ ⊗ **A LA BONNE AUBERGE - LES ROUTIERS** (N° RR MAI 21 096) (Mme Nicole **Verdin**) ☎ 86-55-54-22 Coaches welcome (rest. seats 65). Evening meals.

DARDILLY 69570 Rhône **RD 6 and RD 73 Map 2-A1**
⚑ ⊗ ⌂ **LE CHENE ROND** (N° RR FEV 23 144) (M. Emile **Lagoutte**) 87, Rte Nle 7 ☎ 78-87-15-48 ⇥ 6 Closed Sat midday, Sun; Aug. Evening meals.
⛽ **Service Station LES BRUYÈRES** (N° RR FEV 23 649) (M. Norbert **Berton**) Aire de Paisy ☎ 78-35-73-80 sens Lyon/Paris Open 24 hours. German spoken.
⚑ ⊗ ⌂ **LE RELAIS DE LA RADIO** (N° RR SEP 26 042) (Mme Lucienne **Monnot**) lieu-dit Montcourant ☎ 78-48-01-39 ⇥ 8

Closed Sat evening, Sun; 1 to 24 Aug. Coaches welcome (rest. seats 50). Evening meals.

DARVOY 45150 Loiret **RN 751 Map 13-A1**
♀ ⊗ **LE RELAIS DES ROUTIERS** (N° RR DEC 16 348) (Mme Germaine **Girard**) ☎ 38-59-71-00 Closed Sun afternoon; Aug.

DAX 40100 Landes **RN 647 and 124 Map 20-A2**
♀ ⊗ **AUBERGE DE LA CHALOSSE** (N° RR OCT 22 956) (M. **Pichaud**) 157, avenue Georges Clemenceau ☎ 58-74-23-08 ➡ 4 Closed Sun; Aug. Evening meals.

DECAZEVILLE 12300 Aveyron **RN 140 (axe Brive Mediterranée) Map 22-B1 and 17-B2**
♀ ⊗ **REST. DES USINES** (N° RR OCT 25 132) (Mme Régine **Forsse**)
⊷ 23, faubourg Desseligny ☎ 65-43-15-88 Closed Sat afternoon. Evening meals. Menus 40–105F. Specialities: *écrevisses américaines, cuisses de grenouilles, bavette aux échalottes.*

DECINES 69150 Rhône **RN 517 Map 2-A2**
♀ ⊗ ⌂ **2 Stars NN – HOTEL DE LA POSTE – Chez Simone** (N° RR JUL 18 783) (Mme Marcel **Buisson**) 11, rue d'Alsace ☎ 78-49-19-03 ➡ 34 from 100 to 180F, breakfast to 20F. Restaurant closed Sun, Hotel open. Car park (area 2000 sq.m.) locked at night. Evening meals. English, Spanish, Italian spoken. Bar; dogs allowed; boule played; track and pool near.

DECIZE 58300 Nièvre **RN 81 Map 13-B2**
♀ ⊗ **LE RELAIS BEL-AIR** (N° RR NOV 19 985) (M. and Mme André **Paris**) 164, avenue de Verdun ☎ 86-25-01-86 Closed Sun; Aug. Coaches welcome (rest. seats 44). Meals served until 8pm.

DENEZE-SUR-DOUÉ 49700 Maine-et-Loire **RD 69 Map 12-B2**
♀ ⊗ **LE RELAIS DES ROUTIERS** (N° RR JAN 23 113) (Mme Onillon) ☎ 41-59-21-56.

DENGUIN 64230 Pyrénées-Atlantiques **RN 117 Map 20-B3**
♀ ⊗ ⌂ **2 stars NN LES ROUTIERS DE DENGUIN** (N° RR MARS 26 846) (**Sarl Pyrénées Montagne Océan**) ☎ 59-68-85-15 ➡ 14 English, Spanish, German spoken.

DÉOLS 36130 Indre **RN 151, RN 20 and RN 725 Maps 12-B3 and 13-B1**
♀ ⊗ **L'ESCALE** (Voir Châteauroux).
♀ ⊗ **RELAIS DE L'ESPÉRANCE** (N° RR OCT 26 340) (Mme **Dugué**) route d'Issoudun ☎ 54-22-68-17.

DERBIÈRE 2674 Drôme **RN 7 Map 24-A2**
♀ ⊗ ⌂ **LE RELAIS DES MARRONNIERS** (N° RR AOU 26 022) (M. Dominique **Léorat**) RN 7, La Coucourde ☎ 75-51-06-25 ➡ 6 Closed Sun in winter.

DESERTINES 03630 Allier **RN 145 Map 16-A2**
♀ ⊗ **AUX CHANT'OISEAUX** (N° RR DEC 24 438) (SDF **Pinet**) 79, rue

D

Desertines continued
Ambroise Croizat ☎ 70-05-18-59 Closed Wed; Oct. Evening meals.
♇ ⊗ **LE BON AMI** (N° RR MARS 26 823) (Mme Cecilia **Rocha**) 63, rue de Stalingrad ☎ 70-05-21-16 Closed Tue. Portuguese spoken.

DESVRES 62240 Pas-de-Calais **RN 341 Map 5-A2**
♇ ⊗ ⌂ **LE RELAIS DE LA BELLE CROIX** (N° RR SEP 23 462) (M. **Grumelart-Mielot**) ☎ 21-91-65-81 Longfosse ⊷ 5 English spoken.

DETRIER 73110 Savoie **RD 925 Map 19-A2**
♇ ⊗ **LES SMOUTANS** (N° RR MARS 27 217) (M. Alain **Sigrand**) La Rochette ☎ 79-25-52-59 Closed Sun afternoon. English spoken.

DEUIL-LA-BARRE 95170 Val-d'Oise **RN 428 Map 1-A2**
♇ ⊗ **LE RELAIS DU COQ HARDI** (N° RR SEP 19 940) (M. and Mme **Lantinier**) 62 bis, avenue de la Division Leclerc ☎ 39-64-16-81 Closed Sat; Sun; Aug. Evening meals to order.

DEUX-CHAISES 03240 Allier **Map 16-A3**
♇ ⊗ **LE RELAIS DE L'AMITIÉ** (N° RR AVR 24 904) (M. Louis **Douge**) RN 145 ☎ 70-47-15-64 **Le Montet.**

DEVAY 58300 Nièvre **Map 16-A3**
♇ ⊗ **L'ETRIER** (N° RR MARS 26 842) (M. Jean-Marc **Boutet**) Route Nationale ☎ 86-25-15-65. German spoken.

DIEPPE 76200 Seine-Maritime **RN 15 Map 4-A2**
♇ ⊗ **L'AVENIR** (N° RR JUN 23 856) (M. Benoît **Pan**) 10, Cours de Dakar Port de Commerce ☎ 35-84-18-10 Closed Sat evening, Sun; Aug.

DINAN 22100 C.-du-N. **RN 166 and 176 Map 7-A3**
♇ ⊗ ⌂ **LA MARMITE** (N° RR AOU 23 904) (M. **Bouillet**) 91, rue de Brest ☎ 96-39-04-42 ⊷ 5 Closed Sat evening, Sun. Full-board 140F per night. Coaches welcome (rest. seats 45). English, ⇌ German spoken.

DINARD 35400 I.-et-V. **RN 166 and 168 Map 7-A3**
♇ ⊗ ⌂ **LE CAP HORN** (N° RR MARS 25 837) (M. Jean-Pierre **Treff**) 66, rue de la Gare ☎ 99-46-59-09 ⊷ 4 Closed Christmas to New Year; 15 to 31 Aug. Coaches welcome (rest. seats 32/20). Evening meals.

DISSAY 86130 Vienne **RN 10 Map 15-B1**
♇ ⊗ **LA MOURANDERIE** (N° RR JUL 25 067) (Mme Colette **Berrier**) **CHEZ COLETTE** ☎ 49-52-40-13 or 12 Coaches welcome (rest. seats 150). Evening meals.

DISSAY-SUR-COURCILLON 72500 Sarthe **RN 158 Map 12-A2**
♇ ⊗ **RELAIS MAINE-TOURAINE** (N° RR MAI 21 918) (Mme Colette **Petit**) Route Nationale 158 ☎ 43-44-09-08 Restaurant open 24 hours. Room for weddings, banquets.

D

DIVAJEU 26400 Drôme **RN 538/DLE 26 Map 24-A1**
♀ ⊗ **LES TONNELLES** (N° RR SEPT 26 654) (M. Bernard **Berchaud**) Quartier de Lambres ☎ 75-40-66-82 Closed Sat. Coaches welcome (rest. seats 54 + shaded terrace). Meals served until 9pm. Italian spoken.

DIVES-SUR-MER 14360 Calvados **Map 4-B2**
♀ ⊗ **LE CAFE DU PARKING** (N° RR SEP 26 047) (M. Daniel **Constant**) 2, rue des Frères-Le-Paule ☎ 31-91-24-25 Closed Sun; Aug.

DIZY-LE-GROS 02150 Aisne **RD 336 Map 6-A2**
♀ ⊗ **LE RELAIS FRANCE-EUROPE** (N° RR AOU 194540) (M. Claude **Gantier**) Route de Reims ☎ 23-21-23-15 **Minitel** ⊷ 3 Closed Sun; 15 to 31 Aug. Coaches welcome (3 rooms + heated terrace = 160 seats). Evening meals until 9pm.

DOL-DE-BRETAGNE 35120 Ille-et-Vilaine **RN 12 Map 7-A3**
♀ ⊗ **LE RELAIS DES SPORTS ET DU BON ACCUEIL** (N° RR OCT 23 999) (M. Jean-Yves **Beubry**) 23 bis, rue de Rennes ☎ 99-48-06-14 **Minitel** Coaches welcome (rest. seats 50). Evening meals.

DOLLON 72390 Sarthe **Map 8-B2**
♀ ⊗ **LES LABOUREURS** (N° RR SEPT 26 668) (M. Christopher **Gay**) 2, place de l'Eglise ☎ 43-93-44-06.

DOMFRONT 61700 Orne **RN 12**
♀ ⊗ ⌂ **1 Star NN RELAIS ST-MICHEL** (N° RR JAN 10 298) (M. Michel and Claudine **Prod'homme**) 5, rte du Mont St-Michel ☎ 33-38-64-99 **Minitel** ⊷ 19 from 65 to 120F, breakfast 18–22F. Closed Fri evenings low season. Full-board 130–150F per night, 1000F per 7 days. Coaches welcome (rest. seats 240). Evening
↪ meals until 11pm. Some English spoken. Menus from 45 to 85F. Specialities: *Andouillette au poivre, tarte normande, poulet normande.* Sites to visit: church, château, remains of 11th C chapel.

♀ ⊗ **LA CROIX DES LANDES** (N° RR FEV 23 133) (M. **Farigoul**) ☎ 33-38-51-35.

DOMONT 95330 Val d'Oise **RN 1 Maps 1-A2 and 3-B3**
♀ ⊗ **LA VIELLE AUBERGE** (N° RR JAN 24 085) (M. Roger **Badaire**) 72, Rte Nle 7 ☎ 39-91-01-66 ⊷ 7 Closed Sat, Sun; Aug. Spanish spoken. Evening meals until 9pm.

DOMPIERRE-SUR-BESBRE 03290 Allier **RN 79 Map 16-A3**
♀ ⊗ **LE RELAIS DE LA BESBRE** (N° RR JUN 25 453) (M. Jean-Pierre **Marossa**) 207, avenue de la Gare ☎ 70-34-53-69 Closed Sun; half Sept. Evening meals until 9pm.

DONZENAC 19270 Corrèze **RN 20 Map 17-A1**
♀ ⊗ **RELAIS DE LA POÊLE D'OR** (N° RR SEPT 26 987) (M. Daniel **Vermand**) Av. de Paris ☎ 55-85-72-20. Filling station near.

D

DONZÈRE 26290 Drôme **RN7 Map 24-A2**
♈ ⊗ ⌂ **1 star NN AU BON ACCUEIL** (N° RR OCT 26 701) (M. Jacky **Paunon**) RN 7 ☎ 75-51-64-58 ⊸ 11 Dutch, Spanish spoken.

DORLISHEIM 67120 Bas-Rhin **RN 392 Map 10-B2**
♈ ⊗ ⌂ **LE RELAIS DE LA GARE** (N° RR NOV 9 059) (M. René **Jost**) 4, avenue de la Gare ☎ 88-38-14-28 ⊸ 7 Closed Sat, Sun; from 28 Aug to 15 Sep; 10 days in Oct. Coaches welcome (rest. seats 70). Evening meals.

DOUAI 59500 Nord **RN 17 and 34 Map 5-B3**
♈ ⊗ ⌂ **A L'ÉPI D'OR** (N° RR FEV 22 663) (M. Michel **Barjou**) 38, faubourg d'Arras Lambres ☎ 27-87-04-56 ⊸ 7 Closed Sun. Open 4.30am to midnight.
♈ ⊗ ⌂ **LE RELAIS** (N° RR MARS 25 844 (Mme Jeanine **Deyredk**) 370, rue d'Aniche ☎ 27-88-12-06 ⊸ 8.
♈ ⊗ **LA FLAMANDRIÈRE** (N° RR OCT 26 347) (M. **Tison**) Rte de Tournai ☎ 27-98-55-28 **Minitel** Closed Mon. Coaches welcome (rest. seats 80). Evening meals.

DOUÉ-LA-FONTAINE 49700 M.-et-L. **Map 12-B2**
♈ ⊗ **CHEZ PAUL** (N° RR 27 118) (M. et Mme Paul et Josette **Type**) Zone industrielle Route de Montreuil ☎ 41-59-03-33 Open 24 hours, English and Spanish spoken.

DOULAINCOURT 52270 Hte-Marne **RN 67 Map 14-A1**
♈ ⊗ ⌂ **1 Star NN LE RELAIS DE PARIS** (N° RR JAN 8 214) (M. Denis **Frantzen**) Place Charles de Gaulle ☎ 25-94-61-18 ⊸ 10 Closed Wed (except Jul, Aug); 24 Aug–14 Sep. Full-board 140–150F per night. Evening meals.

DOUSSART 74210 Hte-Savoie **Map 19-A2**
♈ ⊗ ⌂ **1 Star NN LA TOUR DU LAC** (N° RR OCT 26 677) (Mme Lucette **Favre-Bonvin**) SARL Scherfa – La Gare ☎ 50-44-30-37 ⊸ 10 Closed Sun.

DOZULE 14430 Calvados **RN 175 Map 4-B2**
♈ ⊗ ⌂ **LES CHARMETTES** (N° RR FEV 26 804) (M. Patrice **Tanguy**) 1, route de Rouen ☎ 31-79-21-87 ⊸ 4 Closed Sun evening; Oct. German spoken.

DRAGUIGNAN 83300 Var
♈ ⊗ **LE PENALTY** (N° RR FEV 26 437) (M. Guy **Chabrand**) Quartier St Léger, 1, av. de la 1ʳᵉ Armée ☎ 94-68-11-28 **Minitel** Closed Sun; half Aug.

DREUIL-LES-AMIENS 80730 Somme **RN 235 Map 5-A3**
♈ ⊗ **CHEZ JEAN-MARIE ET CHRISTIANE** (N° RR FEV 23 645) (M. Jean-Marie **Dumeige**) 285, avenue Pasteur ☎ 22-43-12-95 Closed Sun; Aug. Coaches welcome (rest. seats 60). Evening meals.

DREUX 28100 Eure-et-Loire **RN 12 and RN 154 Map 8-A3**
♈ ⊗ **LE RELAIS DE LA POSTE** (N° RR SEP 19 506) (Mme **Sedaine**) 2, rue du Général-de-Gaulle ☎ 37-46-12-00 Closed Sun; Aug.

D

♀ ⊗ **LE MARCEAU** (N° RR SEPT 26 998) (M. Jean-Pierre **Parent**) 40/
42, av. du Général Marceau ☎ 37-46-05-57 Closed Sun; Aug.

DROUÉ 41270 L.-et-C. **CD 141 Map 8-B3**
♀ ⊗ **AUBERGE DU CHATEAU** (N° RR JAN 23 605) (M. Marcel
Savouray) 16, place de la République ☎ 54-80-51-47 Closed Sun
evening; Dec. Full-board 120–150F per night. Coaches welcome
(rest. seats 70). Evening meals.

DUNKERQUE 59140 Nord **RN 16 Map 5-A2**
♀ ⊗ ⌂ **AU PANIER FLEURI** (N° RR DEC 23 073) (M. **Playe**) 15-17,
rue du Ponceau ☎ 28-66-76-19 ⇥ 7 Closed Sat (from 2pm), Sun.
Full-board 180–220F per night. Coaches welcome (rest. seats 40).
Evening meals.
♀ ⊗ **CENTRE ROUTIER DE TRANSPORT** (N° RR OCT 23 994) (M.
Serge **Baumans**) Z.I. de Grande Synthe, rue Louis Blanqui ☎ 28-
60-03-64 **Minitel** Closed Sun. Dormitory for lorry-drivers.
Coaches welcome (rest. seats 80). Evening meals.

DURANVILLE 27230 Eure **RN 13 Map 4-B3**
♀ ⊗ ⌂ **BON ACCUEIL** (N° RR DEC 24 457) (M. **Jardin**) RN 13 ☎ 32-
46-83-02 ⇥ 16 Closed Sun; Sept. Evening meals.
♀ ⊗ **Tobacconist LE RELAIS DES ARCADES** (N° RR OCT 25 664)
(M. Claude **Yssambourg**) ☎ 32-46-83-01 Closed Sat afternoon,
Sun; Jul. Evening meals.

DURAVEL 46700 Lot **Map 21-B1**
♀ ⊗ **LE PIED DE MOUTON** (N° RR DEC 26 417) (M. John **Duberley**)
☎ 65-36-50-39 Closed Dec. Evening meals. English spoken.

DURFORT 30170 Gard **Map 23-B1**
♀ ⊗ **LE SANTA FE** (N° RR FEV 24 851) (M. Michel **Vallat**) Rte de St-
Hippolyte ☎ 66-77-57-00 Closed Mon. English, German spoken.

E

ECALLES-ALIX 76190 S.-Marit. **RN 15 Bis Map 4-A3**
♀ ⊗ ⌂ **AUBERGE DE LA FOURCHE** (N° RR AVR 25 867) (M. Serge
Vannier) Tobacconist Hameau de Loumare ☎ 35-95-45-01 ⇥ 5
Closed Sun. Coaches welcome (rest. seats 32). Evening meals.

ECARDENVILLE-LA-CAMPAGNE 27170 Eure **RN 13 Map 4-B3**
♀ ⊗ ⌂ **AUBERGE DU RELAIS** (N° RR JUN 26 928) (Mme Phillippe
Lelièvre) ☎ 32-35-05-32 ⇥ 10 Closed Sun; 2nd fortnight Aug.
English, German spoken.

LES ÉCHELLES 73 360 Savoie **RN 6 Map 2-B3**
♀ ⊗ **L'ESCAPADE** (N° RR JUL 25 997) (M. Jean-Françoise **Daude**) Rte

E

Les Echelles continued

Nle 6 ☎ 79-36-55-99 Closed Sun; last week Aug, 1st week Sept.

ECHEMIRE 49150 M.-et-L. **Autoroute Océane A11 RN 766 Map 12-A2**

♀ ⊗ **LE RELAIS DES ROUTIERS – CHEZ JACQUELINE** (N° RR AOU 20 270) (Mme **Gaillot**) 7, 9, rue Principale Le Bourg ☎ 41-89-19-17 Closed Sun; 1–21 Jun. Coaches welcome (rest. 3 rooms of 45/30 /10 seats).

ECLAIBES 59330 Nord **RN 2 Map 6-A3**

♀ ⊗ **LE ROBINSON** (N° RR JUN 26 270) (M. Elhadi **Manseur**) Rte Nle 2 ☎ 27-61-14-63 Coaches welcome (rest. seats 240). Evening meals.

ECHOUCHE 61150 Orne **RD 924 Ex 24 bis Map 8-A2**

♀ ⊗ ⌂ **HOTEL DE L'OUEST** (N° RR MARS 26 206) (M. Dominique **Bodin**) 27, avenue du Gal-Leclerc ☎ 33-35-12-24 ⊷ 4. Closed Sun evening. Coaches welcome (rest. seats 30/50/100). Evening meals.

ECROUVES-TOUL 54200 M.-et-M. **RN 4 Map 14-A/B1**

♀ ⊗ ⌂ **LE RELAIS MATHY** (N° RR AOU 13 061) (**Mathy SARL**) 875, avenue du 15ᵉ Génie ☎ 83-43-04-27 ⊷ 17 Closed Fri evening, Sat; Jul. Full-board 160F per night. Coaches welcome (rest. seats 50). Evening meals.

ECULLY 69130 Rhone **RN 7 Map 2-A1**

♀ ⊗ **LES ROUTIERS** (N° RR JUIN 26 906) (Mme Sylvie **Taillandier**) 30, Rte de Paris ☎ 78-34-01-40. Closed Sun.

ÉGLISES-D'ARGENTEUIL (LES) 17400 Chte-Marit. **CD 950 Map 15-A2**

♀ ⊗ ⌂ **CHEZ VEDETTE** (N° RR SEP 27 023) (M. Joël **Pilot**) Saint-Jean-d'Angély ☎ 46-59-94-21 ⊷ 5 Closed Sat. afternoon.

ELVEN 56260 Morbihan **RN 166 Map 7-B2**

♀ ⊗ ⌂ **1 Star NN LE RELAIS DE L'ARGOUET** (N° RR AOU 16 177) (M. and Mme André **Le Douarin**) 36, avenue de l'Argouët ☎ 97-53-32-98 ⊷ 12 from 85 to 140F, breakfast to 15F. Closed Sat except high season; Sept. Full-board 155F per night. Coaches welcome (rest. seats 130). Evening meals until 10pm. English spoken. Parking; bar; dogs allowed. Menus from 45 to 120F. Specialities: fish, seafood. Sites to visit: lakes, rivers.

EMBRUN 05200 Htes-Alpes **RN 94 Map 25-A1**

♀ ⊗ ⌂ **1 star NN PONT FRACHE** (N° RR MAI 26 879) (Mme Simone **Faure**) Route de Briançon ☎ 92-43-00-86 ⊷ 20 English, Italian, Spanish, German spoken.

♀ ⊗ **Self-Service Embrunais SUR L'POUCE** (N° RR DEC 25 767) Mme Michèle **Veillon**) Boulevard Pasteur, Réfectoire des Cordeliers ☎ 92-43-27-07 Closed Sun; Christmas holidays. Coach welcome (rest. seats 80). English spoken.

E

EMONDEVILLE 50310 Manche **RN 13 Map 4-B1**

♈ ⊗ **AU COUP DE FREIN** (N° RR MARS 26 825) (Mme Thérèse **Jean**) Montebourg ☎ 33-41-22-74 ⊷ 3 Closed Sat from 2.30pm to Sun evening.

ENNORDES 18380 Cher **RD 30 Map 13-A1**

♈ ⊗ **LE RELAIS DES ROUTIERS** (N° RR JAN 19 620) (Mme Georgette **Champion**) Route Départementale 30 ☎ 48-73-06-36 Closed Sat.

♈ ⊗ **LA SURPRISE** (N° RR DEC 25 240) (Mme Maryline **Auroi**) La Chapelle-d'Angillon ☎ 48-58-26-97 Closed Sat afternoon, Sun; 15 days in Summer. Coaches welcome (rest. seats 40). Evening meals.

ENTRAN 86100 Vienne **A 10 Map 15-B1**

♈ ⊗ **ACCOR L'ARCHE** Aut. A10 Sens Province/Paris ☎ 49-21-75-58 Self service 7am to 10pm. Shop. English spoken.

EPANNES 79270 Deux-Sèvres **RN 11 Map 15-A1**

♈ ⊗ ⌂ **LE RELAIS SUISSE-OCÉAN** (N° RR MAI 8 479) (M. Jacky **Guilloteau**) On edge of the Poitevin Marais, 10km from A23 exit. ☎ 49-04-80-01 ⊷ 10 Closed Sun low season; 15 Sept to 30 Sept. Full-board 140–160F. Coaches welcome (rest. seats 125). Evening meals.

EPERNAY 51200 Marne **RN 3 Map 9-A3**

♈ ⊗ ⌂ **AU BON ACCUEIL** (N° RR JAN 16 390) (Mme Marie-Louise **Prejent**) 13, avenue J.-J. Rousseau ☎ 26-55-23-29 **Minitel** ⊷ 10 Closed Sun; Jan. Full-board 160–200F. Coaches welcome (rest. seats 30/50). Evening meals until 10pm to mid-night.

EPERRAIS 61400 Orne **RD 938 Map 8-B2**

♈ ⊗ **LA PETITE VALLÉE** (N° RR MARS 26 839) (Mme Monique **Germond**) La Petite Vallée, Mortagne ☎ 33-83-91-34. Closed Sun. English spoken.

EPINAL 80000 Vosges **Map 10-A2**

♈ ⊗ **LE RELAIS DE L'ABATTOIR** (N° RR SEPT 26 053) (M. Gérard **Didier**) 63, rue de Nancy ☎ 29-82-32-13 Closed Sun; 14 Jul to 15 Aug. Evening meals.

EPINAY-SUR-SEINE 93800 Seine-Saint-Denis) **RN 14 Map 1-A2**

♈ ⊗ **AU RENDEZ-VOUS DES COCHERS LIVREURS** (N° RR JUIN 26 924) (M. Jean-Francois **Fremont**) 32, Bld Foch ☎ 48-26-80-03 Closed Sun; public holidays.

♈ ⊗ ⌂ **LES OISEAUX** (N° RR JANV 27 155) (Mme Jeanine **Lecointe**) 1, rue de l'Yser ou 12, bd Foch ☎ 42-43-91-38 ⊷ 8 Closed Sun.

EPINEAU-LES-VOVES 89400 Yonne **RN 6 Map 13-A2**

♈ ⊗ ⌂ **LE RELAIS DES 6 BOULES** (N° RR JUL 22 864) (M. Ahmed **Betroune**) 2, route de Chambéry ☎ 86-91-20-45 and 86-91-20-54 Arabic, German spoken.

E

EPINEUIL-LE-FLEURIEL 18360 Cher **Map 16-A2**

♀ ⊗ **LES ROUTIERS** (N° RR JAN 26 154) (Mme Hélène **Bergerat**)
Saulzais-le-Potier ☎ 48-63-02-81 **Minitel** Closed Mon afternoon.
Coaches welcome (rest. seats 60). Evening meals until 9pm.

EPOISSES 21460 Côte-d'Or **Map 13-A3**

♀ ⊗ ⌂ **LA POMME D'OR** (N° RR DEC 24 769) (Mme Monique
Mucherl) Rue des Forges ☎ 80-96-43-01 ⊷ 8 Approved by
Tourist Board. Closed Wed; 1 to 22 Aug. Evening meals until
8.00pm. Full-board 135–140F per night.

EPONE 78680 Yvelines **RN 13 Map 1-A1**

♀ ⊗ **LE RESTAUVERT** (N° RR MAI 26 891) (**Sarl Restauvert**) Route
de Gargenville ☎ 30-95-60-20 Italian spoken.

EPREVILLE-près-LE-NEUFBOURG 27110 Eure **RD 133 Maps 3-B1
and 4-B3**

♀ ⊗ **LE BRABANT** (N° RR MAR 21 020) (M. Raymond **Cochois**) ☎ 32-
35-04-40 Closed Wed; 18 to 28 Aug.

EQUEURDREVILLE 50120 Manche **RD 901 Map 4-A1**

♀ ⊗ ⌂ **RESTAURANT DE LA HAGUE** (N° RR JUN 22 835) (M.
Claude **Lamy**) 120, rue de la Paix ☎ 33-53-14-87 ⊷ 17 Closed
Sun. 1 to 15 Sept. English spoken.

♀ ⊗ **À L'HORIZON** (N° RR DEC 27 117) (Mme Christiane **Casrouge**)
24, rue Surcouf ☎ 33-93-85-85 Closed Sun.

EROME 26600 Drôme **RN 7 Map 18-B3**

♀ ⊗ **AU PETIT COQ BLANC** (N° RR JUN 25 961) (M. Alain **Watrui**)
RN 7 ☎ 75-03-30-13 Evening meals until 1am. English spoken.

ERVILLERS 62121 P.-de-C. **Map 5-B3**

♀ ⊗ **LE RELAIS** (N° RR JUL 26 965) (Mme Muriel **Gillon**) 34, Rte
Nationale ☎ 21-55-83-02 English, German spoken.

ERVY-LE-CHATEL 10130 Aube **D 374 Map 9-B3**

♀ ⊗ **RESTAURANT DE LA GARE** (N° RR FEVR 26 811) (M. Dany
Bordier) Place de la Gare ☎ 25-70-66-36 Closed Tue at 2pm.

ESLETTES (LES) 76710 Seine-Marit. **RN 27 Map 3-A1**

♀ ⊗ **LE RELAX** (N° RR MAI 21 091) (M. Jean **Sorel**) Route de Dieppe
Côte de Malaunay ☎ 35-75-11-70 Closed Wed.

ESNON 89210 Yonne **RN 443 Map 9-B2 13-A2**

♀ ⊗ **LE RELAIS DES AMIS** (N° RR FEV 26806) (Mme Danièle
Ollivon), 20, Route Nationale ☎ 86-56-13-26 **Minitel** Closed Mon
and September. Coaches welcome (rest. seats 70).

ESPALION 12500 Aveyron **RN 120 Map 23-A1**

♀ ⊗ ⌂ **1 Star NN LE RELAIS DES QUATRE ROUTES** (N° RR JAN 26
162) (Mme Marie **Bouteleau**) Quatre Routes ☎ 65-44-01-69 ⊷
⊷ Closed Sun. Full-board 150–200F per night. Evening meals.
Portuguese, Spanish spoken.

E

ESQUERDES 62380 P.-de-C. **RD 211 Map 5-A2**
♀ ⊗ ⌂ **CAFE ROUTIERS D'ESQUERDES** (N° RR MAR 6 466) (Mme Justine **Tassart**) 1114, rue Bernard-Chochoy ☎ 21-98-17-35 ⇥ 7 Evening meals.

ESSARTS (LES) 85140 Vendee **RN 160 Map 11-B3**
♀ ⊗ **LE PINIER** (N° RR MAR 20 423) (Mme Jacqueline **Dupont**) ☎ 51-62-81-69 Closed Fri evening, Sat. Evening meals.
♀ ⊗ **CAFE RESTAURANT DES TOURISTES** (N° RR MAI 26 544) (Mme Chantal **Rousselot**) 35, rue de Gaulle ☎ 51-62-83-52 Coaches welcome (rest. seats 40).

ESSARTS-LE-ROI (LES) 78690 Yvelines **RN 10 Maps 1-B1–9-A1**
♀ ⊗ **LE RELAIS DE L'ARCOAT** (N° RR JAN 25 793) (SARL **ARCOAT**) 39 Rte Nle 10 ☎ 30-41-60-53 Closed Sat evening, Sun. English spoken.
♀ ⊗ **A LA GRACE DE DIEU** (N° RR JUL 25 055) (M. Daniel **Bigot**) Rte Nle 10 ☎ 30-41-60-04 Closed Sat, Sun; Aug. Coaches welcome (rest. seats 110). Evening meals.

ESSERTENNE-ET-CECEY 70100 Haute-Saône **CD 70 Map 14-A3**
♀ ⊗ **LES ROUTIERS** (N° RR NOV 27 105) (M. Pascal **Roy**) rue de la Gare ☎ 84-67-41-66 Closed Wed pm.

ESTABLES 43160 Hte-Loire **RN 106 and Dle 35 Map 17-B3**
♀ ⊗ **LE RELAIS D'ESTABLES** (N° RR OCT 26 076) (M. Gérard **Fournerie**) Félines, La Chaise-Dieu ☎ 71-00-92-11 Open 24 hours.

ESTREÉS-DENIECOURT 80660 Somme **RN 336 Maps 5-B3 and 6A1**
♀ ⊗ ⌂ **L'AUBERGE DE LA MAIRIE** (N° RR AVR 21 466) (Mme Claudette **Demuynck-Dehenry**) Péronne exit Autoroute A1 to Amiens ☎ 22-85-20-16 ⇥ 4 Closed Sat, Sun; Aug. Full-board 130–140F. Coaches welcome (rest. seats 100–120). Evening meals.

ESTREES-MONS-EN-CHAUSSEE 80200 Somme **RN 29 Maps 5-B3–6-A1**
♀ ⊗ **A LA POMME D'API** (N° RR FEV 14 686) (M. Albert **Gras**) 28, Route Nationale ☎ 22-85-60-04 ⇥ 3 Closed Sun; Aug. Coaches welcome (rest. seats 40). Evening meals.

ETAGNAC 16150 Chte **RN 141/948 Map 15-B2**
♀ ⊗ **RELAIS D'ÉTAGNAC** (N° RR AVR 25 376) (M. Christian **Labrousse**) ☎ 45-89-21-38 ⇥ 10 Coaches welcome (4 dining rooms). Filling station, tobacconist, newsagent. English spoken.

ETAIS-LE-SAUVIN 89840 Yonne **Map 13-A2**
♀ ⊗ **LES ROUTIERS** (N° RR AVR 24 913) (Mme Mireille **Picot**) rue de la Gare ☎ 86-47-25-19 Evening meals.

ETALANS-NODS 25580 Doubs **RN 57 Map 14-B3**
♀ ⊗ **AUBERGE DU GOUFFRE DE POUDREY** (N° RR FEV 24 110) (Mme Elisabeth **Gorrissen**) Rte Nle 57 ☎ 81-59-20-43 Closed Jan.

E

Etalans-Nods continued

Coaches welcome (rest. seats 100). Evening meals. Dutch, English, German spoken.

ETALONDES 76260 S.-Mme **RD 925 Map 4-A3**
♀ ⊗ **LA BAHUTIÈRE** (N° RR JUL 25 984) (M. Éric **Castelain**) 24, rte Nationale ☎ 35-86-88-01 Closed Sun. Evening meals until 10.30pm. English spoken.

ETAMPES 91150 Essonne **RN 20 Map 9-B1**
GARAGE DES ROUTIERS (N° RR JAN 15 508) (M. Roger **David** Unic Agent and Westinghouse brake-fitters RN 20 South of Etampes ☎ 64-94-56-18

ETOILE 26800 Drôme **RN 7 Map 24-A1**
♀ ⊗ 🏠 **ROUVEYROL** (N° RR JAN 26 134) (M. Roland **Rouveyrol**) RN 7 ☎ 75-61-62-06 Fiancey ⊶ 13 Closed Sun. Evening meals. English, German spoken.

ETOUVELLES 02000 Aisne **RN 2 Map 6-B1**
♀ ⊗ 🏠 **CHEZ JEANNOT** (N° RR MAR 16 908) (M. J.-M. **Serre**) 30, Rue de Paris, D542 ☎ 23-20-63-26 ⊶ 9 Closed Sat, Sun and August. Evening meals. Coaches welcome (rest. seats 120).

ETRELLES 35370 l.-et-V. **see VITRE**

EU 76260 Seine-Maritime **RN 15 Bis Map 4-A2**
♀ ⊗ 🏠 **LE RELAIS DE L'ETOILE** (N° RR JUN 16 132) (M. Maurice **Pajot**) 37, boulevard Thiers ☎ 35-86-14-89 ⊶ 10 Evening meals.

EVANS 39700 Jura **Map 14-B3**
♀ ⊗ **RELAIS 73** (N° RR MAI 25 992) (Mme Marguerite **Bardey**) Chez Guiguille ☎ 84-71-15-97 Coaches welcome (rest. seats 70). Evening meals.

EXMES 61310 Orne **RD 14, 26 Map 8-A2**
♀ ⊗ **RELAIS SAINT-LÉONARD** (N° RR DEC 763) (M. Michel **Soulabaille**) Bourg St. Léonard ☎ 33-67-17-03 Closed Sun; Aug.
♀ ⊗ 🏠 **LE RELAIS DU COMMERCE** (N° RR JUN 21 556) (Mme Fernande **Simon**) Grande-Rue ☎ 33-39-93-04 ⊶ 4 Full-board 140–180F per night. Coaches welcome (rest. seats 200). Evening meals.

EYGUIANS 05300 Hautes-Alpes **RN 75 Maps 24-B2–25-A1**
♀ ⊗ 🏠 **1 Star NN LE RELAIS DE LA GARE** (N° RR NOV 15 439) (Mme Michelle **Robert**) ☎ 92-66-20-08 ⊶ 15 Closed Jan. Full-
⚓ board 165–190F per night. Evening meals.

EYMOUTIER Voir ST-AMAND-LE-PETIT 87120 Hte-Vienne

EZY-SUR-EURE 27530 Eure **RD 143 Map 8-A3**
♀ ⊗ 🏠 **LE RELAIS LE TERMINUS** (N° RR AVR 17 514) (Mme Madeleine **Veisen**) 16, bld Ulysse-Lavertu – place de la Gare ☎ 37-64-73-24 ⊶ 10 Closed Fri 2.00pm, Sat. Open Sun midday. Closed Aug. Evening meals.

FABREGUES 34690 Hérault **RN 113 Map 23-B2**
ⵟ ⊗ **BAR LE 113** (N° RR AOU 24 303) (Mme Josette **Avignon**) 36,
avenue Georges-Clémenceau ☎ 67-85-12-86 Closed Sun; Oct.
Coaches welcome (rest. seats 45). Evening meals.

FALAISE 14700 Calvados **RN 158 Map 6-A2**
ⵟ ⊗ ⌂ **LE RELAIS CHEZ DURAND** (N° RR OCT 21 674) (M.
Christian **Durand**) 33, avenue d'Hastings ☎ 31-90-04-67 **Minitel**
— 5 Closed Sun; public holidays; Jul. Evening meals until 9.30pm.

FALCK 57550 Moselle **RD 23 Map 10-A1**
ⵟ ⊗ **KRAUSER** (N° RR AVR 26 220) (M. Guy **Louvet**) 2, rue Hargaten
☎ 87-82-60-69 Evening meals.

FALLERON 85670 Vendée **RN 753 and D 34 Map 11-B2**
ⵟ ⊗ **CHEZ COLETTE** (N° RR AOU 24 657) **Tobacconist** (M. and
Mme Didier **Charrier**) 54, Rue Nationale ☎ 51-35-50-22 Closed
Sat afternoon, Sun. Coaches welcome (rest. seats 50). Evening
meals.

FAOUET (LE) 56320 Morbihan **RN 782 Map 7-B2**
ⵟ ⊗ ⌂ **LE RELAIS DES HALLES** (N° RR MAR 4 067) (M. and Mme
Le Puil) 19, rue du Soleil ☎ 97-23-07-66 — 8 Closed Sun; Sept.
Evening meals. English spoken.
ⵟ ⊗ **TY CRAVIC** (N° RR JUIN 27 308) (Mme Josiane **Herbaux**) ☎ 94-
23-07-04 Closed Sun and August. Evening meals served to 11pm.

FARE-LES-OLIVIERS (LA) 13380 B.-du-R. **RN 113 Map 24-B3**
ⵟ ⊗ ⌂ **LE RELAIS PROVENÇAL** (N° RR MAI 22 352) (Mme Odette
Camarasa) Route National 113 ☎ 90-57-65-62 — 8 Closed Sun; 15
Aug to 1 Sept. Spanish, Italian spoken.

FARGUES-SUR-OURBIZE 47700 Lot-et-Garonne **RN 655 Map 21-A1**
ⵟ ⊗ **LE RELAIS DES ROUTIERS** (N° RR FEV 22 218) (Mme Michèle
Téchene) ☎ 53-93-04-54 — 4 Closed Wed from 2–7pm. Half
board 95F, full board 125F per night. Coaches welcome (3 dining
rooms = 200 seats). Evening meals. Spanish spoken.

FAUVILLE-EVREUX 27930 Eure **D 57 Maps 3-B1 and 4-B3**
ⵟ ⊗ ⌂ **LES AILES** (N° RR MAI 25 390) (Mme Mauricette **Quenel**) rue
de Fauville ☎ 32-39-28-18 — 12 English, German, Spanish
spoken.

FAVEROLLES-SUR-CHER 41400 L.-and-C.)
Voir MONTRICHARD

FECAMP 76400 Seine-Maritime **RD 925 Map 4-A3**
ⵟ ⊗ **RELAIS DU CHEMIN DE FER** (N° RR AVR 25 899) (M. Jean-
Marie **Lefèbvre**) 29/31 quai-Bérigny ☎ 35-28-06-17 Closed Sat,
Sun evening; 20 Dec–20 Jan. Evening meals until 9pm.

FEISSONS-SUR-ISERE 73260 Savoie **Map 19-B2**
ⵟ ⊗ **LE RELAIS DES ROUTIERS** (N° RR OCT 24 699) (M. Michel
Ruffier) between Albertville and Moutiers (take 1st right after

F

Feissons-sur-Isere continued
Cevins) ☎ 79-22-50-97 **Minitel** Closed weekends. Some English, German spoken.

FELINES 07340 Ardèche **RN 82 Map 24-A1**
♈ ⊗ ⌂ **1 Star NN LE RELAIS DE LA REMISE** (N° RR JUN 25 032) (M. Jacky **Laurencin**) Route Nationale 82 ☎ 75-34-82-22 ⊸ 4 Closed Sat, Sun; Dec to Mar. Full-board 135–155F per night. Coaches welcome (rest. seats 130 + 80 on terrace). Evening meals.

FENOUILLER (LE) 85800 Vendée **RD 754 Map 11-B2**
♈ ⊗ ⌂ **LA MADELON** (N° RR JAN 26 137) (M. Fulbert-Gérard **Pouvreau**) 64, rue du Centre, St-Gilles-Croix-de-Vie ☎ 51-55-05-35 ⊸ 20 Coaches welcome (rest. seats 110). Full-board 140–152F per night. Evening meals. English spoken.

FERDRUPT 88360 Vosges **RN 66 Map 10-A3**
♈ ⊗ **PLEIN AIR VOSGES ALSACE** (N° RR AVR 24 566) (M. Michel **Guenot**) ☎ 29-25-03-51 Full-board available. Coaches welcome (rest. seats 65). Evening meals.

FERRIÈRE (LA) 79390 Deux-Sevres **RN 148 bis Map 15-A1**
♈ ⊗ **AU BON ACCUEIL** (N° RR JUN 25 469) (Mmes **Bilheu-Berger**) Thenezay ☎ 49-63-03-01 Closed Thur evening; last 2 weeks Jan, Aug. Coaches welcome (rest. seats 65). Evening meals.

FERRIERES-EN-BRAY 76220 S.Marit **RN 31 Map 3-A2**
♈ ⊗ ⌂ **HOTEL DU CHEMIN DE FER** (N° RR MAI 24 573) (M. Jean **Feret**) 26, av. de la Gare ☎ 35-90-01-61 ⊸ 10 Closed Sat, Sun. Full-board 110–135F per night. Coaches welcome (rest. seats 90). Evening meals until midnight.

FERTE-BERNARD (LA) 72400 Sarthe **RN 23 Map 8-B3**
♈ ⊗ **ACCOR L'ARCHE** (M. G. **Bisson**) Autoroute A11 ☎ 43-93-41-02 Self-service restaurant 7.00am–11.00pm. Shop.

FERTE-GAUCHER (LA) 77320 S.-et-M. **RN 34 Map 9-A2**
♈ ⊗ **LE RELAIS DE L'EST** (N° RR SEP 19 501) (M. Bruno **Gapillou**) 4, avenue de la Gare ☎ 64-04-01-90 Closed Sun; Aug. Evening meals until 10pm. German spoken.

see also SANCY-LES-PROVINS

FERTE-SAINT-AMBREUIL (LA) 71420 Saône-et-Loire **Autoroute A-6 Map 18-B1**
♈ ⊗ **CAFE ROUTE ACCOR** (M. Jean-Jacques **Viau**) Aire de Service de Sennecey-le-Grand Direction Paris-Province ☎ 85-44-21-79 Open 7.00am–10.00pm weekends, 24 hours weekdays. Self-service restaurant. Shop. English spoken.
♈ ⊗ **ACCOR L'ARCHE** (Mme **Marie-Claude Debrune**) Aire de St-Ambreuil Direction Province-Paris Autoroute A-6 ☎ 85-44-20-64 Self-service restaurant open 24 hours. Shop.

F

FIANCEY-PAR-LIVRON 26250 Drôme **RN 7 Maps 18-B3 and 24-A1**
♀ ⊗ ⌂ **RELAIS DU SUD-EST** (N° RR MAI 26 552) (M. André **Courbier**) RN 7 ☎ 75-61-61-19 ⊷ 9 English and German spoken. Closed Sun. Evening meals served till 11pm. Coaches welcome (Rest. seats 52).

FIANCEY see **ÉTOILE**

FIENVILLERS PAR CANDAS 80500 Somme **Map 5-A3**
♀ ⊗ **LE RELAIS FLEURI** (N° RR OCT 27 070) (Mme Sylviane **Doriol**) 66, route Nationale ☎ 22-32-51-78 Closed Sat and Sun. Polish spoken.

FIGEAC 46100 Lot **Map 17-B2**
♀ ⊗ **LE RELAIS DES CHASSEURS** (N° RR MAI 23 792) (Mme **Wilhem**) La Vayssière ☎ 65-34-12-33 ⊷ 8 Closed Sat at 6pm to Mon morning. Full-board 130-135F per night. Coaches welcome (rest. seats 50). Evening meals. Spanish, English spoken.

FIRBEIX 24450 Dordogne **RN 21 Map 17-A1**
♀ ⊗ **LE RELAIS DES SPORTS** (N° RR JUN 21 548) (M. René **Beaubatit**) Nationale 21 ☎ 53-52-82-53 Closed Oct. Coaches welcome (rest. seats 100). Evening meals.

FISMES 51170 Marne **RN 31 Map 6-B1**
♀ ⊗ ⌂ **LE LION ROUGE** (N° RR AVR 24 200) (M. Michel **Sohier**) 6, route de Soissons ☎ 26-78-12-63 ⊷ 5 Closed Sun. Evening meals until 10pm.

FITOU 11510 Aude **RN 9 Map 23-A3**
♀ ⊗ ⌂ **1 Star RELAIS LE PARADOR** (N° RR MAI 27 273) (M. Robert **Morhain**) Cabanne de Fitou ☎ 68-45-79-11 ⊷ 50 70 to 170 F Petit-déjeuner to 18 and 25 F. German, Spanish and Italian spoken. Evening meals served to 12pm.

FIX-SAINT-GENEYS 43320 Hte-Loire **RN 7 Map 25-A2**
♀ ⊗ **RELAIS DU COL** (N° RR OCT 18 858) (Mme **Gallien**) ☎ 71-57-02-67 Closed Sun.

FLASSANS-SUR-ISSOLE 83340 Var **RN 7 Map 25-A2**
♀ ⊗ **REST LE NOCTURNE** (N° RR AVR 12 797) (M. Robert **Gualco**) Nationale 7, quartier de la Bourette ☎ 94-69-71-33 Closed Sat;
⇱ Dec. Coaches welcome (rest. seats 140). Italian spoken. Evening meals.
♀ ⊗ **RELAIS DE L'ISSOLE** (N° RR NOV 27 083) (Mme Monique **Nottoli**) ☎ 94-59-64-84. Filling station near-by.

FLAVIAC 07000 Ardèche **Map 24-A1**
♀ ⊗ **LES ROUTIERS** (N° RR DEC 26 407) (M. Didier **Garrayts**) Place Émile-Crémière ☎ 75-65-77-57 ⊷ 7 Closed Sun; Sept.

FLAVY-LE-MARTEL 02520 Aisne **Maps 5-B3 and 6-A1**
♀ ⊗ **LE RELAIS DES ROUTIERS** (N° RR FEV 26 178) (M. Jean-Paul **Brière**) 17, rue André-Brûlé ☎ 23-52-51-31 Closed Sat.

F

FLERS 61100 Orne **RD 924 and RD 18 Map 8-A1/2**
  ☺ ⦾ 🏠 **HÔTEL DES TOURISTES** (N° RR DEC 26 758) (M. Maurice-**Dupont**) 80, rue de Paris ☎ 33-65-25-57 ⏣ 12 Closed Sun.
  ☺ ⦾ **LE PRIEURÉ** (N° RR JAN 26 795) (M. Lionel **Pailleux**) La Lande Patry ☎ 33-64-83-12

FLERS-EN-ESCREBIEUX 59128 Nord **RN 43 Map 51-B2/3**
  ☺ ⦾ **AU BON CASSE-CROÛTE** (N° RR OCT 27 050) (M. Raymond **Dufour**) 59, route Nationale ☎ 27-86-69-41 Closed Sat and Sun.

FLEURANCE 32500 Gers **RN 21 Map 21-B2**
  ☺ ⦾ **REST. DU STADE** (N° RR MAR 22 261) (M. Alphonse **Pujade**) place de l'Eglise ☎ 62-06-02-23 Closed Sat; June. Coaches welcome (rest. seats 160). Evening meals.

FLEURE 86340 Vienne **RN 147 Map 15-B1**
  ☺ ⦾ **AUX AMIS DE LA ROUTE** (N° RR JUIN 26931) (Mme Michèle **Gulonnet**) Route de Poitiers ☎ 49-42-60-25

FLEURIEU-SUR-SAÔNE 69250 Rhône **CD 433 Map 2-A1**
  ☺ ⦾ **LA CABANE** (N° RR AVR 26 492) (M. Jean-Robert **Richard**) 54, rte de Lyon ☎ 78-91-40-60 Closed Sat, Sun; Aug. Coaches welcome (rest. seats 80). English, Italian spoken.

FLEURIEUX-S/ARBRESLE 69210 Rhône **RN 7 Map 18-A2**
  ☺ ⦾ **AUBERGE DES CÔTEAUX LYONNAIS** (N° RR DEC 26 748) (M. Pierre **Caceres**) ☎ 74-26-97-90 Closed Sun. Spanish spoken.

FLEURY 60240 Oise **Map 3-B2**
  ☺ ⦾ **LA TABLE DE FLEURY** (N° RR JANV 26797) (M. Yvan **Marie**) Gran-de-Rue ☎ 44-49-04-60.

FLEURY-SUR-ORNE 14000 Calvados **RN 162 Map 4-B2**
  ☺ ⦾ **RELAIS DE LA POMME D'OR** (N° RR OCT 21 680) (Mme Emilienne **François**) 20, route d'Harcourt ☎ 31-82-36-87 Closed Sun; public holidays; Aug.

FLEVIEU 69360 Rhône **CD 12 Map 2-B1**
  ☺ ⦾ **LE GAULOIS** (N° RR MARS 27 237) (M Hen-Pierre **Coursat**) 2, rue Saint-Nicolas Ternay ☎ 78-73-07-34. English spoken.

FLIREY 54470 M.-et-M. **RN 958 Map 14-B1**
  ☺ ⦾ **LE RELAIS CHEZ JACQUES** (N° RR MAI 12 261) (Mme Marthe **Warin**) ☎ 83-81-15-73 ⏣ 4.

FLIXECOURT 80420 Somme **30 m RN1**
  ☺ ⦾ **LES FLONFLONS DU BAL** (N° RR DEC 26 768) (M. Jean-Marc **Rohaut**), 16 rue Georges- Clémenceau ☎ 22-51-36-34 English spoken.

FOIX 09000 Ariège **RN 20 Map 22-A3**
  ☺ ⦾ 🏠 **LE RELAIS DU SOLEIL D'OR** (N° RR AOU 20 527) (M. Jean **Coumes**) 57, avenue du Ml-Leclerc ☎ 61-65-01-33 ⏣ 6 Closed Sun Nov to May.

FOLLIGNY 50320 Manche **RD 924 Map 8-A1**
Ⓨ ⊗ ⌂ **LE RELAIS DU LION D'OR** (N° RR OCT 24 716) (Mme **Héon**)
🕀 Le Repas ☎ 33-61-32-77 ⇥ 7 Closed Feb. English spoken.

FONDETTES 37230 I.-et-L. **RN 152 Map 12-A2**
Ⓨ ⊗ **LE BEAU MANOIR** (N° RR DEC 24 458) (M. Alain **Barre**) 6, quai
de la Guignière ☎ 47-42-01-02 Closed Sat, Sun; public holidays.
15 days in Aug; 15 days in Dec. Coaches welcome (rest. seats
64). Evening meals (except Fri).

FONTAINE-LE-COMTE 86240 Vienne **RN 11 near to RN 10 Map 15-B1**
Ⓨ ⊗ **AUBERGE DE LA GARENNE** (N° RR AVR 25 386) (Mme
Michelle **Guerin**) ☎ 49-57-01-22 **Minitel** Closed Sun; Aug.
Coaches welcome (rest. seats 70). Evening meals until 11pm.

FONTAINE-SAINT-MARTIN (LA) 72114 Sarthe **RN 23 Map 12-A2**
Ⓨ ⊗ **LE RELAIS DU CHENE VERT** (N° RR FEV 16 890) (Mme
Flameych) ☎ 43-29-80-84 Closed Sat, Sun; 3 weeks Aug; 2 weeks
Dec. Evening meals.

FONTAINE-SIMON 28240 E.-et-L. **RD 2 and 25 Map 8-A/B3**
Ⓨ ⊗ ⌂ **AU BON COIN** (N° RR JAN 23 108) (M. **Durand**) rue de la
Mairie La Loupe ☎ 37-81-84-98 ⇥ 10 Closed Fri; Full-board 130–
150F per night. Evening meals.

FONTAINE UTERTE 02210 Aisne **Map 6-A1**
Ⓨ ⊗ **ETOILE DU BERGER** (N° RR SEPT 27 006) (Mme Jeannine
Munie) Bohain ☎ 23-07-90-26 Closed Sun. Filling station at 3 kms.

FONTENAY-SUR-LOING 45210 Loiret **RN 7 Map 9-B2**
Ⓨ ⊗ **LE RELAIS DES CENT BORNES** (N° RR DEC 21 722) (M.
Martin) Nationale 7 ☎ 38-95-82-06 Open 24 hours. Closed 9 to 24
Aug. Coaches welcome (rest. seats 70). Evening meals.

FONTVANNES 10190 Aube **Map 9-B3**
Ⓨ ⊗ ⌂ **AUBERGE DE LA VANNE** (N° RR JAN 26 425) (M. Michel
Dubrulle) 1, rue Léandre-Denis ☎ 25-70 37-60 ⇥ 8 Closed Sun.

FONTVERGNES 12300 Aveyron **RN 140 (main Brive-Méditerranée road) Maps 22-B1 and 17-B2** see Decazeville
Ⓨ ⊗ **REST. DES USINES** (N° RR OCT 25 132) (Mme Régine **Forsse**)
23, faubourg Desseligny Decazeville ☎ 65-43 15-88 Closed Sun.
🕀 Evening meals served until 11pm.

FORMERIE 60220 Oise **Map 3-A2**
Ⓨ ⊗ ⌂ **CAFE DE LA PAIX** (N° RR MAI 24 576) (Mme Françoise
Merlin) 8, rue Dornat ☎ 44-46-17-08 **Minitel** ⇥ 6 Closed Sun
afternoon; Full-board 120F per night. Coaches welcome (rest.
seats 60). Evening meals.

FOS-SUR-MER 13270 Bouches-du-Rhône **Map 24-A3**
Ⓨ ⊗ ⌂ **1 Star NN MA CAMPAGNE** (N° RR FEV 26 167) (M. Bernard
Silhol) 42, avenue Jean-Jaurès ☎ 42-05-01-66 or 42-05-00-11 ⇥ 25

F

Fos-sur-Mer continued

Closed Sat afternoon to Mon morning. Full-board 150–180F per night. Coaches welcome (rest. seats 300). Evening meals. English, Italian, Spanish spoken.

♀ ⊗ **LE MOULIN** (N° RR OCT 25 135) (Mme Gisèle **Lefèbvre**) plage du Cavaou ☎ 42-05-48-38 **Minitel** Coaches welcome (rest. seats 80). Evening meals. English spoken.

⊗ **LE RELAIS DE LA GARE** (N° RR OCT 25 684) (sté de la Gare **Godart**) quartier de la Gare ☎ 42-06-43-43 Closed Sun. Evening meals.

♀ ⊗ **RELAIS DE LA FOSSETTE — Chez Annie et Guy** (N° RR MAR 25 317) (M. Guy **Hologne**) quartier de la Fossette ☎ 42-05-30-01 Closed Sat, Sun; Aug. Coaches welcome (rest. seats 80). Evening meals.

FOUCARMONT 76340 S.-Mme **RN 28 Map 4-A2**
♀ ⊗ **LE RELAIS ROUTIERS** (N° RR JAN 25 275) (Mme **Bénard**) RN 28 ☎ 35-93-91-50 Closed Sat. Evening meals.

♀ **CHEZ FRANÇOISE** (N° RR JUN 25 458) (Mme Françoise **Maubert**) 35, rue Douce ☎ 35-93-70-37 Closed Sat; 15 to 30 Aug.

FOUGERES 35300 Ile-et-Vilaine **RN 12 Map 8-B1**
♀ ⊗ ⌂ **1 Star NN AUX AMIS DE LA ROUTE** (N° RR SEP 23 992) (M. Michel **Bastien**) 6, bld St-Germain ☎ 99-99-07-62 ⊷ 12 from 90–100F, breakfast to 20F. Full-board 150–180F per night. Coaches welcome (rest. seats 90). Evening meals. English, German spoken. Parking (1000 vehicles). Bar; dogs allowed; Recreation (fishing, watersports). Sites to visit: Saint-Mâlo, Mont St Michel, countryside and châteaux.

FOUILLOUSE (LA) 42480 Loire **RN 82 Map 2-B1**
♀ ⊗ **LE RELAIS** (N° RR JAN 24 830) (Mme Louise **Bonnet**) locally 'Les Molineaux' ☎ 77-30-13-51 Closed Sat, Sun; 14 Jul to 15 Aug. Evening meals.

FOUQUEVILLE 27370 Eure **RN 840 and RD 81 Map 3-B1**
♀ ⊗ **LE GRAND CERF** (N° RR JUN 25 457) (Mme Jocelyne **Buquet**) RD 840 ☎ 32-35-30-06 Amfreville-la-Campagne Closed Sun.

FRAISSE-HAUT 15300 Cantal **Map 17-A2**
♀ ⊗ ⌂ **1 Star NN HOTEL DES CIMES** (N° RR AOU 26 656) (M. Christophe **Cros**) RN 122 Laveissière ☎ 71-20-07-42 **Minitel** ⊷ 20 Full-board 142–152F per night. Coaches welcome (2 dining rooms = 90 places). Evening meals.

FRANCUEIL 37150 Indre-et Loire **RN 76 Map 12-A/B3**
♀ ⊗ **LE RELAIS DES CHÂTEAUX** (N° RR MAI 8 494) (M. Bernardatte **Bourbonnais**) Blère ☎ 47-23-96-30 Closed Sun; Mon morning. Evening meals until 10 pm.

FRASNE 25560 Doubs **RD 471/49 Map 14-B3**
♀ ⊗ **L'ARC-EN-CIEL** (N° RR MARS 26 477) (M. Claude **Guyon**) 94, Gran-du-Rue ☎ 81-49-83-68 Closed Tue; Jul (8 days). Evening meals.

F

FRÉJUS 83600 Var **RN 7 Map 25-B2**
♀ ⊗ 🏠 **1 Star NN LES TROIS CHÊNES** (N° RR AVR 16 518) (Mme Monique **Laurent**) Route de Cannes ☎ 94-53-20-08 ⊸ 18 all with showers (5 with own WC) from 140–200F, breakfast 22–25F. Access for disabled. Coaches welcome (rest. seats 100). Evening meals. English, German, Italian spoken. Parking; bar; boules played; recreations (swimming pool, tennis courts near). Sites to visit: Gorges du Verdon, Lakes of Saint Cassien.

FRESNES-EN-TARDENOIS 02130 Aisne **Autoroute A4**
♀ ⊗ **RELAIS DU TARDENOIS** (Mme **Pongnan**) Autoroute A4 Fresnes-en-Tardenois ☎ 23-70-23-16 Self-service restaurant open 6.30am to 10.30pm. Entrance cards for lorry drivers. Shop, TV, rest room.

FRESNES-MAZANCOURT 80320 Somme **RN 17 Map 5-B3**
♀ ⊗ **L'ESCALE DES ROUTIERS** (N° RR SEPT 27 010) (M. Jean-Claude **Guerquin**) ☎ 22-85-28-50 Closed Sat and Sun.

FRETEVAL 41160 Loir-et-Cher **RN 10 Map 12-A3 and 8-B3**
♀ ⊗ **LE PLESSIS** (N° RR MAR 21 862) (Mme Gilberte **Thirouard**) ☎ 54-82-65-28 Open 5.00am to mid-night. Closed Sat; Aug. Full-board available. Coaches welcome (rest. seats 60). Evening meals.

FRIÈRES-FAILLOUEL 02700 Aisne **Map 6-A1**
♀ ⊗ **CHEZ MARTINE** (N° RR JUL 26 007) (Mme Martine **Rouillat**) 19, place André-Ruller.

FROISSY 60480 Oise **RN1 Map 3-A2**
♀ ⊗ 🏠 **LE BEAUVAIS BRETEUIL** (N° RR JUIL 26 962) (M. Raymond **Julen**) Bois Saint-Martin ☎ 44-79-13-09 ⊸ 5 Closed Sun and three weeks in August. Evening meals served to 11pm.

FROMENTEL par PUTANGES 61210 Orne **RN 24 Bis and 809 Map 8-A2**
♀ ⊗ **LE RELAIS DE L'AIGLE D'OR** (N° RR AVR 25 365) (M. Didier **Creteau**) D 924 Paris/granville ☎ 33-96-21-00 ⊸ 3 Closed Sat, Sun; Aug. Coaches welcome (rest. seats 40). Evening meals. Italian, English spoken.

FRONTIGNAN 34110 Hérault **RN 112 Map 23-B2**
♀ ⊗ 🏠 **LE RELAIS DES VOYAGEURS** (N° RR JUL 26 003) (M. Marcel **Rosso**) 12, rue du Puits-Pascal ☎ 67-48-12-34 **Minitel** ⊸ 6 Closed Sun, Oct to May; 20 Dec to 10 Jan. Coaches welcome (rest. seats 40). Evening meals. English, Italian spoken.

FROUARD 54390 M.-et-M **RN 57 Maps 10-A1/2 and 14-B1**
♀ ⊗ **AU RELAIS DES SPORTIFS Chez Raph** (N° RR JAN 14 656) (M. Raphaël **Capezzali**) 1, rue de la Salle ☎ 83-49-03-52 Closed Mon; Sept.
♀ ⊗ **LA GRANDE CHOPE** (N° RR JUL 21 168) (Mme Christiane **Pallagi**) 4, rue de la Gare ☎ 83-49-05-64 Closed Sat, Sun; Aug.

F

FUILET (LE) 49000 Maine-et-Loire **Map 12-B1**
♀ ⊗ **CHEZ ALPHONSE ET MONIQUE** (N° RR DEC 26 394) (Mme Monique **Bodo**) 1, rue de la Blandinière ☎ 41-70-52-58 Closed Aug. Evening meals until 9.30pm.

FUMAY 08170 Ardennes **RN 51 Map 6-A2**
♀ ⊗ ⌂ **1 Star NN LE RELAIS DU LION** (N° RR AVR 21 465) (Mme Édith **Potier**) 41, rue de la Gare ☎ 24-41-10-27 ⏤ 11 Closed Sun; Sept. Full-board 140F, Half-board 85F per night. Evening meals.

FUMEL 47500 Lot-et-Garonne **Map 17-A1 and 21-B1**
♀ ⊗ **BAR DE LA SOIERIE** (N° RR NOV 27 098) (Mme Liliane **Lafon**) 88, avenue de l'Usine
⊗ **SALON DE THÈ-CRÈPERIE CHEZ DANIEL** (N° RR DEC 27 113) (M. Daniel **Herranz**) Centre Commercial de Florimont ☎ 53-40-92-60 English spoken. Closed Sun.

FUVEAU 13970 B.-du-R. **RN 96 Map 24-B3**
♀ ⊗ **AUBERGE DU CHATEAU** (N° RR JUN 25 962) (Mme Claudette **Charried**) RN 96 ☎ 42-58-60-10 Closed Tue.

G

GAËL 35290 1.-et-V. **Map 7-B3**
♀ ⊗ **LE RELAIS DES SPORTS – REST. CHEZ ANNICK** (N° RR MAI 24 970) (Mme Annick **Rebillard**) Place des Tileuls ☎ 99-07-72-39 **Minitel** ⏤ 4 Closed Fri pm. Coaches welcome (rest. seats 150). Evening meals.

GAGES 12630 Aveyron **RN 88 Map 22-B1 10 Km from Rodez**
♀ ⊗ ⌂ **1 Star NN LE RELAIS DE LA PLAINE** (N° RR DEC 20 920) (Mme Yvonne **Dallo**) ☎ 65-42-29-03 ⏤ 22 Closed Sat; Oct. Full-board 150–185F per night. Coaches welcome (rest. seats 120). Evening meals.

GALBSHEIM 67760 Bas-Rhin Map 10-B1/2
♀ ⊗ ⌂ **2 star NN EUROP RELAIS** (N° RR FEV 22 226) (M. **Lepron**) Route du Rhin ☎ 88-96-43-33 ⏤ 22 Closed Fri, pm, Sat and 15/8 to 31/8. German spoken.

GAMACHES 80220 Somme **Map 4-B2**
♀ ⊗ **LES ROUTIERS** (N° RR FEVR 25 817) (M. Claude **Reffay**) 20, place du Général Lederc ☎ 22-26-16-33.

GAN 64290 Pyr.-Atl **RN 134 Maps 20-B3 and 21-A3**
♀ ⊗ ⌂ **1 Star NN HOTEL MODERNE** (N° RR DEC 23 568) (M. Patrick **Piette**) 41–43, place de la Mairie ☎ 59-21-54-98 ⏤ 15 from 58 to 105F, breakfast to 15F. Closed Sun; 15 days Aug. Coaches

welcome (rest. seats 180). Evening meals until 9pm. Bar; dogs allowed.

♀ ⊗ 🏠 **LE RELAIS DES VOYAGEURS** (N° RR OCT 25 710) (M. Jean-Michel **Bonis**) 9, rue Henri IV ☎ 59-21-56-38.

GAP 05000 Hautes-Alpes **Map 25-A1**
♀ ⊗ 🏠 **ALPES DAUPHINE** (N° RR JUN 25969) (M. André **Farizy**) Quartier de la Descente RN 85 (Napoléon) ☎ 92-51-47-15 ⊷ 5 Open all year. Coaches welcome (rest. seats 60). English, German, Italian spoken.

GARGES-LES-GONESSE 95140 Val-d'Oise **RD 84 Maps 1-A and 2-3**
♀ ⊗ 🏠 **LE RELAIS DU MONT-KEMMEL** (N° RR FEV 14 714) (M. André **Courbron**) 194, avenue de Stalingrad ☎ 39-86-33-35 ⊷ 6 Closed Sat, Sun; public holidays; Aug.

GASVILLE see MAINVILLIERS

GAVRELLE 62580 Pas-de-Calais **Map 5-B3**
♀ ⊗ **RELAIS DE LA CHAUMIÈRE** (N° RR SEPT 27 013) (M. Franck **Courcelle**) 21, route Nationale ☎ 21-58-16-99 English spoken.

GENAY par SEMUR-EN-AUXOIS 21140 Côte-d'Or **Map 13-A3**
♀ ⊗ **AU PONT DE GENAY** (N° RR SEP 23 942) (Mme Josette **Goubard**) ☎ 80-97-03-32 Closed Tue.

GENIS 24160 Dordogne
♀ ⊗ 🏠 **LE PÉRIGORD Bar LE XV Excideuil** (N° RR SEPT 26 323) (M. **Jarjanette**) Le Bourg ☎ 53-52-47-11 **Minitel** ⊷ 10 Closed Sun (out of season). Full-board 130–160F per night. Coaches welcome (rest. seats 45). Evening meals.

GENNEVILLIERS 92230 Hauts-de-Seine **Map 1-A2**
♀ ⊗ **LES ROUTIERS** (N° RR SEPT 26 664) (Mme Anne-Maria **Vidalenc**) 39, avenue Marcel-Paul ☎ 47-92-11-70 Closed Fri evening, Sat, Sun; 3 weeks Aug. Evening meals served until 9pm.

GER 64550 Pyrénées-Atlantiques **RN 117 Map 21-A3**
♀ ⊗ 🏠 **A LA CLÉ D'OR** (N° RR AVR 20 706) (M. Robert **Coudert**) ☎ 62-31-50-56 ⊷ 4 Closed Sat afternoon, Sun; 15 Aug–15 Sept. Evening meals.

GER 50850 Manche **RD 157 Map 8-A1**
♀ ⊗ 🏠 **HOTEL DES FLEURS** (N° RR MAI 23 293) (M. Gilbert **Thomas**) La Grande-Rue ☎ 33-59-06-15 ⊷ 8.

GERARDMER 88400 Vosges **RN 417 Bis Map 10-A2**
♀ 🏠 **1 Star NN LE GAI RELAIS** (N° RR MAR 13 462) (M. Michel **Viry**) 59, boulevard de la Jamagne ☎ 29-63-05-96 ⊷ 7 Closed Sun afternoon. Full-board 150–165F per night. Coaches welcome (rest. seats 45/2 rooms). Evening meals until 8.00 pm. Bar food, snacks.

G

GERMIGNY-DES-PRÉS 45110 Loiret **RD 60 Map 13-A1**

Y ⊗ 🏠 **HOTEL DE LA PLACE** (N° RR JAN 25 250) (Mme **Maillard**)
Le Bourg Châteauneuf ☎ 38-58-20-14 **Minitel** ◄ 13 Closed Fri;
Feb. Full-board 130–160F per night. Coaches welcome (rest.
seats 180). Evening meals.

GERMIGNY-SUR-YONNE 89600 Yonne **RN 5 Maps 9-B2 and 13-A2**

Y ⊗ 🏠 **SARL LE RELAIS DES ROUTIERS** (N° RR MAI 23 806) Rte de
Genève ☎ 86-35-06-39 **Minitel** ◄ 9 Closed Sun.

GERTWILLER 67140 Bas-Rhin

Y ⊗ **RELAIS DES GOURMETS** (N° RR JUIL 27 324) (M. Hubert **Klein**)
154, route de Strasbourg ☎ 88-08-92-69 Closed Tues and mid Feb
to mid March. English and German spoken. Evening meals
served until 11.30pm.

GHYVELDE 59254 Nord **Map 5-B2**

Y ⊗ **CAFE ST-SÉBASTIEN** (N° RR OCT 26 712) (Mme Edith **Marie
Rubben**) 161, rue Nationale ☎ 28-26-61-95 Closed Tue; 17 Aug–
17 Sept. Dutch spoken.

GIBERVILLE 14730 Calvados **RN 175 Map 4-B2**

Y ⊗ **AU VERT GALANT** (N° RR MAI 26 892) (M. Jean-Luc **Outre-
quin**) 19, route de Rouen ☎ 31-72-36-52 Closed Sun; Aug. English
spoken.

GIDY see ORLEANS SARAN)

GIEN 45500 Loiret **RN 140 Map 13-A1**

Y ⊗ **AUBERGE DE LA CROIX-BLANCHE** (N° RR NOV 9 042) (Mme
Chauvel **Michonnet**) 17, route de Bourges ☎ 38-67-28-95 Closed
Fri evening; 24 Dec to 5 Jan. No evening meals.

Y ⊗ **CAFÉ DU NORD** (No RR OCT 27 054) (Mme Suzanne **Botineau**)
51, place de la Victoire ☎ 38-67-32-98 Closed Sun and first 2
weeks of August. English spoken.

Y ⊗ 🏠 **AU RELAIS NORMAND** (N° RR OCT 27 055) (M. Pierre
Montceau) Sarl, 64, place de la Victoire ☎ 38-67-28-56 ◄ 9
Closed Sun.

GIÈVRES 41130 Loir-et-Cher **RN 76 Map 12-B3**

Y ⊗ ⛽ **Petrol/oil LE RELAIS DE NORAY** (N° RR SEP 21 206) (M.
Michel **Ribeau**) ☎ 54-98-64-00 **Minitel** Closed Sat afternoon; end
Sept/beginning Oct. Evening meals. English, German spoken.

Y ⊗ **LA BALANCELLE** (N° RR JUL 26 946) (Mme Francine
Brialy), 1, route de Romorantin ☎ 54-98-64-76.

GISORS 27140 Eure **RN 15 Map 3-B2**

Y ⊗ **BAR DE L'AVENUE** (N° RR JUN 26 564) (M. **Roussel**) Sarl Tina,
95, route de Dieppe ☎ 32-27-19-45 Closed Sun; 15–30 Aug.
Evening meals served until 9pm. English spoken.

GLACERIE (LA) 50470 Manche **RN 13**

Y ⊗ **LE RELAIS DE LA GLACERIE** (N° RR SEPT 26 034) (M. Paul
Roupsard) near Conforama ☎ 33-44-13-54 **Minitel** Closed Sun;

14 Jul to 3 Aug. Coaches welcome (rest. seats 80). Evening meals until 9pm.

GLENIC 23380 Creuse **RN 140 and RD 940 Map 16-B1**
♀ ⊗ ⌂ **LA PERGOLA** (N° RR JUN 25 021) (M. André **Laforme**) Le Pont ☎ 55-52-93-38 ↤ 14 Closed Oct.

GLOS-SUR-RISLE 27290 Eure **Map 4-B3**
♀ ⊗ **RELAIS LAFORGE** (N° RR NOV 24 758) (Mme Micheline **Salm**) La Forge **Montfort-sur-Risle** ☎ 32-56-16-34 Closed Sun.

GODEWAERSVELDE 59270 Nord **RN 348 Map 5-A1**
♀ ⊗ **LE CUSTOM** (N° RR JUIL 26 961) (M. Antoine **Trassaert**) "Callicanes" ☎ 28-43-33-87 Service station opposite. Dutch spoken.

GOLBEY 88190 Vosges **RN 66 Maps 14-B1/2 and 10-A2**
♀ ⊗ **RELAIS DU PETIT CERF** (N° RR MAI 26 888) (M. Christian **Kuntz**) 63, rue du Gl-Leclerc ☎ 29-34-23-25. Closed Sun.

GONESSE 95500 Val-d'Oise **Map 1-A3**
♀ ⊗ ⌂ **CHEZ COCO** (N° RR JAN 25 265) (M. André **Baugé**) 43, rue de Paris ☎ 39-85-01-26 ↤ 9 Closed Sun afternoon 2.30 pm.

GONNEVILLE-SUR-HONFLEUR 14600 Calvados **Map 4-B2**
♀ ⊗ **LE MERLE BLANC** (N° RR DEC 24 775) (M. **Renault**) Honfleur ☎ 31-89-11-98 Closed Mon afternoon; Aug; 20 to 31 Dec. Coaches welcome (rest. seats 42). Evening meals. English spoken.

GORRON 53120 Mayenne **RN 806 Map 8-B1**
♀ ⊗ ⌂ **1 Star NN LE RELAIS DU BOCAGE – AU RENDEZ-VOUS DES ROUTIERS** (N° RR FEV 14 232) (Mme **Bibron**) 9, rue Corbeau Paris ☎ 43-04-61-74 ↤ 10 Full-board 160–200F per night. Coaches welcome (rest. seats 100). Evening meals.

GOUESNIÈRE (LA) 35350 Ile-et-Vilaine **RD 4 Map 7-A3**
♀ ⊗ **LE RELAIS DES ROUTIERS** (N° RR JUL 21 599) (Mme M.-T. **Bourgalais**) Le Bourg ☎ 99-58-80-57 ↤ 16 with showers. Closed Sun; 15–30 Aug. Full-board 135–140F per night. Coaches welcome (rest. seats 120). Evening meals.

GOURDON 46300 Lot **RN 704 Map 17-B1**
♀ ⊗ ⌂ **LE RELAIS DE LA MADELEINE** (N° RR JUL 18 770) (Sarl **Barbes**) Boulevard de la Madeleine ☎ 61-41-02-63 ↤ 16 Closed Sun in winter, Oct. Full-board 165–185F per night. Coaches welcome (rest. seats 55 + terrace). Evening meals.

GOURIN 56110 Morbihan **RD 1/769 Map 7-B2**
♀ ⊗ ⌂ **AUBERGE DE TOUL-AN-CHY** (N° RR MAI 26 541) (M. Joseph **Hilliou**), 20, rue de la Libération ☎ 97-23-43-77 ↤ 9 Closed Sat. Evening meals served. English spoken.

GOUSSAINVILLE 95190 Val-d'Oise **Map 1-A3**
♀ ⊗ **AUX SPORTS** (N° RR MAR 24 885) (M. Marcel **Dufros**) 22, avenue Albert Sarrault ☎ 39-88-10-84 Closed Sat.

G

GOUSTRAINVILLE par DOZULE 14430 Calvados **RN 815 Map 4-B2**
♉ ⊗ **LE RELAIS DES ROUTIERS** (N° RR DEC 11 933) (M. Daniel **Duval**) ☎ 31-79-21-90 Closed Sun; Aug.

GOUZON 23230 Creuse **Map 16-B2**
♉ ⊗ **CHEZ HÉLÈNE** (N° RR NOV 26 380) (Mme Hélène **Kowalski**) Trois Fonds ☎ 55-81-75-98 Polish spoken.

GRAINVILLE 27380 Eure **RN 14 Map 3-A1**
♉ ⊗ **LE RELAIS DE GRAINVILLE** (N° RR JUN 26 563) (Mme Edwige **Wahrenberger**) 40, route Nationale ☎ 32-48-06-28 Closed Sun. Coaches welcome (rest. seats 100 in 2 rooms). Evening meals 5pm–8pm.

GRAINVILLE-LANGANNERIE 14190 Calvados **RN 158 Map 8-A2 4-B2**
♉ ⊗ **CHEZ DOMINIQUE** (N° RR SEPT 27 031) (M. Dominique **Laine**) Route Nationale ☎ 31-90-51-00 Closed Sun. English spoken.

GRAMAT 46500 Lot **RN 140 and D 677 Map 17-B1**
♉ ⊗ ⌂ **2 Stars NN LE RELAIS DU CENTRE** (N° RR FEV 13 419) (Société **Grimal**: M. André **Grimal et Fils**) Place de la Republique ☎ 65-38-73-37 **Minitel** ⊷ 14 from 150 to 250F, breakfast to 24F. Telephone, TV in room. Access for disabled. Closed Sat low season. Coaches welcome (rest. seats 100). Evening meals. English spoken. Parking; bar; dogs allowed; TV room; terrace. Menus 60–80F. Specialities: *Foie gras et confit de canard, Cassoulet maison, Salade quercynoise*. Sites to visit: Roc – Amadoux, Gouffre de Padirac (10 kms).

GRAND-BREUIL (LE) par ROUILLÉ 86480 Vienne **RN 150 Map 15-A1**
♉ ⊗ **LE RELAIS DE LA BONNE AUBERGE CHEZ DÉDÉ** (N° RR JUN 19 800) (M. André **Rousseville**) ☎ 49-43-90-62 ⊷ 6 Closed Sun; 23 Dec to 9 Jan.

GRAND-FOUGERAY (LE) 35390 I.-et-V. **RN 137 Map 11-A2**
♉ ⊗ ⌂ **1 Star NN RELAIS DE LA BELLE ÉTOILE** (N° RR MAI 25 407) (M. Roland **Pirot**) Le Belle Étoile ☎ 99-08-42-59 Closed Sun. English spoken.

GRAND QUEVILLY 76120 Seine-Maritime **Map 3-A1**
♉ ⊗ ⌂ **HÔTEL DU CADRAN** (N° RR JUIN 27 301) (M. Phillippe **Delafenestre**) 1, rue Pierre-Corneille ☎ 35-69-69-34 ⊷ 7 English spoken. Evening meals.

GRANDE-AU-BOIS (LA) see SAINTE-MENEHOULD Marne

GRANDE-SYNTHE 59760 Nord **Map 5-A2**
⌂ **LA BIGUINE** (N° RR NOV 26 390) (M. Denis **Jaeger**) 176, route de Spycker ☎ 28-27-88-32 ⊷ 5 Closed Sun. Full-board 140–160F per night. Coaches welcome (rest. seats 60). Evening meals until 11pm. English, German spoken.

G

GRANDE-VALLÉE (LA) 37110 I.-et-L. **see VILLEDOMER**

GRAULHET 81100 Tarn **RN 631 Map 22-B2**
Y ⊗ **LE DOMINO** (N° RR OCT 25 146) (Mme Lucienne **Fallières**)
Place du Jourdain ☎ 63-34-43-74 Spanish spoken.

GRAVELINES 59820 Nord **RN 40**
Y ⊗ **CAFÉ DE L'AGRICULTURE** (N° RR 24 414) (Mme Raymonde
Blanckaert) 52, avenue Jean-Jouhaux ☎ 28-23-05-50 Closed Aug.

GRAVIGNY 27930 Eure **RN 154 Maps 3-B1 and 4-B3**
Y ⊗ 🏠 **HOTEL DES SPORTS** (N° RR OCT 23 513) (Mme Annick
Chrétien) 109, avenue A.-Briand ☎ 32-33-16-19 ⊷ 7.

GREMONVILLE 76790 Seine-Maritime **RD 20 Map 4-A3**
Y ⊗ **LA CHAUMIERE** (N° RR JAN 26 776) (M. Christian **Lemasurier**)
Motteville ☎ 35-56-45-65 English spoken.

GRENOBLE 38100 Isère **Maps 19-A3 and 24-B1**
Y ⊗ **LE CAFÉ DU NORD** (N° RR AOU 23 415) (Mme Bernadette
Bonnet) 44, Grand rue Monestier-de-Clermont ☎ 76-34-03-73
Closed Sun 2.00 pm.

GRIGNY 69250 Rhône
Y ⊗ **LE PHOENIX** (N° RR JUIL 27 320) (M. Michel **Lelarge**) 80, rue
de Bouteiller ☎ 78-73-03-72 Closed Sat pm, Sun and 7/7 to 15/7.
English, Spanish and Italian spoken. Evening meals.

GRIMAUD 83360 Var **Map 25-A2**
Y ⊗ 🏠 **LE RESTAUROUTE** (N° RR JAN 24 815) (M. Bernard **Gentile**)
Rte Nationale 98 **St Pons-les-Murs** ☎ 94-56-03-75 **Minitel** ⊷ 10
Closed Sun; Dec. Coaches, reservations only (rest. seats 80; 150
in season). Evening meals. English, German, Dutch, Italian
spoken.

GRISOLLES 82170 T.-et-G. **RN 20 and 113 Map 22-A2**
Y ⊗ **LE RELAIS DE LA GARE** (N° RR FEV 25 807) (M. Pierre
Dupuis) RN 20 ☎ 63-67-31-83 Coaches welcome (rest. seats 55).
Evening meals. English spoken.

GUEMAR 68970 Haut-Rhin **RN 83 Map 10-B2**
Y ⊗ 🏠 **A L'ANGE** (N° RR MAR 24 173) (M. Claude **Meinrad**) 16, Rte
de Sélestat ☎ 89-71-83-03 ⊷ 14 Closed Sat. 15 Dec to 15 Jan.
Evening meals. German, English, Italian spoken.

GUER near BELLEVUE-COETQUIDAN 56380 Morbihan **RN 772 and
773 Map 7-B3**
Y ⊗ 🏠 **LE RELAIS DE L'UNION** (N° RR MAR 20 131) (M. Oliver
Guérin) ☎ 97-75-71-46 ⊷ 6 Closed Sun; Aug. Evening meals.
Y ⊗ 🏠 **LE LION D'OR** (N° RR JANV 27 167) (M. Pierre **Poirier**) 7,
place de la Gare ☎ 97-22-00-26 ⊷ 5 Closed Sun.

GUERCHE-DE-BRETAGNE (LA) 35130 I.-et-V. **RN 178 Map 8-B1**
Y ⊗ 🏠 **LE RELAIS DU PONT D'ANJOU** (N° RR JUN 19 813) (M.

G

Guerche-de-Bretagne continued
▭ **Moussu**) 11, faubourg d'Anjou ☎ 99-96-23-10 ⊷ 12 Closed Sat evening. Full-board 145–165F per night. Coaches welcome (rest. seats 70).

GUEREINS 01090 Ain **RN 17 Map 18-B2**
♀ ⊗ **LA CROISÉE** (N° RR MAI 26 551) (M. Michel **Manains**) La Croisée de Guereins ☎ 74-66-14-93 Closed Sun; Tue from 4pm; 15 Aug–1 Sept. Evening meals.

GUÉRIGNY 58130 Nievre **RD 977 Map 13-B2**
♀ ⊗ ⌂ **HOTEL DU COMMERCE** (N° RR NOV 26 095) (M. Gérard **Page**) ☎ 86-37-32-77 ⊷ 7 Closed Sun in winter; 20 Dec to 5 Jan. Full-board 140–150F per night. Evening meals until midnight. German spoken.

GUILBERVILLE 50160 Manche **RN 175 Maps 4-B1 and 8-A1**
♀ ⊗ **LE POTEAU** (N° RR MAI 15 941) (M. Fredy **Menant**) Le Poteau ☎ 33-56-73-10 **Minitel** Closed Sat; Christmas holiday. Evening meals until midnight. English, German spoken.

GUILLON 89420 Yonne
♀ ⊗ **ACCOR L'ARCHE** (M. **Prioul**) Autoroute Aire de Maison Dieu ☎ 86-32-11-34 Self-service restaurant.

GUIPAVAS 29215 Finistère **CD 712 Map 7-A1**
♀ ⊗ ⌂ **LE RELAIS DU LION D'OR** (N° RR NOV 8 075) (Mme **Troadsec**) 52, rue de Paris ☎ 98-28-00-33.

GUJAN MESTRAS 33470 Gironde **Map 20-A1**
♀ ⊗ **LA MOUCLADE** (N° RR FEV 27 183) (Mme Marcelle **Judas**) 150, avenue de Lattre-de-Tassigny ☎ 56-66-56-00 Closed Tues and 1/12 to 15/12.

GUMBRECHTSHOFFEN 67110 Bas-Rhin 500m from **RN 62 RD 242 Map 10-B1**
♀ ⊗ **AU SOLEIL – Chez Bernard et Lili** (N° RR AOU 22 020) (Mme Liliane **Peifer**) 30, Rue Principale ☎ 88-72-90-77 ⊷ 3 Closed Sun afternoon; Aug. Full-board 90–130F per night. Coaches welcome (rest. seats 130/50). Evening meals. German spoken.

GUMERY 10400 Aube **RD 439 Map 9 A/B2**
♀ ⊗ ⌂ **AU RELAIS** (N° RR FEV 27 194) (Mmes Évelyne et Jacqueline **Visse**) 3, rte de Sens ☎ 25-39-16-01 ⊷ 10 Closed Sun afternoon. English spoken.

GURUNHUEL 22390 Côtes-du-Nord **RN 787 Map 7-A2**
♀ **AU RENDEZ-VOUS DES CHASSEURS ET DES PECHEURS – Chez Gilberte** (N° RR JUL 19 429) (M. and Mme Yves **Georgelin**) Kérambellec ☎ 96-21-81-00 **Minitel** Closed Jul. Coaches welcome (rest. seats 50).

HABSHEIM 68440 Haut-Rhin **RN 66 Map 10-B3**
Y ⊗ **A LA VILLE DE MULHOUSE** (N° RR OCT 21 676) (Mme
Gabrielle **Lehmann**) 76, rue du Général-de-Gaulle ☎ 89-44-31-33
Closed Sun unless booked. Coaches welcome (rest. seats 150/50/
45). German, English spoken.

HAGONDANGE 57300 Moselle **RN 53 Map 10-A1 and 6-B3**
Y ⊗ ⌂ **LE RELAIS DES AMIS** (N° RR JAN 16 412) Mme Yolande
Tarter) 36, rue de Metz ☎ 87-71-46-63 ⊷ 42 **Hôtel du Centre 1
star NN** 7, rue Anatole-France ☎ 87-71-47-64 Closed Sun; first 3
weeks Aug.

HAIE-FOUASSIÈRE (LA) 44690 Loire-Atl Clisson N 359 Map 11-B3
Y ⊗ **LE RABELAIS** (N° RR FEV 26 433 bis) (M. **Budes**) 1, rue de
Seures ☎ 40-54-87-76 Closed Sun; Aug. English, German spoken.

HAILLICOURT 62940 Pas-de-Calais **Map 5-B2**
Y ⊗ **L'ABREUVOIR** (N° RR OCT 25 148) (Mme Suzanne **Lemoine**)
30, rue du 1er Mai ☎ 21-62-26-54 English Spoken.

HALLENNES-LEZ-HAUBOURDIN 59320 Nord **RD 941 Map 5-B1**
Y ⊗ **AUX AMIS DE LA ROUTE** (N° RR MAR 23 705) (Mme Micheli-
ne **Masfrand**) 329, rue de Général-de-Gaulle ☎ 20-07-14-24
Minitel Showers. Closed Sat, Sun; Aug. Shop.

HALLUIN 59250 Nord **RN 17 Map 5-B1**
Y ⊗ **LE CELTIC** (N° RR JUN 25 447) (Mme Roberte **Claisse**) 260, rue
de Lille ☎ 20-94-75-54 Closed Sun; Aug. Evening meals. English
spoken.
Y ⊗ **AU ROUTIER** (N° RR OCT 26 687) (M. Richard **Kozior**) 196, rue
de la Lys ☎ 20-23-88-20 Closed Sat afternoon, Sun afternoon; Aug.
Polish, Yugoslav, Dutch spoken.

HARDRICOURT 78250 Yvelines **RN 190 Map 1-A1**
Y ⊗ **LA DEVINETTE** (N° RR NOV 26 367) (M. Michel **Lemoine**) 30,
boulevard Michelet ☎ 34-74-06-32 Closed Sat, Sun; Aug. Evening
meals.

HAVRE (LE) 7660 S.-Marit **RN 13 Bis Map 4-A/B2**
Y ⊗ **LE RELAIS DES ROUTIERS** (N° RR NOV 23 550) (Mme Marie-
Pierre **Priser**) 57, rue Marceau ☎ 35-25-06-44.
Y ⊗ **A LA PIPE (S.A. Garonne)** (N° RR OCT 24 367) (M. Didier
Eudes) 128, Bld de Graville ☎ 35-24-54-48 Closed Sun; 15 days in
Sept. Full-board. Coaches welcome (rest. seats 75/85). Evening
meals. English spoken.
Y ⊗ **LE P'TIT COMPTOIR** (N° RR JUN 26 558) (M. Bernard **Rondel**)
31, rue du Général Faidherbe ☎ 35-42-78-72 Closed Sun; Christ-
mas to New year. Coaches welcome (2 dining rooms = 60 seats).
Evening meals. English spoken.
Y ⊗ **AU TÉLÉPHONE** (N° RR OCT 24 393) (M. Gérard **Percepied**)
173, Bld Amiral Mouchez ☎ 35-25-40-35 English spoken.
Y ⊗ **LA RASCASSE** (N° RR MAI 24 955) (Mme Gislène **Villey**) 2, rue
Gustave Nicolle ☎ 35-24-50-05 Closed Sat, Sun; Jul. Evening
meals.

H

Havre continued

♀ ⊗ 🏠 **LE WELCOME** (N° RR OCT 27 048) (Mme Marie-Pierre **Priser**) Quai Southampson ☎ 35-43-17-84 ⤚ 10

♀ ⊗ **AU PETIT MOUSSE** (N° RR FEV 27 178) (M. Patrice **Munster**) 19, rue Amiral Courbet ☎ 35-25-13-43 Closed Sat pm and Sun. German spoken.

♀ ⊗ **TANTE JEANNE** (N° RR MARS 27 232) (M. Claude **Sauvage**) 72/74, rue Paul-Marion ☎ 35-26-40-54

HAYE-DU-PUITS (LA) 50250 Manche RN 800 Map 4-B1
♀ ⊗ **LE RELAIS LES AMIS** (N° RR MAI 24 572) (M. Louis **Le Filliastre**) 16, rue du Château ☎ 33-46-03-42 Closed Sun in winter. Coaches welcome (rest. seats 150).

HAYE-PESNEL 50320 Manche **RD 7 Map 8-A1**
♀ ⊗ **LE RELAIS CHEZ ARMELLE** (N° RR AOU 15 766) (Mme Armelle **Jacquette**) Rue de la Libération ☎ 33-61-50-83 Closed Sat, Sun; Dec. Full-board guest rooms. Coaches welcome (rest. 2 rooms seat 50). Evening meals.

HAYONS-ESCLAVELLES par NEUFCHATEL-EN-BRAY (LES) 76270 Seine-Maritime **RN 28 and 29 Map 3-A1**
♀ ⊗ 🏠 **AUX AMIS DES ROUTIERS** (N° RR AOU 25 620) (M. Pierre **Durieu**) ☎ 35-93-13-15 ⤚ 8 Closed Sun; Dec. Car park. English spoken.

HEBERGEMENT (L') 85260 Vendée **RN 763 Maps 11-B3 and 12-B1**
♀ ⊗ **LE RELAIS DES ROUTIERS** (N° RR NOV 24 408) (M. **Bretin**) 17, rue Georges-Clemenceau ☎ 51-42-80-71 Closed Sat; Aug (3 weeks). Evening meals.

HENDAYE 64700 Pyr.-Atl. **RN 10 Map 20-A3**
♀ ⊗ **LE RELAIS DES ROUTIERS CHEZ MARCEL-FRANCO-ESPAGNOL** (N° RR MAI 18 415) (Mme **Mongobert**) Pont International 11, avenue d'Espagne ☎ 59-26-73-00 and 26-78-95 Closed Sun; Aug. Evening meals. German spoken.

♀ ⊗ **BAR-RESTAURANT DU PONT** (N° RR OCT 27 071) (M. Richard **Mas**) 17, avenue d'Espagne ☎ 59-20-73-96 Closed Sun and 15th to 30th August. Spanish spoken.

HERBIERS (LES)85500 Vendée **RN 160 Map 11-B3**
♀ ⊗ 🏠 **1 star NN L'ORÉE DES BOIS VERTS** (N° RR OCT 27 044) (M. René **Joulin**) Route des Sables ☎ 51-91-00-18 ⤚ 7 Closed Sun pm and Christmas to New Year. Parking, bar, dogs allowed (except in the restaurant), TV room. Visit puy du fou, Abbey.

HERMANVILLE-SUR-MER 148800 Calvados **CD 514 Map 4-B2**
♀ ⊗ **LE LUDO** (N° RR SEPT 27 020) (Mme Josianne **Gueniot**) 37, boulevard de la 3ᵉ D.I.B. ☎ 31-96-84-55. English spoken.

HERMITAGE (L') 35590 I.-et-V. **RD 125 Map 7-B3**
♀ ⊗ **LE VILLAGE** (N° RR JUN 25 964) (Mme **Cosnier**) 23, rue de Rennes ☎ 99-64-03-31 Closed Sun; Aug. Coaches welcome (rest. 3 rooms seat 90). Evening meals.

H

HERMITAGE-LORGE (L') 22150 C.-du-N. **RD 168 Map 7-A2**
♀ ⊗ 🏠 **LE SOLEIL D'OR** (N° RR SEPT 26 031) (Mme Huguette **Maillard**) Le Paly ☎ 96-42-11-39 **Minitel** ⏤ 9 Closed Sun evening. Full-board 140–200F per night. Coaches welcome (rest. seats 125). Evening meals.

HEUDEBOUVILLE 27400 Eure **RN 15 Map 3-B1**
♀ ⊗ 🏠 **AU TROU NORMAND** (N° RR AVR 25 387) (M. Guy **Fort**) Louviers ☎ 32-40-18-00 ⏤ 5 Closed Sun; Aug.

HINGLE (LE) 22100 C..-du-N. **RN 166 Map 7-A3**
♀ ⊗ 🏠 **LE RELAIS DES ROUTIERS** (N° RR JUL 24 633) (M. Rémy **Pessel**) place de la Gare Les Granits ☎ 96-83-58-45 ⏤ 6 Closed Sun. Full-board. Coaches welcome (rest. seats 80). Evening meals. English spoken.

HIRSON 02500 Aisne **RN 43 Map 6-A2**
♀ ⊗ 🏠 **MARLENE ET JULIANO** (N° RR SEP 26 644) (M. **Lonnoy-Corsini**) 151, avenue Joffre ☎ 23-58-14-03. Closed Sun evening.

HOLTZWIHR 68320 Haut-Rhin **Map 10-B2**
♀ ⊗ **AU TONNEAU D'OR** (N° RR DEC 76 769) (M. Patrick **Vonders-cher**) 99, rue Principale ☎ 89-47-41-24 Closed Mon; Feb. German spoken.

HOPITAL-CAMFROUT (L') 29224 Finistere **RN 170 Map 7-A1**
♀ ⊗ **LE RELAIS DES ROUTIERS** (N° RR DEC 21 301) (M. Bernard **Hamery**) Le Bourg ☎ 98-20-01-21 Closed 15 Aug to 1 Sept. Coaches welcome (rest. seats 160).

HOPITAL-SUR-RHINS (L') par ST-CYR-DE-FAVIERES 42132 Loire **RN 7 Map 18-A2**
♀ ⊗ 🏠 **LE RELAIS DES ROUTIERS** (N° RR MARS 9 420) (M. **Lagoutte**) ☎ 77-64-80-13 ⏤ 7 Closed Sat; Aug. Coaches welcome (rest. seats 35). Evening meals until 9.00pm.
♀ ⊗ **RELAIS ALSACIEN** (N° RR JUL 26 618) (M. Marcel **Terrier**) Saint- Cyr de Favières ☎ 77-64-81-01 Closed Sat, Sun; Jul. Coaches welcome (rest. seats 25).

HOSPITALET DU LARZAC (L') 12230 Aveyron **RN 9 Map 23-A1**
♀ ⊗ 🏠 **2 star RELAIS ESPACE** N° RR AVR 27 243) (Mme Ginette **Gineste**) RN 9 Aérodrome Millau-Larzac ⏤ 10 Open 6am to 11pm. English and Spanish spoken. Self service menu. Parking for 120 cars.

HOSTENS 33125 Gironde **RN 205 Map 20-B1**
♀ ⊗ **AU BON ACCUEIL** (N° RR NOV 22 561) (Mme **Laouilleau**) ☎ 56-88-50-63 Closed Sun.

HOTTOT LES BAGUES 14250 Calvados **CD9 Map 4-B2**
♀ ⊗ **LE RELAIS DE LA MANCHE** (N° RR JANV 26 794) (M. Roland **Jeanne**) Route de Caumont ☎ 31-80-81-72. Closed Sat afternoon, 2 weeks in Feb/Sept.

H

HOUCHES (LES) 74310 Hte-Savoie **RN 205 Map 19-B2**
♀ ⊗ **RELAIS DU CHATELARD** (N° RR JUL 26 593) (M. Bernard **Chibaudel**) Passy Le Chatelard ☎ 50-47-21-62 Closed Sun. Spanish spoken.

HOURTIN 33990 Gironde **Map 20-A1**
♀ ⊗ **LE NOUVEAU NICE** (N° RR NOV 27 100) (M. Phillippe **Roberel**) 6, rue du Médoc ☎ 56-09-21-13 English and Spanish spoken.

HOUSSAYE-EN-BRIE (LA) 77610 S.-et-M. **RN 36 Map 9-A1**
♀ ⊗ ⌂ **AUBERGE DU COUCOU** (N° RR JUL 26 607) (MM. Christian and Jacky **Broust**) La haute-Gonière ☎ 64-07-40-75 English spoken.

HOUSSOYE (LA) 60390 Oise **RN 181 Map 3-B2**
♀ ⊗ ⌂ **LE RELAIS DU CHEVAL BLANC** (N° RR SEP 15 790) (Mme **Juttier**) ☎ 44-81-40-23 ⊷ 6 Closed Sun.

HUILLY-SUR-SEILLE 71290 S, et L. **RN 175 Map 18-B1**
♀ ⊗ ⌂ **CHEZ DAFFY** (N° RR JAN 26 135) (Mme Michel **Orange**) ☎ 85-40-00-65 Closed Wed. Evening meals served.

HUISSEAU-EN-BEAUCE 41310 L.-et-C. **RN 10 Map 12-A3**
♀ ⊗ **LES PLATANES** (N° RR SEPT 27 001) (M. Hubert **Breton**) ☎ 54-82-81-46 Closed Sat afternoon; Sun. Filling station near.

HUMIERES 62130 Pas-de-Calais **Map 5-A3**
♀ ⊗ **LA SEMEUSE Fina Station** (N° RR MAR 24 537) (Mme Berthe **Ternisien**) ☎ 21-41-85-77 **Minitel** Coaches welcome (rest. seats 50). Evening meals.

HUSSEREN WESSERLING 68470 Haut-Rhin **RN 66 Map 10-B3**
⊗ **RELAIS DU PONT ROUGE** (N° RR JANV 26 783) (Mme Juliana **Menzione**) 36, route Nationale ☎ 89-82-14-81. Italian spoken.

HUTTENHEIM 67230 Bas-Rhin **RN 83 Map 10-B2**
♀ ⊗ **AU JARDIN DES ROSES** (N° RR SEPT 27 027) (M. Maurice **Schneider**) Près Benfeld ☎ 88-74-41-44 Closed Sat and August. German spoken.

HYENVILLE 50660 Manche **RD 971 Map 8-A1**
♀ ⊗ **LE RELAIS DE LA SIENNE** (N° RR MARS 26 481) (Mme Éliane **Mayor**) Le Pont Hyenville-Quettreville-sur-Sienne ☎ 33-07-56-03 **Minitel** ⊷ 8 Closed Sat. English spoken.

HYERES 83400 Var **RN 98 Map 25-A3**
♀ ⊗ ⌂ **RELAIS DU GROS PIN** (N° RR MAI 21 935) (Mme Antoinette **Durante**) 15, avenue Paul-Renaudel ☎ 94-97-63-26 ⊷ 8 Closed Sun; Christmas, New Year.

HYERES-PAROISSE 25110 Doubs **RN 73 Maps 10-A3 and 14-B3 see BAUME-LES-DAMES**

I

IMLING SARREBOURG 57400 Moselle **RN 4 Map 10-B2**
🍷 ⊗ **RELAIS DE LA FERME** (N° RR DEC 25 757) (M. Jean-Luc **Steiner**) Rte de Sarrebourg RN 4 ☎ 87-23-68-72 Closed 15 days in beginning Aug, 15 days Dec, Jan. Coaches welcome (rest. seats 50). Evening meals. German spoken.

INTVILLE-LE-GUETARD 45300 Loiret **see PITHIVIERS**

ISLE-ADAM (L') 95290 Val-d'Oise **RN 322 Map 3-B2**
🍷 ⊗ **AU RALLYE Chez Paulette** (N° RR FEV 18 325) (Mme Paulette **Combes**) 71, rue de Pontoise ☎ 34-69-08-24 Closed Sat evening, Sun evening; Aug.

ISLE-D'ABEAU (L') par BOURGOIN-JALLIEU 38300 Isère **Autoroute A43 Map 2-B2**
🍷 ⊗ **L'ARCHE** Autoroute A3, Bourgoin-Jallieu ☎ 74-27-27-91 Self-service restaurant. Open 7.00am to 11.00pm. Shop.

ISLE-JOURDAIN (L') 32600 Gers **RN 124 Map 22-A2**
🍷 ⊗ **L'OLYMPIA** (N° RR SEP 19 912) (M. Michel **Amour**) 5, rue de la République ☎ 62-07-01-35 Closed Sun; Aug. Evening meals.

ISSANKA 34770 Hérault Commune de GIGEAN **RN 113 Map 23-B2**
🍷 ⊗ Ⓗ **2 Stars NN LE RELAIS GARRIGOU** (N° RR DEC 21 730) (M. Gilbert **Cornevin**) ☎ 67-78-71-30 🛏 8 + Studio and flats. Closed Sat, Sun low season; Christmas to New Year. Full-board 190–195F per night, 2 people 340F. Coaches welcome (rest. seats 360). Evening meals, served until 11pm.

ISSOIRE 63500 Puy-de-Dôme **RN 9 Map 17-A3**
🍷 ⊗ **LE CHAPEAU ROUGE** (N° RR FEV 15 540) (M. André **Jouve**) route de St-Germain ☎ 73-89-14-74 Closed Sun; Aug. Evening meals, served until midnight.
🍷 ⊗ Ⓗ **AU REPOS DES ROUTIERS** (N° RR NOV 25 746) (Mme Ginette **Clauzin**) Veneix ☎ 73-96-62-01 🛏 7 Full-board 150F per night. Coaches welcome (rest. seats 90). Evening meals.

ISSOUDUN 36100 Indre **RN 151 Map 13-B1**
🍷 ⊗ **LE RELAIS DE LA CROIX-ROUGE** (N° RR AOU 22 432) (M. Claude **Grosyeux**) 14, faubourg de la Croix-Rouge ☎ 54-21-04-91 🛏 5 Closed Sun. Full board 160F per night. Coaches welcome (rest. seats 70). Evening meals. English, German, Italian, Turkish spoken.
🍷 ⊗ **LE RELAIS DES SPORTS** (N° RR OCT 24 378) (M. and Mme Guy **Bertaud**) 8, route de Bourges ☎ 54-21-50-30 Closed Sat; 10 to 25 Aug. Evening meals.

IS-SUR-TILLE 21120 Côte-d'Or **RN 459 Map 14-A3**
🍷 ⊗ **LE RELAIS DU MIDI** (N° RR JUL 17 848) (M. **Chalopet**) place Villeneuve ☎ 80-95-07-51 Coaches welcome (rest. seats 60).

ISTRES 13800 Bouches-du-Rhône **Map 24-A/B3**
🍷 ⊗ Ⓗ **LE COMMERCE** (N° RR JUN 26 919) (M. Jacky **Larno**) 6, Bld J.J. Pratt ☎ 42-55-01-11 🛏 9 Spanish, Portuguese and German spoken.

I

IVRY-EN-MONTAGNE 21340 Côte-d'Or **RN 6 Map 13-B3**
♀ ⊗ ⌂ **1 Star NN RESTAU MOTEL LE CHALET D'IVRY** (N° SEPT
26 642) (M. Alain Ben **Fedhila**) RN 6 ☎ 80-20-21-18 ⊷ 10
German, English, Italian, Arabic spoken.

IVRY-SUR-SEINE 94200 Val-de-Marne **Map 1-B2**
♀ ⊗ **CHEZ PAINDAVOINE** (N° RR JUL 26 598) (M. François **Ver-
dière**) 11, Quai Marcel Boyer ☎ 46-71-36-37 Closed Sun. Evening
meals.

J

JALLAIS 49510 M.-et-L. **RN 756/RD 15 Maps 11-B3 and 12-B1**
♀ ⊗ ⌂ **2 Stars NN LE RELAIS DE LA CROIX VERTE Son Restaurant Le Vert Galant** (N° RR MARS 18 345) (M. **Gaillard**)
Centre ville 1, rue Jean-de-Sagmond ☎ 41-64-10-12 and 64-20-22
⊷ 25 from 148 to 220F, breakfast to 21F, telephone, T.V. Closed
Fri. evening off season. Full-board 160–220F per night. Coaches
welcome (rest. seats 175). Evening meals. English, German
spoken. Car park; bar; dogs allowed. Menus from 59–135F.
Specialities: *salade de rillauds d'Anjou chauds, Brochet de Loire
au beurre blanc, Civet de porcelet Saint-Hubert.* Sites to visit:
⊷ vineyards of Muscadet and Anjou, Museum of Cholet.

JANZE 35150 I.-et-V. **RN 777 Maps 7-B3 and 8-B1**
♀ ⊗ **LE RELAIS DE ROUTIERS** (N° RR JAN 20 967) (M. Michel
Métayer) 5, Jean-Marie Lacire ☎ 99-47-05-10. Coaches welco-
me. (2 dining rooms = 400 places). Evening meals until 8pm.

JARNAC 16200 Charente **RN 141 Map 15-A2**
♀ ⊗ **LES ROUTIERS** (N° RR AOU 22 910) (Mme Maryse **Bouffinie**)
77, rue Pasteur ☎ 45-81-02-40 Closed Sun. Coaches welcome
(rest. seats 55). Evening meals.

JARRIE 38560 Isere **RN 85 Maps 19-A3 and 24-B1**
♀ ⊗ **LES ROUTIERS Chez Michel and Lucie Relais du Pont** (N° RR
AVR 25 378) (M. and Mme **Bellosguardo-Rochas**) ☎ 76-68-85-38
Closed Sun. Evening meal served until 8.30pm.

JARS 18420 Cher **RN 723 Map 13-B1**
♀ ⊗ **LE RELAIS DES ROUTIERS** (N° RR JUL 11 601) (Mme **Castag-
nie**) ☎ 48-58-70-44 Evening meals.

JAYAT 01340 Ain **CD 975 Map 18-B1**
♀ ⊗ ⌂ **1 star NN LE RELAIS DE JAYAT** (N° RR DEC 27 132) (M.
Jean-Pierre **Rousselle**) Montrevel-en-Bresse ☎ 74-30-84-69 ⊷ 12
English spoken.

J

JOIGNY 89300 Yonne **RN 943 Maps 9-B2 and 13-A2**
☺ Ⓢ **RELAIS DE LA PROMENADE** (N° RR JUL 26 586) (M. Maurice **Deschamps**) 17, avenue Jules Hémery ☎ 86-62-18-13 Closed Sun.

JOSSELIN 56120 Morbihan **RN 24 Map 7-B3**
☺ Ⓢ **LA ROCHETTE** (N° RR AOU 22 002) (Mme Annie **Le Corre**) 128, rue Glatinier ☎ 97-22-27-29 Closed Sat, Sun low season. Coaches welcome (rest. seats 95). Evening meals. English spoken.

JOUE-EN-CHARNIE 72540 Sarthe **RN 157 Map 8-B2**
☺ Ⓢ **RESTAURANT DU CHEVAL BLANC** (N° RR JUIL 23 400) (M. **Lalande**) ☎ 43-88-42-13

JUGON-LES-LACS 22270 Côtes-du-Nord. **N12 near Dole exit Map 7-A3**
☺ Ⓢ **LES VALLÉES** (N° RR SEPT 26 645) (Mme Paulette **Hervé**) Dole ☎ 96-31-64-62 Closed Mon afternoon. English spoken.

JUMELLIERE (LA) 49120 M.-et-L. **RD 961 Map 11-A3**
☺ Ⓢ **LE RELAIS DE LA BOULE D'OR** (N° RR JAN 12 009) (M. and Mme **Sécher**) 2, rue du Val de Loire ☎ 41-64-33-23 ⏩ 4 Closed Sun. Full-board 130–150F per night. Coaches welcome (rest. seats 55). Evening meals.

JURANVILLE 45340 Loiret **RN 375 and RD 31 Map 9-B1**
☺ Ⓢ **L'AUBERGE DES ROUTIERS** (N° RR JUN 24 611) (M. Maryse **Rocher**) **Pavé de Juranville** ☎ 38-33-24-61 Closed Sun evening; Dec. Evening meals.

JURQUES 14260 Calvados **RN 177 Maps 4-B2 and 8-A1**
☺ Ⓢ **AU BON ACCUEIL Tobacconist/Newsagent** (N° RR OCT 25 123) (M. Daniel **Stalpaërt**) route de Vire ☎ 31-77-81-17 ⏩ 3 Evening meals.
☺ Ⓢ ⌂ **HOTEL DE LA GARE** (N° RR OCT 26 706) (M. Michel-Jacques **Cauchepin**) route de Vire ☎ 31-77-81-20 ⏩ 4 Closed Sat. English spoken.

JUSSAC 15250 Cantal **RN 122 Map 17-B2**
☺ Ⓢ **LE RELAIS DES ROUTIERS** (N° RR OCT 19 556) (Mme Denise **Lasgouttes**) Route Nationale ☎ 71-47-65-61 Closed Sun; beginning Aug.

JUVISY-SUR-ORGE 91260 Essonne **RN 7 Map 1-B2**
☺ Ⓢ **LE JOFFREY** (N° RR JANV 27 147) (M. Patrick **Thierry**) 45, av. de la Cour-de-France ☎ 69-21-27-50 Closed Sun.
☺ Ⓢ **LE RELAIS DE LA MARINE** (N° RR NOV 26 389) (M. François **Sciabbarrasi**) 61, quai J.-P. Thimbault ☎ 69-21-28-65 ⏩ 6 Closed Sat afternoon, Sun. Italian spoken.

JUZANVIGNY 10500 Aube **RD 400 Map 9-B3**
☺ Ⓢ **CHEZ JACKY ET ROSE** (N° RR FEV 21 789) (M. Jacques **Deflin**) ☎ 25-92-80-57 and 25-92-60-06 ⏩ 3. Closed Aug. Evening meals

K

KERGONAN-LANGUIDIC 56440 Morbihan **RN 24 Map 7-B2**
♊ ⊗ **LE RELAIS DES ROUTIERS** (N° RR JUL 20 785) (M. **Le Garrec**)
9, rue du Commerce ☎ 97-65-87-03 Closed Sat; end Dec.

KERHOSTIN 56510 Morbihan **D 768 Map 11-A1 see SAINT-PIERRE-QUIBERON**

KESKASTEL 67260 Bas-Rhin **RN 61 Map 10-A/B1**
♊ ⊗ ⌂ **1 Star NN LE RELAIS L'ALSACE** (N° RR JUN 15 259) (Mme **Lenjoint**) 11, rue du Faubourg ☎ 88-00-11-04 ⊷ 8 Closed Fri evening, Sat; mid Jul to mid Aug.

KINGERSHEIM 68470 Haut-Rhin **Map 10-B3**
♊ ⊗ ⌂ **AU CHASSEUR VERT** (N° RR JUIN 26 561) (Mme Kheria **Mabrouk**) 5, rue de Guebwiller ☎ 89-52-36-47. English, German spoken.

KNUTANGE 57240 Moselle **RN 52 Map 6-B3**
♊ ⊗ ⌂ **1 Star NN LE RELAIS DU STADE** (N° RR NOV 25 197) (Mme Rada **Radojcic**) 180, rue Victor-Rimmel ☎ 82-84-12-47 ⊷ 15 Closed Sat. German, some Italian spoken.

KOGENHEIM 67230 Bas-Rhin **RN 83 Map 10-B2**
♊ ⊗ ⌂ **A L'ÉTOILE** (N° RR AOUT 26 624) (M. and Mme Robert **Rapp**) 36, route de Strasbourg ☎ 88-74-70-02. Closed Mon; Jan. Coaches welcome (rest. seats 80). Evening meals served until midnight. German spoken.

KRUTH 68820 Haut-Rhin **Map 10-B3**
♊ ⊗ ⌂ **2 Stars NN AUBERGE DE FRANCE** (N° RR OCT 22 987) (M. **Ruffenach**) 20, Grande-Rue ☎ 89-82-28-02 ⊷ 16 Closed Thur; Nov. Full-board 150F per night. Coaches welcome (rest. seats 120). Evening meals. German spoken.

L

LABATUT 40300 Landes **RN 117 Map 20-A/B2**
♊ ⊗ ⌂ **LA GUINGUETTE** (N° RR JUL 26 968) (M. Christian **Begu**) ☎ 58-98-18-82 ⊷ 5 Spanish spoken. Filling station near.

LABEGUDE 07200 Ardèche **RN 102 Maps 23-B1 and 24-A2**
♊ ⊗ ⌂ **LE RELAIS DE LA POSTE** (N° RR AVR 8 426) (M. Maurice **Teyssier**) Route Nationale 64 ☎ 75-37-40-25 ⊷ 12 Closed Sun in winter, Sept. Full board 140–155F per night. Coaches welcome (rest. seats 55). Evening meals.

LABENNE 40530 Landes **RN 10 Map 20-A2**
♊ ⊗ ⌂ **HÔTEL BOUDIGAU** (N° RR DEC 25 221) (M. Francis **Be-**

gards) Nationale 10 ☎ 59-31-40-18 ⊸ 6 Closed Sat/Sun; public holiday. Open 6am to 10pm.

🏆 **Esso Service Station** (N° RR MAI 24 589) (Mme Marie-Josephe **Dillenschneider**) Autoroute A63 Aire de Labenne Ouest ☎ 59-31-47-73.

LABROYE par HESDIN 62140 Pas-de-Calais RD 928 Map 5-A3
🍷 ⊗ **Tobacconist LE RELAIS DES ROUTIERS – Chez Georgette** (N° RR AOU 19 459) (Mme Georgette **Flicourt**) route du Val d'Authie ☎ 21-86-83-10 Closed last 2 weeks Sept. Coaches welcome (rest. seats 95). Evening meals.

LABRUGUIERE 81290 Tarn RN 621 Map 22-B2
🍷 ⊗ 🏠 **1 Star NN LE RELAIS DE LA MARMITE** (N° RR JAN 24 073) (M. René **Ozanne**) 35, avenue Henri-Simon ☎ 63-50-21-19 ⊸ 16 Closed Sat, Sun; 15 days Aug. Coaches welcome (rest seats 60). Full board from 130–150F. Evening meals served until 9pm.

LACAPELLE MARIVAL 46320 Lot CD 940 Map 17-B1/2
🍷 ⊗ 🏠 **LE RELAIS DU SEGALA** (N° RR JAN 26 788) (M. Jean **Cagnac**) Route de Leyne ☎ 65-40-81-91. English, Spanish spoken.

LACAUNE 81230 Tarn RD 622 Map 22-B2
🍷 ⊗ 🏠 **LE CHALET** (N° RR NOV 26 736) (M. Joseph **Delpino**) 14, rue André Théron ☎ 65-40-81-91. English, Spanish spoken.

LADON 45270 Loiret RN 60 Maps 9-B1 and 13-A1
🍷 ⊗ 🏠 **LE RELAIS DE LADON** (N° RR FEVR 25 829) (M. Pierre **Guillaumin**) 400, avenue du 24 Novembre ☎ 38-95-51-32 ⊸ 7 Closed Sun. Full-board 120F per night. Coaches welcome (rest. seats 55). Evening meals.

🍷 ⊗ 🏠 **LES RUCHERS DU PARC** (N° RR JUIL 26 951) (Mme Ghislaine **Thiriau**) 240, route de Bellegarde ☎ 38-95-56-69 Closed Tue afternoon, all day Wed. English spoken.

LAFITTE-LOT 47320 L. et G. RN D 666 Map 21-B1
🍷 ⊗ **LES AMIS DE LA ROUTE** (N° RR NOV 26 085) (Mme Jeannette **Briot**) Dle 666 ☎ 53-84-08-98 **Minitel** Closed every other Sun; 1 to 15 Aug. Evening meals. English, Spanish spoken.

LAFOX 47270 L.-et-G. RN 113 Map 21-B1/2
🍷 ⊗ 🏠 **1 Star NN LE RELAIS TOULOUSAIN** (N° RR JAN 22 155) (M. and Mme **André**) 113, route de Toulouse ☎ 53-68-54-83 **Minitel** ⊸ 27. Closed Sat evening, Sun. Last 2 weeks in Aug. Full-board 165-185F per night. Coaches welcome (restaurant seats 220). Evening meals. Spanish, Italian spoken.

LAGEON 79200 Deux-Sèvres RN 138 and RD 79 Maps 12-B2 and 15-A1
🍷 ⊗ 🏠 **LE RELAIS DES ROUTIERS – Le Sampiero** (N° RR JUL 12 348) (M. Robert **Garandeau**) ☎ 49-69-82-11 ⊸ 5 Closed Sat, Sun; Aug. Italian spoken. Evening meals.

🍷 ⊗ 🏠 **CHEZ MARINETTE** (N° RR SEPT 27 003) (Mme Marie-Reine

L

Lageon continued

Vignaud) ☎ 49-69-86-57 ⌐ Open 5.30 am – l am. Italian, some German spoken. Filling station near.

LAISSAC 12310 Aveyron **RN 88 Map 23-A1**

♀ ⊗ ⌂ **1 Star NN LES PALANGES** (N° RR MAR 26 856) (M. Claude **Manenc**) avenue de Rodez ☎ 65-69-60-38 ⌐ 17 English, Italian spoken.

LALOUBERE 65310 Htes-Pyr. **RD 135 Map 21-A3**

♀ ⊗ ⌂ **1 Star NN HÔTEL DES PYRENEES** (N° RR AOU 16 207) (Mme Michelle **Cazamayou**) 13, rue du Ml-Foch ☎ 62-93-19-62 ⌐ 9 from 80–100F, breakfast 18–20F. Access for disabled. Closed Sun. Aug. Full board 155F per night. Evening meals until 9pm. Car park; bar; dogs allowed. Sites to visit: Lourdes (17 kms), Pic du Midi, Pyrenees. English, Spanish, Italian spoken.

LAMAGISTERE 82360 T.-et-G. **RN 113 Map 21-B2**

♀ ⊗ **CHEZ BOMPA** (N° RR AVR 23 774) (M. Gilbert **Bompa**) 86, avenue Saint-Michel ☎ 63-39-91-56 **Mintel** Closed Sat. l to 15 Aug. Coaches welcome (rest. seats 100). Evening meals until 11pm. Spanish, Italian spoken.

LAMBALLE 22400 Côtes-du-Nord **RD 12 Map 7-A3**

♀ ⊗ ⌂ **2 Stars NN LA TOUR D'ARGENT** (N° RR JAN 3 713) (M. Claude **Mounier**) 2, rue du Docteur Lavergne ☎ 96-31-01-37 ⌐ 15 in 1 Star NN ⌐ 16 in 2 Stars NN. from 95–250F, breakfast 24–30F, telephone, TV. Closed Sat, 15 days in Jun. Coaches welcome (rest. seats 50). Evening meals. English spoken. Car park; bar; dogs allowed; TV room; amusements (pool table, table tennis). Menus 65–150F. Specialities: *crevettes grillées, Canard à l'orange, coquilles Saint-Jacques.* Sites to visit: Saint-Malo, Le
⌂ Mont St. Michel.

LAMBESC 13410 B.-du-R. **RN 7 Map 24-B3**

♀ ⊗ **RELAIS DE LA GARE** (N° RR AVR 26 044) (Mme Germaine **Lansac**) Bld des Coopèratives ☎ 42-92-97-60 Closed Sun. Coaches welcome (rest. seats 70). Evening meals. Italian spoken.
♀ ⊗ **LE VOLTAIRE** (N° RR JUN 26 923) (M. Albert **Reymond**) Cros du Loubon ☎ 42-92-72-19 ⌐ 8 Open 6am – 1pm. Italian spoken. Filling station (8 pumps).

LAMONZIE-ST-MARTIN 24130 Dordogne **RD 936 Maps 15-B3 and 21-B1**

♀ ⊗ **LA POMME D'OR** (N° RR AVR 23 762) (M. Giuseppina **Perna**) La Force ☎ 53-24-04-00 Closed Sat; Aug. Italian spoken.

LAMOTTE-DU-RHONE 84500 Vaucluse **RN 994 Map 24-A2**

♀ ⊗ **CAFE DE LA PAIX** (N° RR OCT 26 060) (M. Gérard **Dewez**) ☎ 90-30-41-89 ⌐ 7 Closed Sun. Full board 150–180F per night. Coaches welcome (rest. seats 62). Evening meals until 9pm.

LANCON-DE-PROVENCE 13680 B.-du-R. **RN 113 Map 24-B3**

♀ ⊗ **RELAIS DES FOURCHES** (N° RR FEV 26 166) (M. Vincent

Florio) RN 113 Quartier des Fenage ☎ 90-42-71-21 ➼ 5 Closed Sat afternoon, Sun. Full-board. Coaches welcome (rest. seats 120). Evening meals. Spanish, Italian spoken.

LANCON-DE-PROVENCE 13680 B.-du-R. **Autoroute A7**
⊗ **RELAIS DE PROVENCE** (Sté Accor) Autoroute A7 Aire de Lancon-de-Provence ☎ 90-53-90-25 Self-service restaurant, open 6 to midnight, 24 hours Jun to Sept. Carpark, TV, exchange, telephones. Tobacconist. Newsagent.
⊉ **Total Service Station – RELAIS DU SENEGUIER** A7 ☎ 90-53-18-18.

LANDE-SUR-EURE (LA) 61290 Orne **Map 8-A3**
⊻ ⊗ **RELAIS DE LA TOUR** (N° RR FEV 26 808) (M. Edouard **Simon**) Le Bourg ☎ 33-73-65-00.

LANDES 17380 Charente-Marit. **RN 139 Map 15-A2**
⊻ ⊗ ⌂ **AUX AMIS DE LA ROUTE** (N° RR MARS 26 218) (M. Robert **Picard**) Tonnay Boutonne ☎ 46-59-73-12 ➼ 4 Full-board 140F. Evening meals.

LANDEVANT 56690 Morbihan **RN 165 Map 7-B2**
⊻ ⊗ **LE RELAIS DU PELICAN** (N° RR JUL 6 281) (M. **Bourn**) 14, rte
⊷ Nle ☎ 97-56-93-12 Closed Mon evening/Tue; Oct.

LANDIVISIAU 29230 Finistère **RN 12 Map 7-A1**
⊻ ⊗ ⌂ **LE TERMINUS** (N° RR JUN 17 822) (M. Raymond **Floch**) 94, avenue Foch ☎ 98-68-02-00 ➼ 15 Closed Sat; 1 to 31 Aug. Full board available. Coaches welcome (rest. seats 80). Evening meals. Menus 50–70F. Specialities: seafood. English spoken.

LANDRECIES 59550 Nord **RN 45 Map 6-A1**
⊻ ⊗ ⌂ **1 Star NN LE RELAIS DUPLEIX** (N° RR NOV 11 882) (M. **Mathieu**) Ville Basse ☎ 27-84-70-46 ➼ 12.
⊻ ⊗ **LE SAMBRETON** (N° RR AOU 23 896) (M. and Mme Monique **Lacoche SARL**) Guise road. ☎ 27-84-81-58. Closed Sat afternoon, Sun afternoon; 15–30 Aug.

LANDRETHUN-LE-NORD 62250 Pas-de-Calais **RD 234 and 231 Map 5-A2**
⊻ ⊗ **A LA DESCENTE DES VOYAGEURS** (N° RR JUN 24 244) (Mme Nelly **Brisbout**) ☎ 21-92-85-55. ➼ 3 Full board 160F per night. Coaches welcome (rest. seats 60). Evening meals.

LANESTER 56600 Morbihan **RN 24 Map 7-B2**
⊻ ⊗ ⌂ **1 Star NN LE RELAIS DE LA ROTONDE** (N° RR NOV 15 440) (M. **Mercier**) 120, rue Jean-Jaurès ☎ 97-76-06-37 ➼ 14 Closed Sat afternnon, Sun; 15 days in Aug, Christmas, New Year. Full board 150 per night. Coaches welcome (rest. seats 40). Evening meals until 8.30pm.
⊻ ⊗ **LE RELAIS DU PONT-DU-BONHOMME** (N° RR OCT 23 963) (M. Lucien **Phillippe**) avenue du Pont-du-Bonhomme ☎ 97-76-51-23 Closed Aug. Coaches welcome (rest. seats 400/200).

L

LANGOGNE 48300 Lozère **RN 102 Map 17-B3**
⊻ ⊗ 🏠 **1 Star NN HOTEL DU LUXEMBOURG** (N° RR AVR 22 750)
(Mme Adrienne **Chabalier**) place de la Gare ☎ 66-69-00-11 ⊷
14 Closed Jan. Full-board 150–160F per night. Coaches welcome
(rest. seats 60). Evening meals.

LANGON 33210 Gironde **RN 113 and RN 132 Autoroute A61 Maps
20-B1 and 21-A1**
⊻ ⊗ 🏠 **HÔTEL RESTAURANT DARLOT** (N° RR MAR 14 293) (M.
Jean-Paul **Darlot**) 10, rue Dotézac ☎ 56-63-01-36 ⊷ 11 Closed
Sun 15 Aug to 5 Sept. Full-board 150–173F per night. Coaches
⊷ welcome (rest. seats 80). English, Spanish spoken. Menus up to
52F. Specialities: *civet de lièvre, cèpes à la bordelaise, Sailmis de
palombe.*

LANGON MENNETOU-SUR-CHER 41320 Loir-et-Cher
⊻ ⊗ 🏠 **RELAIS DE LANGON** Sté JADF Nle 76 (N° RR SEPT 26 312)
☎ 54-96-44-32 **Minitel** Closed Sat, 2pm to Mon, 5am; 15–30 Aug.
Coaches welcome (rest. seats 70). Evening meals until midnight.

LANGRES 52200 Haute-Marne **RN 19 Map 14-A2**
⊻ ⊗ 🏠 **RELAIS DE LA COLLINIÈRE** (N° RR JUL 26 601) (Mme
Élisabeth **Guerra**) ☎ 25-87-03-27 ⊷ 8 Closed Sun. Coaches
welcome (rest. seats 40). Evening meals. Portuguese spoken.
⊻ ⊗ 🏠 **A LA BONNE AUBERGE** (N° RR AVR 16 016) (M. Marcel
Baumann) Faubourg de la Collinière ☎ 25-87-09-18 ⊷ 6 Closed
Sun; Christmas; beginning May. Full-board 110–140F per night.
Coaches welcome (rest. seats 50/20). Evening meals.

LAINISCAT 22 570 C.-du-N. **Map 7-B2**
⊻ ⊗ **CHALET DES ROUTIERS** (N° RR SEPT 25 638) (Mme Catherine
Morvan) Gare de Gouarec ☎ 96-24-90-93 Closed Sun in Jan or
Feb. Evening meals. English spoken.

LANNION 22300 Côtes-du-Nord **Map 7-A2**
⊻ ⊗ 🏠 **LE RELAIS DE LA CROIX ROUGE** (N° RR DEC 23 571)
(Mme **Pasquiou**) Croix Rouge Ploumilliau route de Morlaix ☎ 96-
35-45-08 ⊷ 14.

LAONS 28270 Eure-et-Loir **RD 4 Map 8-A3**
⊻ ⊗ **LES ROUTIERS** (N° RR JUL 24 649) (Mme Suzanne **Rio**) 2, Place
du Carrefour ☎ 37-38-10-21 Closed Thur afternoon.

LAPALISSE 03120 Allier **RN 7 and RD3 Map 16-A3**
⊻ ⊗ 🏠 **1 Star NN LE CHAPON DORÉ** (N° RR FEV 26 814) (M. Jean-
Luc **Lalauze**) 2, avenue du 8 Mai 1945 ☎ 70-99-09-51 ⊷ 8. (4 with
shower) from 65–130F, breakfast to 18.50F. Closed Sun. Car park;
bar; dogs allowed; recreations (*pétanque*). Places to visit: zoo,
châteaux.
⚑ **Avia Service Station – LES ROUTIERS** (N° RR FEV 23 666) (M.
Serge **L'Habitant**) 48, avenue du 8-Mai ☎ 70-99-10-08 Closed Sun
(except summer). English, German spoken.

L

LAPALME 11480 Aude **RN 9 Map 23-A3**
♈ ⊗ 🏠 **LE CHANTECLAIR** (N° RR AVR 26 867) (M. Maurice **Preignan**) ☎ 68-48-15-03 ⊷ 7.

LAPALUD 84840 Vaucluse **RN 7 Map 24-A2**
♈ ⊗ 🏠 **LE RELAIS DE LA CROISIERETTE** (N° RR AVR 24 183) (M. Daniel **Régnier**) RN 7 ☎ 90-40-32-88 ⊷ 4 Closed Sat, Sun; 15 to 31 Aug. Evening meals.

LAPANOUSE-SERVERAC 12150 Aveyron **RN 595 Map 23-A1**
♈ ⊗ **LE RELAIS DES ROUTIERS** (N° RR DEC 21 736) (M. Roger **Arnal**) route de Rodez ☎ 65-71-60-44.

LAPEYRADE 40240 Landes **RD 933 Map 21-A2**
♈ ⊗ 🏠 **LE RELAIS DES BRUYÈRES** (N° RR JANV 27 161) (SARL Palm Gérnte Mme Aline **Lallemant**) Labastide d'Armagnac ☎ 58-93-61-16 ⊷ 11 Closed Sun evening and Tues morning (except 15/6 to 15/9, and Nov to Dec.) English and Spanish spoken.

LAPTE 43200 Hte-Loire **RD 105 Map 18-A3**
♈ ⊗ 🏠 **AUX POUSSINS** (N° RR JUN 26 925) (Mme Sabine **Dziergwa**) Le Bourg ☎ 71-59-37-76. ⊷ 13 Closed Wed afternoon; Nov. Filling station (Elf) at 3 kms, closed Tue.

LARDIN (LE) 24570 Dordogne **RN 89 Map 17-A1**
♈ ⊗ 🏠 **RELAIS ST-LAZARE** (N° RR MAI 26 248) (Mme Denise **Baril**) La Galibe RN 87 ☎ 53-51-37-45 ⊷ 10.

LAROUILLIES 59219 Nord **RN 2 Map 6-A1/2**
♈ ⊗ **L'AVESNOIS** (N° RR MARS 26 834) (M. and Mme Kléber **Moreau**) ☎ 27-59-22-88 English spoken.

LARRAZET 82500 Tarn-et-Garonne **RD 928 Map 22-A1**
♈ ⊗ **AUBERGE DE LA BARBACANE** (N° RR JANV 26 798) (M. Roland **Cancel**) route d'Auch ☎ 63-20-71-29 ⊷ 5 Closed Mon afternoon.

LAUSSEIGNAN-BARBASTE 47230 L.-et-G. **RN 655 Map 21-A2 see BARBASTE**

LAVAL 53000 Mayenne **RN 162 and RD 53 Map 8-B1**
♈ ⊗ **LE RELAIS DE NIAFLES** (N° RR NOV 22 994) Autoroute A81 exit 3 Niafles Changé-les-Laval ☎ 43-53-76-15 Closed Sat afternoon, Sun; 1 to 23 Aug. Coaches welcome (rest. seats 150). Evening meals until 10pm.
♈ **BAR DE LA GARE** (N° RR JUL 25 493) (Mme Claudia **Helbert**) 107, avenue Robert Buron ☎ 43-53-94-88 Coaches welcome (rest. seats 27).

LAVANS-LES-DOLE 39700 Jura **RN 73 Map 14-A3**
♈ ⊗ 🏠 **LE PANORAMIC** (N° RR MAI 26 238) (Mme Nadège **Hardy**) Orchamps ☎ 84-81-21-41 ⊷ 10.

L

LAVARDAC 47230 L.-et-G. **RN 655 Map 21-B1**
♀ ⊗ ⌂ **LE RELAIS** (N° RR FEV 25 299) (M. Patrick **Caillau**) 8, allée des Alliés ☎ 53-65-54-35 ⊸ 8 Closed Fri 3.00pm, Sat 3.00pm. English spoken.

LAVEISSIERE 15300 Cantal **RN 122 Map 17-A2**
♀ ⊗ ⌂ **LE ROCHER FLEURI** (N° RR NOV 26 092) (M. Claude **Chevallier**) La Grande-Granilh ☎ 71-20-01-77 ⊸ Closed Sun, Oct.

LAVERSINES 60510 Oise **RN 31 Map 3-A2**
♀ ⊗ **LE RELAIS ROUTIERS** (N° RR MAI 25 416) (Mme Nadine **Fontaine**) 90, rue St-Germain ☎ 44-07-75-80 Closed Sat and Sun.

LEDENON 30210 Gard **RN 86 Map 24-A2**
♀ ⊗ ⌂ **RELAIS DE LEDENON** (N° RR AVR 25 889) (M. **Brunel and Co**) Nationale 86 ☎ 66-37-12-83 ⊸ 7 Closed Sat, Sun; public holidays. No rooms let Fri night. English spoken.

LENCLOITRE 86140 Vienne **RD 725 Maps 15-B1 and 12-B2**
♀ ⊗ **LE CHAMP DE FOIRE** (N° RR AVR 24-552) (Mme Michelle **Guignon**) 18, place du Champ de Foire ☎ 49-90-74-91 ⊸ 4 Closed Sun. Coaches welcome (rest. seats 70). Evening meals.
♀ ⊗ **AU 14** (N° RR JUIL 26 934) (M. André **Pernelle**) 2, place du Champ de Foire ☎ 49-90-71-29 Closed Sun. Filling stations opposite and at 200m.

LEROUVILLE 55200 Meuse **RD 964 Map 14-A1**
♀ ⊗ **LE RELAIS DE L'HOTEL DE VILLE** (N° RR MAR 24 171) (Mme Hélène **Ruse**) 23, Rue Nationale ☎ 29-91-06-16 Closed Wed. German spoken.

LESCHELLES 02170 Aisne **RN 30 Map 6-A1**
♀ ⊗ **LE RELAIS DES QUATRE CHEMINS** (N° RR OCT 13 164) (M. Pierre **Rousseaux**) ☎ 23-97-04-88 ⊸ 2 Closed Aug.

LESMONT 10500 Aube **RN 60 Map 9-B3**
♀ ⊗ **LA GUINGUETTE** (N° RR FEV 21 002) (M. Paul **Meurville**) ☎ 25-77-26-48 Closed Mon afternoon.
♀ ⊗ **LE RELAIS DES LACS** (N° RR AOU 23 425) (M. Jacky **Kappler**) RN 60 ☎ 25-77-45-35 or 77-44-68 Closed Mon morning.

LESQUIN 59810 Nord **Map 5-B1**
♀ ⊗ **CHEZ PASCAL** (N° RR MARS 25 854) (Mme Christiane **Montaigne**) 23, rue Voltaire ☎ 20-86-25-84 Closed Sat, Sun. Evening meals until midnight. English spoken.

LESSARD-EN-BRESSE 71440 S-et-L. **RN 78 Map 18-B1**
♀ ⊗ **RELAIS DU SOLEIL** (N° RR MARS 26 857) (Mme Jeanine **Cristofini**) Place de L'Église ☎ 85-96-40-57 English spoken. Filling station near.

L

LEUE (LA) (Commune de la REORTHE) 85210 Vendee **RN 137 Map 11-B3**
♀ ⊗ ⌂ **LE RELAIS DES ROUTIERS** (N° RR AVR 20 714 bis) (MM. **Charbonneau** and **Dariet**) ☎ 51-94-41-46 ⌐ 7 Closed Sat, Sun; Jul. Coaches welcome (rest. seats 29). Evening meals until 10pm.

LÉVIGNAC-DE-GUYENNE 47120 L.-et-G. **708 D green Map 21-A1**
♀ ⊗ ⌂ **1 Star NN CHEZ DENISE** (N° RR OCT 25 675) (M. Jean **Mamie**) Al. des Promenades ☎ 53-83-72-12 **Minitel** ⌐ 10 Full-board 155–165F. Coaches welcome (rest. seats 200). Evening meals.

LEYMENT 01150 Ain **RN 84 Map 2-A2**
♀ ⊗ ⌂ **LE RELAIS DE LA GARE** (N° RR FEV 27 190) (M. Marcel **Bessière**) 34, rue de la Gare ☎ 74-34-94-30 ⌐ 7 Closed Tues pm and Wed pm, 22/12 to 2/1.

LEZINNES 89160 Yonne **RD 905 Map 13-A3**
♀ ⊗ ⌂ **LE RELAIS DES VOYAGEURS** (N° RR OCT 25 701) (M. Serge **Vermeulen**) 41, Route Nle 905 ☎ 86-75-61-49 ⌐ 9. Coaches welcome. Evening meals.

LIBOURNE 33500 Gironde **RN 89 Map 15-A3**
♀ ⊗ **MOULIN BLANC** (N° RR JANV 27 171) (Mme Geneviève **Fernandez**) 132, av. Georges-Clemenceau ☎ 57-25-01-61 ⌐ 9 Spanish, Italian and German spoken.

LIGARDES 32650 Gers **RN 131 and RD 36 Map 21-B2**
♀ ⊗ **LE RELAIS CHEZ DUDULE** (N° RR MAR 21 820) (M. Francis **Dulong**) Route d'Agen ☎ 62-28-12-62.

LIGNANE 13540 B.-du-R. **RN 7 Map 24-B3**
♀ ⊗ **LE RELAIS DE LIGNANE** (N° RR MAR 21 453) (M. Christian **Mondin**) Nationale 7 ☎ 42-92-51-15 Coaches welcome (rest. seats 50). Meals served 11.30am to 2pm and evening. HGV parking.

LIGNOL 56160 Morbihan **RD 782 Map 7-B2**
♀ ⊗ ⌂ **RELAIS DES VOYAGEURS** (N° RR DEC 26 126) (M. Bernard **Le Solliec**) 4, rue de la Marie ☎ 97-27-03-48 **Minitel** ⌐ 7 Closed Mon 1.30pm. Coaches welcome (rest. seats 200). Evening meals.

LIGNOL-LE-CHATEAU 10200 Aube **RD 19 Map 9-B3**
♀ ⊗ **CHEZ CAROLINE** (N° RR DEC 26 150) (Mme Caroline **Aubriot**) Bar s/Aube ☎ 25-92-01-06 and 25-92-01-08 Closed Sat evening 8.00pm, Sun evening. Coaches welcome (rest. seats 80). Evening meals until 1.00am.

LIGNY-EN-BARROIS 55500 Meuse **Map 14-A1**
♀ ⊗ **RELAIS DE L'EUROP** (N° RR JUIL 26 943) (M. Mario **Fodde**) ☎ 29-78-00-83 Closed Sun evening. Filling station near.

L

LILLE 59000 Nord **R 17 Map 5-B1 6-A3**
♀ ⊗ **L'EDELWEISS** (N° RR MAR 25 332) (Mme Monique **Duthoit**)
205, rue d'Arras ☎ 20-52-45-29 Closed Aug. Dutch spoken.

LIMAY 78520 Yvelines **Map 3-B2**
♀ ⊗ **LA MARMITE** (N° RR AOU 25 617) (M. Claude **Pesta**) 1, rte de
Meulan ☎ 34-78-65-52 **Minitel** Closed Sun. Evening meals ex-
cept Fri. Polish, English, Spanish, Portuguese spoken.

LIMOGES 87000 Haute-Vienne **RN 20 Map 16-B1**
♀ ⊗ **CHEZ BICHON** (N° RR DEC 23 057) (M. **Houard**) 68, avenue de
Lattre-de-Tassigny ☎ 55-30-68-83 Closed Sat; Evening meals
until 9pm. English, Spanish spoken.

LINAS-MONTLHÉRY 93310 Essonne **RN 20 Map 1-B2**
♀ ⊗ **LE JUBILÉ** (N° RR SEPT 25 095) (M. Jacques **Boissier**) ☎ 64-90-
64-45 et 90-23-87.

LIPOSTHEY-PISSOS 40410 Landes **RN 10 Map 20-B1**
♀ ⊗ ⌂ **LE RELAIS CHEZ ALINE** (N° RR MAR 10 433) (Mme **Gros**) ☎
58-82-30-30 ⊷ 7 Closed Sat in winter; Christmas holidays; Full-
board 145–150F per night. Coaches welcome (rest. seats 80)
Evening meals.

LIRE 49530 M.-et-L. **RN 763 Map 11-A3**
♀ ⊗ **CHEZ ANGÈLE** (N° RR JUL 25 474) (M. Jean-Claude **Gouraud**)
Les Fourneaux ☎ 40-83-13-10 Closed Mon afternoon; Aug.

LISIEUX 14100 Calvados **RN 13 and CD 579 Map 4-B2**
♀ ⊗ ⌂ **RELAIS PARIS-CHERBOURG** (N° RR MAI 21 902) (M. and
Mme **Pestel**) 113, avenue du Six-Juin ☎ 31-62-06-38 ⊷ 6 Closed
Sun evening; Sept for 15 days. Full board 158,80F per night.
Coaches welcome (rest. seats 40). Evening meals.
♀ ⊗ **PILE OU FACE** (N° RR JUN 25 443) (Mme Gisèle **Bellemont**) 68,
Bld Herbet Fournet ☎ 31-62-06-09 Closed Sun. Coaches welco-
me (rest. seats 52). Evening meals.
♀ ⊗ **LE RELAIS DE L'AGRICULTURE** (N° RR MARS 27 212) (M.
Andre **Fiaut**) 23, rue du Gal-Leclerc ☎ 31-31-44-18 ⊷ 10 Closed
Sun.

LISSAY LOCHY 18340 Cher **RD 28/73 Map 13-B1**
♀ ⊗ **AUBERGE DES MAISONS ROUGES** (N° RR MARS 26 473) (M.
Robert **Leger**) Levet ☎ 48-64-76-07 **Minitel** Closed Sat; Dec.

LES LISSES 91100 Villabe Essonne **Autoroute A6 Map 1-B2**
♀ ⊗ **RESTOP DES LISSES** (N° RR RA-4) (M. Jean **Lamotte**, J.-C.
Després) Aire de Service des Lisses ☎ 60-86-22-51 Self-service
restaurant 11.00am to 10.00pm. TV. Showers.

LIT ET MIXE 41170 Landes **CD 652 Map 20-A2**
♀ ⊗ **Grill RESTO GRILL** (N° RR OCT 27 056) (M. Phillippe **Labro**)
route de Mimizan ☎ 58-42-84-91 English spoken.

LIVRON-SUR-DROME 26250 Drôme)
Ⴘ ⊗ 🏠 **AUBERGE MACAMP** (N° RR JUIL 27136) (Mme Josiane **Vocanson**) Francy ☎ 75-61-73-91 **Minitel** ⊷ **17** Evening meals.

LODEVE 34700 Hérault **RN 9 Map 23-A2**
Ⴘ ⊗ **LE RELAIS DE LA FONTAINE D'AMOUR** (N° RR JUN 21 149) (Mme Renée **Granier**) Nationale 9 ☎ 67-44-02-77. Closed Tue. Evening meals.
Ⴘ ⊗ **RELAIS DE LA CROIX** (N° RR JUN 26 910) (M. Jean-Dennis **Roig**) Cartels ☎ 67-44-00-72 ⊷ 5 Closed weekends; 10–30 Oct. Filling station 5kms. Car park (3,300 m²).
Ⴘ ⊗ 🏠 **LE RELAIS DE L'ESCALETTE** (N° RR FEV 24 852) (M. Lucien **Mirman**) Rte Nationale 9 ☎ 67-44-01-14 ⊷ 22 Closed Sat; Oct. Full-board 150–170F per night. Coaches welcome (rest. seats 80). Evening meals. English, Italian, Spanish spoken.

LOGE (LA) par THEILLAY 41390 Loir-et-Cher **RN 20 Map 13-B1**
Ⴘ ⊗ 🏠 **1 Star NN LE RELAIS DE LA LOGE** (N° RR JAN 25 249) (M. Guy **Paillaud**) ☎ 54-83-37-20 ⊷ 40 Open 24 hours. Coaches ⊷ welcome (rest. seats 170). Evening meals. English spoken.

LOIGNE-SUR-MAYENNE 53200 Mayenne **Map 12-A1**
Ⴘ ⊗ **CHEZ MANU** (N° RR NOV 26 391) (M. Manuel **Alonso**) 2, rue de Bretagne ☎ 43-07-29-62 Closed Mon until Midday; 15 days in Aug. Evening meals. English spoken.
Ⴘ ⊗ **CAFÉ DES SPORTS** (N° RR JUIN 27 314) (M. José **Atlan**) 2, rue de la Roche-du-Maine ☎ 43-07-19-10 Closed Mon pm and first two weeks of August. English spoken. Evening meals.

LOIRE 49480 Maine-et-Loire **Map 11-A3**
Ⴘ ⊗ **LE RELAIS DES SPORTS** (N° RR AVR 24 551) (M. Phillippe **Audouin**) Bourg ☎ 41-92-20-64.

LOISON-SOUS-LENS 62218 P.-de-C **Map 5-B3**
Ⴘ ⊗ 🏠 **LE PRÉSIDENT** (N° RR MARS 27 221) (M. **Fauer**) 7/9, rue de Lille ☎ 21-78-51-95 ⊷ 5 Closed Sun.

LOISY 54700 PONT-A-MOUSSON Meurthe-et-Moselle **Autoroute A-31 Maps 10-A1 and 14-B1**
Ⴘ ⊗ **RESTAURANT TOURNEBRIDE** Aire de service de Pont-à-Mousson Loisy ☎ 83-81-18-89 Food served 11.30am to 3.00pm, 7.00pm to 10.00pm. Open 24 hours in summer. English, Spanish spoken.
⛽ **Les Routiers Total Service Station – LE RELAIS DE L'OBRION** (N° RR AVR 22 779) (**Cogesta**) Autoroute A31 Pont-à-Mousson ☎ 83-81-03-85 Open 24 hours. English, Spanish, Italian spoken.

LONGEAU-LE-VALLINOT 52600 Haute-Marne **RN 67 Map 14-A2**
Ⴘ ⊗ 🏠 **L'AUBERGE ROUTIERE** (N° RR AVR 17 783) (M. Georges **Groscolas**) ☎ 25-88-42-16 ⊷ 10 Closed Sat evening in winter, Sept. Full-board 140–145F per night. Coaches welcome (rest. seats 60).

L

Longeau-le-Vallinot continued
♀ ⊗ ⌂ **LE CAFÉ DES ROUTIERS** (N° RR JUL 21 994) (Mme Edwige **Denis**) Rte Nle ☎ 25-88-40-51 ⊷ 7 Closed Fri evening. Full-board 130–150F. Coaches welcome (rest. seats 50/25). Evening meals.

LONGEVILLE-LES-SAINT-AVOLD 57740 Moselle **Autoroute A32 Map 10-A1 see ST-AVOLD**
♟ **Antar Service Station RELAIS SARRE LORRAINE** (N° RR JUL 25 043) (M. Jean-Pierre **Duytschaevel**) Autoroute A32 ☎ 87-92-23-89 Open 24 hours English, German spoken.

LONGLAVILLE 54810 M.-et-M. **RN 52 Map 6-A3**
♀ ⊗ **LE RELAIS DE LA DOUANE** (N° RR AVR 18 684) (Mme Liliane **Gaudelet-Bonnarue**) 8, avenue du Luxembourg Frontière France-Luxembourg ☎ 82-23-29-19 Closed Aug. English, German spoken.

LONGUE 49160 M.-et-L. **RN 138 and RD 4 Map 12-A2**
♀ ⊗ **LE RELAIS DES SOUVENETS** (N° RR SEP 25 632) (Mme Réjane **Taugourdeau**) RN 147 ☎ 41-52-13-86 Closed Sat afternoon, Sun. Evening meals.
♀ ⊗ **RELAIS DE LA GARE** (N° RR AVR 26 499) (M. Pascal **Desert**) 22, rue Michel-Couet ☎ 41-52-10-37.

LONGUEAU 80330 Somme **RN 35 Map 5-A3**
♀ ⊗ ⌂ **LE RELAIS DE L'HOTEL DE VILLE** (N° RR SEP 23 944) (M. Konider **Bellaredj**) 105, avenue Henri-Barbusse ☎ 22-46-16-14 ⊷ 10 Closed Sun. English, Arabic spoken.

LONS 64140 Pyr.-Atl. **see PAU**

LORIOL 26270 Drôme **RN 7 Map 24-A1**
♀ ⊗ **RELAIS SAINT PAUL** (N° RR MARS 26 214) (M. Albert **Begot**) RN 7 ☎ 75-61-76-31 Closed Mon.

LORRIS 45260 Loiret **RD 961 Map 13-A1**
♀ ⊗ **LE RELAIS DES ROUTIERS** (N° RR AOU 16 655) (M. Baptiste **Charbonnier**) 21, Grande-Rue ☎ 38-92-40-64 Closed Wed afternoon.
♀ ⊗ ⌂ **AUBERGE DE LA CROIX ROUGE** (N° RR MARS 26 861) (M. Jean-Yves **Charrier**) 28, rue Guillaume de Lorris ☎ 38-92-47-03. Open 7am – 9pm. Filling station at 700 metres.

LOUDEAC 22600 C. du N. **Map 7-B2**
♀ ⊗ **RELAIS DU STOP** (N° RR OCT 20 868) (M. **Kerizoret**) Le Haut Breuil ☎ 96-28-01-76.
♀ ⊗ ⌂ **1 Star NN REST. LES ROUTIERS** (N° RR JANV 26 426) (M. and Mme Dominique **Le Cozannet**) 7, rue Lavergne ☎ 96-28-01-44 ⊷ 40 from 60–110F, breakfast 14F, telephone in room. Closed Fri evening; Sun evening; Aug. Full board 130–180F per night. Coaches welcome (rest. seats 180). Car park; bar; dogs allowed.

LOUHANS 71500 S.-et-L. **RN 78 Map 18-B1**
♀ ⊗ **LE ROUTIERS** (N° RR MAR 18 031) (Mme **Alexandre**) 19, rue

Lucien Guillemot ☎ 85-75-11-75. Closed Sun; Aug. Coaches welcome.

LOULAY 17330 Charente-Marit. **RN 150 Map 15-A2**

♈ ⊗ ⌂ **LE RELAIS CHEZ NENETTE** (N° RR OCT 20 856) (Mme Renée **Rullier**) place de-Gaulle ☎ 46-33-80-59 ⇤ 5 Closed Sun (except by arrangement). Coaches welcome (rest. seats 100/30). Evening meals.

♈ ⊗ **LE COUCOU** (N° RR MAI 26 536) (Mme Antoinette **Couturier**) Tout-y-Faut Vergne ☎ 46-33-90-16 Closed Sat off season.

LOUPE (LA) 28240 Eure-et-Loir **RN 23 Map 8-B3**

♈ ⊗ **LA HURIE CHEZ BEATRICE** (N° RR OCT 26 029) (Mme Béatrice **Collin**) La Hurie St-Victor-de-Buthon ☎ 37-81-30-38 Closed Sun. Evening meals in winter. English spoken.

LOUPLANDE 72780 Sarthe **RN 768 Map 8-B2**

♈ ⊗ ⌂ **LE RELAIS DE L'HOTEL DE FRANCE – Les Routiers** (N° RR MAR 11 344) (M. and Mme **Fretault**) ☎ 43-88-52-18 ⇤ 7 Closed Fri, 1pm; Aug. Full-board 120–150F per night. Coaches welcome (rest. seats 160). Evening meals.

LOUVIERS 27400 Eure **RN 154 Map 3-B1**

♈ ⊗ **AU RENDEZ-VOUS DES SPORTIFS Chez Jeannot** (N° RR OCT 22 546) (M. Jean **Hébert**) 27, avenue Winston-Churchill ☎ 32-40-02-00 Closed Sat, Sun; public holidays; Jul.

♈ ⊗ **LE RELAIS DES ROUTIERS** (N° RR MAR 23 714) (Mme **Quesney**) 13, rue de Paris ☎ 32-40-29-22 Closed Sun. Coaches welcome (rest. seats 100). Evening meals until 1am.

LUART (LE) 72390 Sarthe **near RN23/RD29 Map 8-B2**

♈ ⊗ **LES LABOUREURS** (N° RR SEPT 26 668) (M. **Gay**) 2, Place de L'Eglise, Dollon ☎ 43-93-44-06 Closed alternative Sun. English spoken.

LUBBON 40240 Landes **RD 933 Map 21-A2**

♈ ⊗ ⌂ **LE RELAIS CHEZ MAMY** (N° RR FEV 20 116) (M. Louis **Nicoletto**) ☎ 58-93-60-47 ⇤ 9 Closed Sat evening; Oct. Coaches please reserve (rest. seats 70). Evening meals. Italian spoken.

LE LUC 83340 VAR **RN 7 Map 25-A2**

♈ ⊗ ⌂ **2 stars NN PARIS-SAINT-TROP** (N° RR NOV 27 082) (M. Antoine **Jacobs**) ☎ 94-69-71-64 ⇤ 17 English spoken.

LUÇAY LE MALE 36360 Indre **Map 12-B3**

♈ ⊗ ⌂ **LE DAUPHIN** (N° RR MARS 26 843) (M. Patrick **Rebout**) 7, Place Verdun. ☎ 54-40-41-17 ⇤ 5 Car park (3,000 m^2). Filling station (7.30am – 8.30pm)

LUCEAU 72500 Sarthe **RN 138 Map 12-A2**

♈ ⊗ **LA CROIX DE PAILLE** (N° RR OCT 24 744) (M. **Moreau**) Route du Mans **Château du Loir** ☎ 43-44-05-50 **Minitel** Closed Sat evening, Sun except for banquets; Aug. Meals served until 1am.

L

LUDE (LE) 72800 Sarthe **Map 12-A2**
♀ ⊗ **LE RELAIS DES PECHEURS** (N° RR DEC 23 061) (M. **Moire**) 14, boulevard de l'Hospice ☎ 43-94-61-03 Closed Sun afternoon in winter. Coaches welcome (rest. seats 40/25). Evening meals.

LUMBRES 62380 Pas-de-Calais **Map 5-A2**
♀ ⊗ **HOTEL MODERNE** (N° RR SEPT 26 271) (M. Pierre **Fichaux**) 18, rue François-Cousin ☎ 21-39-62-87 Closed Sun; Aug.

LURE 70200 Haute-Saône **RN 19 Maps 10-A3 and 14-B2**
♀ ⊗ ⌂ **LE PETIT RELAIS** (N° RR JUL 24 643) (Mme Monique **Carrière**) 4, rue Albert Mathiez ☎ 84-30-03-53 ⇌ 8 Closed Sun. Evening meals. Coaches welcome (rest. seats 18).

LUSIGNY-SUR-BARSE 10270 Aube **RN 19 Map 9-B3**
♀ ⊗ ⌂ **AUBERGE DES PRAIRIES** (N° RR NOV 25 173) (Mme Monique **Mireux**) ☎ 25-41-20-32 ⇌ 5 Full-board 145–150F per night. Coaches welcome (rest. seats 60). Evening meals.

LUSSAC-LES-CHATEAUX 86320 Vienne **RN 147 Map 15-B1**
♀ ⊗ **LE CHENE VERT** (N° RR AVR 26874) (Mme Alexandrine **Dos Reis Martins**) 14, avenue Léon-Pineau ☎ 49-48-40-30 Closed Sat, Sun. English, Italian, German, Spanish, Portuguese spoken. Car park (2,000m^2) Filling station (7am – 12pm).

LUSSANT 17680 Charente-Maritime **CD 739 Map 11-B1**
♀ ⊗ ⌂ **CHEZ MOI** (N° RR AOUT 26 983) (SARL **Guerin and Sons**) Le Bourg ☎ 46-83-42-44 ⇌ 10 English spoken. Filling station near.

LUTTERBACH 68460 Haut-Rhin **RN 66 Map 10-B3**
⛽ **Elf Service Station – LE RELAIS DES CHEVREUILS** (N° RR DEC 24 039) (M. Roland **Heid**) RN 66 ☎ 89-52-14-66 Closed Sun. German spoken.

LUTZ-EN-DUNOIS 28200 Eure-et-Loir **Map 8-B3**
♀ ⊗ ⌂ **LA RENCONTRE** (N° RR JUIN 27 299) (M. Francis **Berrier**) ☎ 37-45-18-08 ⇌ 5 Closed Sun.

LUZENAC-GARANOU 09250 Ariège **RN 20 Map 22-A3**
♀ ⊗ ⌂ **LE RELAIS DES ROUTIERS** (N° RR DEC 24 041) (Mme Marie **Pires**) Avenue de la Gare ☎ 61-64-47-13 ⇌ 9 Spanish, Portuguese spoken.

LYON 69007 Rhône **RN 6 and 7 Maps 2-A2 and 18-B2**
♀ ⊗ **LES ROUTIERS** (N° RR JUL 21 983) (M. Pierre **Sala**) 21, quai Perrache ☎ 78-37-75-86 Closed Sat, Sun; Aug. Evening meals.

MABLY 42300 Loire **see ROANNE**

M

MADELEINE-BOUVET (LA) 61110 Orne **RD 920 and 36 Map 8-B3**
♀ ⊗ **LE RELAIS PECHEURON** (N° RR OCT 24 355) (M. Alain
Jouanneau) Le Bourg ☎ 33-73-93-00 Closed Wed afternoon; 15
days in Feb. English spoken.

MAGNAC-BOURG 87380 Hte-Vienne **RN 20 Map 17-A1**
♀ ⊗ **LE RELAIS PARIS-TOULOUSE** (N° RR JUL 24 629) (M.
Meriadec) ☎ 55-00-81-53 Closed Wed; (except Jul, Aug).
Coaches welcome (rest. seats 35). Evening meals until 1am.

MAGNAN 32110 Gers **CD 6 Map 21-A2**
♀ ⊗ **LE FER À CHEVAL** (N; RR SEPT 27 022) (Mme Melanie
Bolajuzon) route le Houga-Nogaro ☎ 62-09-04-24 Closed Tues
pm.

MAGNANAC par VILLEMUR-SUR-TARN 331340 Haute-Garonne **RN
630 Map 22-A2**
♀ ⊗ ⌂ **LE RELAIS DE LA GARE** (N° RR OCT 24 737) (Mme
Fabienne **Degoul**) 65, rue de Beauvais ☎ 34-67-20-70 ⇔ 10
Closed Sun. Portuguese spoken.
♀ ⊗ ⌂ **CHEZ FRANÇOISE** (N° RR SEPT 26 331) (Mme **Rossi**) ☎ 61-
09-01-87 or 61-09-32-72 ⇔ 3 Closed Sun; 15 to 22 Aug. Evening
meals until 9pm.

MAGNY-EN-VEXIN 95420 Val d'Oise
♀ ⊗ **RELAIS DE LA GARE** (N° RR OCT 24 737) (Mme **Degoul**) 65,
rue de Beauvais ☎ 34-67-20-70 Full-board 125–155F per night.
Coaches welcome (rest. seats 50). Evening meals.

MAGNY-LA-CAMPAGNE 14270 Calvados **RD 40 Map 4-B2**
♀ ⊗ **A LA VALLÉE D'AUGE – Tobacconist** (N° RR AVR 21 502)
(Mme Marie-Thérèse **Sevin**) ☎ 31-20-04-20 Service station.
Closed Tue; Jul.

MAINBORGÈRE (LA) 85320 Vendée **RD 746 Map 11-B3**
♀ ⊗ **LE RELAIS ROUTIER DE LA MAINBORGÈRE** (N° RR AVR 23
763) (M. Michel **Hémery**) Mareuil-sur-Lay ☎ 51-31-91-24 Closed
Sat, Sun. Evening meals until 8.30pm.

MAINVILLIERS 28300 Eure-et-Loire
♀ ⊗ **CAFÉ ROUTE** Autoroute A11 (M. Philippe **Blanc**) Aire de
Gasville Paris-Province direction ☎ 37-31-62-42 Self-service restaurant open 6.45am to 11.00pm.
♀ ⊗ **CAFÉ ROUTE** (M. Éric **Grujaro**) Autoroute A11 Province-Paris
direction Aire de Bois Paris ☎ 27-31-62-41 Self-service restaurant
open 7.00am to 10.30pm.

MAISON DIEU see GUILLON

MAISON-NEUVE Commune QUENOCHE-par-RIOZ 70190 Haute-
Saône **RN 57 Maps 10-A3 and 14-B2/3**
♀ ⊗ ⌂ **LES ROUTIERS MAISON NEUVE** (N° RR NOV 26 371) (Mme

M

Maison-Neuvre continued

Marie-Hélene **Moureau**) ☎ 84-91-80-54 ⊸ 9 Closed Sun in winter; beginning of Jan. Full-board 130–150F per night. Evening meals.

MAISONS-LAFITTE 78600 Yvelines **Porte Maillot Map 1-A2**

♀ ⊗ **LE RALLYE** (N° RR FEV 23 650) (M. Jacques **Lalanne**) 17, rue des plantes ☎ 39-62-44-28 Closed Sun; Aug.

MALAKOFF 92240 Hts-de-Seine **RN 306 Map 1-B2**

♀ ⊗ **BAR LE DÉPART** (N° RR OCT 24 399) (M. Armand **Alle**) 64, avenue Pierre Brossolette ☎ 46-57-76-05 Closed Sun; Aug. Evening meals.

MALE 61260 Orne **RN 23 Map 8-B3**

♀ ⊗ ⌂ **HOTEL DE LA BELLE RENCONTRE** (N° RR OCT 25 129) (M. André **Carle**) Le Gibet ☎ 37-49-68-85 ⊸ 6 Closed Sun (except for coaches, banquets). Coaches welcome (rest. seats 130). Evening meals.

MALEMORT 19360 Corrèze **RN 89 Map 17-A1**

♀ ⊗ **CHEZ PAULETTE** (N° RR JAN 23 604) (Mme Paulette **Vergne**) 2, avenue Pierre et Marie Curie ☎ 55-24-28-14 Closed Sun; Aug. Coaches welcome (rest. seats 90).

MALTAVERNE Commune de TRACY-LOIRE 58150 Nièvre **RN 7 Map 13-B2**

♀ ⊗ **LE RELAIS DES ROUTIERS** (N° RR OCT 24 007) (M. **Robillot**) ☎ 58-28-15-34 Closed Sat afternoon, Sun; 10 to 31 Aug. Evening meals.

♀ ⊗ **LA TASSÉE** (N° RR NOV 24 409) (M. Maurice **Chet**) RN 7 Cosne-sur-Loire ☎ 86-26-11-76 Closed Sun (coach parties, public holidays bookable); 5 to 25 Aug; 1 week at Christmas. Coaches welcome (rest. seats 70). Evening meals. English spoken.

MANS (LE) 72000 Sarthe **RN 23 Map 8-B2**

♀ ⊗ **CHEZ GABY** (N° RR MARS 27 235) (Mme Marie-Thérèse **Coutable**) 8, rue du Pied-Sec ☎ 43-84-24-48 Closed Sat pm, Sun and August.

♀ ⊗ **L'AUTO-CLUB** (N° RR JUN 23 340) (M. Rémy **Adet**) 239 bis, avenue Bollée ☎ 43-84-70-73 Closed Sun and the week of August 15th. Coaches welcome (rest. seats 60) Evening meals served until 9.30 pm.

MANTES-LA-JOLIE 78200 Yvelines **RN 13 Map 1-A1**

♀ ⊗ ⌂ **LA CURE D'AIR** (N° RR FEV 26 175) (M. Jean-Claude **Ammar**) 161, bld du Mal-Juin ☎ 30-94-29-15 **Minitel** ⊸ 9 Closed Sat. Coaches welcome (rest. seats 200). Evening meals.

♀ ⊗ **LE NOVELTY** (N° RR MAI 26 535) (Mme Marc **Laurent**) 47, rue de la Papeterie ☎ 30-94-03-04 Closed Sun; Aug.

MANTES-LA-VILLE 78200 Yvelines **RN 13 Map 1-A1**

♀ ⊗ **LA DEMI-LUNE** (N° RR DEC 26 129) (Mme Nicolas **Petitpas**) 51, boulevard Roger Salengro ☎ 34-77-03-66 Closed Sat afternoon, Sun.

♀ ⊗ **LE HOUDAN BAR** (N° RR AVR 23 747) (M. Mohamed **Benariba**) 43, route de Houdan ☎ 34-77-06-11 **Minitel** Closed Sun. Meals served until 9pm.

MANTHELAN 37240 Indre-et-Loire **Map 12-B3**
♀ ⊗ **LE RELAIS DE LA CROIX-VERTE** (N° RR SEP 21 626) (Mme **Martin**) 25, rue Nationale ☎ 47-92-80-16 English spoken.
♀ ⊗ **RELAIS DE LA PROMENADE** (N° RR MAI 26 243) 5, Mail de la Mairie ☎ 47-92-80-39 Evening meals. English spoken.

MARAIS (AUX) 60000 Oise **RN 181 Map 3-A2**
♀ ⊗ **AU GRAND "R"** (N° RR NOV 26 369) (M. Marcel **Boutoille**) 125, route de Gisors ☎ 44-48-18-66 **Minitel** Closed Sun; 5–27 Aug. Evening meals until 9pm.

MARANS 17230 Charente-Maritime **RN 137 Map 11-A1**
♀ ⊗ ⌂ **LE POINT DU JOUR** (N° RR JUL 26 291) (**SARL Gérard**) 2, rue des Moulins ☎ 46-01-14-54 and 46-01-10-38. Evening meals.

MARCHE (LA) 58400 Nièvre) RN 7 Map 13-B2
♀ ⊗ **LE RELAIS DES ROUTIERS** (N° RR JAN 22 150) (M. Jany **Larive**) ☎ 86-70-14-11 Closed Wed and 10th to 20th June.

MARCHELEPOT 80200 Somme **Map 5-B3**
♀ ⊗ ⌂ **HOTEL DU PARC – Rest. Oriental – Chez Dahmane** (N° RR MAR 24 531) (M. Dahmane **Houady**) Rte Nationale 17 ☎ 22-84-04-85 ⇥ 6.

MARCONNELLE 62140 P.-de-C. **Map 5-A2**
♀ ⊗ **LE DAUPHIN** (N° RR MAR 24 870) (Mme Josiane **Dauphin**) 948, Rte Nationale 39 ☎ 21-86-83-64 Closed Wed.

MAREAU-AUX-BOIS 45300 Loiret **Map 9-B1**
♀ ⊗ **AUBERGE DE MONTAFILAN** (N° RR OCT 26 689) (M. Phillipe **Tissier**) 2, rue Montafilan ☎ 38-34-05-23.

MARES (LES) 27160 Eure **RD 840**
♀ ⊗ **LE RELAIS DES MARES** (N° RR NOV 26 743) (M. **Guiot**) Les Chesnes-Breteuil-sur-Iton ☎ 32-29-85-09 Closed Sun.

MAREUIL-SUR-LAY 85320 Vendée **RN 746 Map 11-A1**
♀ ⊗ ⌂ **LE STOP BAR** (N° RR AVR 19 037) (M. Claude **Chavignois**) rue Principale ☎ 51-30-52-72 ⇥ 5 Closed Sat.

MAREUIL-SUR-OURCQ 60890 Oise **RD 936 Map 3-B3**
♀ ⊗ **RESTAURANT DE BOURNEVILLE** (N° RR SEP 22 927) (Mme Huguette **Picard**) 7, rue de Meaux à Bourneville ☎ 23-96-72-11 Evening meals until 8pm.

MARGON 28400 Eure-et-Loir **Map 8-B3**
♀ ⊗ **L'ESPÉRANCE** (N° RR OCT 26 360) (M. Marc **Robinet**) Nogent-le-Rotrou ☎ 37-52-19-03 **Minitel** Evening meals served.

M

MARIGNAC 31440 Haute-Garonne **Map 21-B3**
♀ ⊗ ⌂ **1 NN LE PIC DU GAR** (N° RR MAI 27 289) (M. Henri
Fourment) Rue Jean-Jaurès ☎ 61-79-50-57 ⊷ 25 Rooms 80–130F
Breakfast 15 to 20F. Spanish spoken. Evening meals.

MARGUERITTES 30320 Gard **A9 Map 24-A2/3**
♀ ⊗ ⌂ **LE RELAIS DE LA PINÈDE** (N° RR OCT 26 066) (Mme
Monique **Brouzet**) ☎ 66-26-03-63 Closed Sun low season. Spanish
spoken.

MARLES-LES-MINES 62540 Pas-de-Calais **Map 5-A1**
♀ ⊗ **LE 74** (N° AVR 26 877) (M. Bertrand **Schatt**) 74, rue Jean-Jaurès
☎ 21-65-53-71 English, German spoken.

MARMANDE 47200 L.-et-G. **RN 113 and 133 Map 21-A1**
♀ ⊗ ⌂ **2 Stars NN LE RELAIS DU LION D'OR** (N° RR AOU 17 345)
⇥ **(Ets Beaulieu SARL)** 1, rue de la République ☎ 53-64-21-30 ⊷
50 Open 24 hours. English, Spanish, Italian spoken.
♀ ⊗ ⌂ **LE RELAIS** (N° RR FEV 24 860) (M. Hervé **Pouchet**) 93, bld
Ulysse-Casse ☎ 53-64-26-96 ⊷ 8 Closed Sun.

MAROLLES par BROUE 28260 E.-et-L. **RN 12 Map 8-A3**
♀ ⊗ **AU RELAIS DE MAROLLES** (N° RR SEP 18 193 (Mme Viviane
⇥ **Beauvais**) 44, rue Georges-Bréant ☎ 37-43-20-50 Closed Sat
(except for banquets); Sun; 1st fortnight Aug. Coaches welcome
(3 dining rooms = 150 seats). Evening meals until midnight.
Specialities: *Escalope normande, Omelette aux pleurotte*, Grills.
Menus 55–85F.

MAROLLES-SUR-SEINE 77130 S.-et-M. **RN 51 Map 9-B2**
♀ ⊗ **LE RELAIS DES PECHEURS ET DES CHASSEURS** (N° RR NOV
19 566) (Mme **Bodic**) 70, Grande Rue ☎ 64-31-32-20 ⊷ 3.

MAROLLETTE 72600 Sarthe **Map 8-B2**
♀ ⊗ **LE RENDEZ-VOUS DES CHASSEURS** (N° RR SEPT 26 038) (M.
Norbert **Vaidie**) Le Bourg ☎ 43-97-67-00 Closed Tue; 1st fort-
night Aug. Coaches welcome (rest. seats 95). Evening meals.

MARQUEFAVE 31390 Hte-Gar. **RN 117 Map 22-A2**
♀ ⊗ ⌂ **1 Star NN LE RELAIS CHEZ ROGER** (N° RR JUL 13 851) (M.
Roger **Descuns**) ☎ 61-87-85-07 ⊷ 10 from 60 to 80F, access for
disabled. Closed Sun; Oct. Evening meals. Car park; bar; dogs
allowed; recreations (fishing, shooting); sports (*pétanque*).

MARSAC EN LIVRADOIS 63940 Puy-de-Dôme **CD 906 Map 17-A3**
♀ ⊗ ⌂ **1 Star NN LE KALLISTE** (N° RR AVR 26 516) (M. Yves
Graglia) ☎ 73-95-60-78 ⊷ 18 from 80 to 130F, breakfast 15–18F.
Closed Fri afternoon; mid Sept to mid Oct. Car park; bar; dogs
allowed; recreations (zoo, fishing, walks); museum.

MARSAN 32270 Gers **RN 124 Map 21-B2**
♀ ⊗ **RELAIS GRILL 124** (N° RR SEPT 26 990) (M. Fernand **Castaing**)
Aubiet ☎ 62-65-63-43 Closed Sat evening, Sun; 25–31 Dec.
English spoken. Filling station near.

M

MARSEILLE 13000 B.-du-R. **RN 8 Map 24-B3**
♀ ⊗ **LE RELAIS DE L'INDEPENDANCE** (N° RR SEP 21 657) (Mme **Potoudis**) 234, bld de Paris ☎ 91-91-21-89 Closed Sun.
♀ ⊗ **LE RELAIS DES AMIS** (N° RR JUN 15 693) (M. Raymond **Servière**) 188, boulevard de Paris ☎ 91-62-60-76 **Minitel** Closed Sun; public holidays; Aug. Coaches welcome (rest. seats 60). Evening meals.
♀ ⊗ **AUX DELICES DE MOUREPIANE** (N° RR OCt 25 136) (M. Daniel **Barnabon**) 578, chemin du Littoral ☎ 91-46-08-11 Closed Sun. Coaches welcome (rest. seats 100). Evening meals. Italian spoken.
♀ ⊗ **LE RELAIS** (N° RR OCT 26 342) (Mlle **Tommeau**) 40, quai du Lazaret ☎ 91-90-93-02 Closed Sat, Sun.
♀ ⊗ ⌂ **O'ROUTIERS-ANJOLY** (N° RR MAI 27 274) (M. William **Lequem**) Centre Routier Z.A. d'Anjoly ☎ 42-75-19-60 **Minitel** ⌐ 47 with shower. English, Spanish and Italian spoken. Evening meals served until midnight.
♀ ⊗ ⌂ **1 star NN BEAULIEU-GLARIS** (N° RR NOV 27 085) (M. Yvon **Garros**) 1/3 Place des Marseillaises ☎ 91-90-70-59 ⌐ 35 Closed Sat and Sun (hotel always open). English and Arabic spoken.

MARTEL 46600 Lot **RD 703 Souillac-Figeac Map 17-B1**
♀ ⊗ **LA FONTANELLE – CHEZ FRANÇOISE** (N° RR OCT 26 073) (Mme Françoise **Anger**) Avenue de Nassogne ☎ 65-37-31-59 ⌐ 4 Closed Wed afternoon in winter; Wed in summer, 2.00pm to 6.00pm. Full-board 140F per night. English spoken.

MARTIGNE-FERCHAUD 35640 I.-et-V. **RN 178 Maps 8-B1 and 12-A1**
♀ ⊗ ⌂ **LE RELAIS DU POT D'ETAIN** (N° RR JAN 10 229) (Mme Yvonne **Bouteiller**) 10, Grand Rue ☎ 99-47-90-12 ⌐ 8 Closed Sun afternoon. Evening meals served.

MARTINCAMP 76270 S.-Mme **RD 915 Map 3-A1**
♀ ⊗ **RELAIS DE LA FORET D'EAWY** (N° RR DEC 26 404) (M. Michel **Yon**) Neufchâtel-en-Bray ☎ 35-93-07-03 Closed Wed; end Aug. Coaches welcome (rest. seats 50). Evening meals. English spoken.

MARVEJOLS 48100 Lozère **RN 9 Map 17-B3**
♀ ⊗ ⌂ **1 star NN REST DE LA PAIX** (N° RR NOV 26 735) (M. Jean-Jacques **Bourguignon**) 2, ave Brazza ☎ 66-32-10-17 ⌐ 19 **English, Spanish spoken.**

MASSERET 19510 Corrèze **RN 20 Map 17-A1**
♀ ⊗ ⌂ **LE RELAIS DES VOYAGEURS** (N° RR DEC 21 714) (M. Alain **Saturnin**) Route Nationale 20 ☎ 55-73-40-11 ⌐ 7 Closed Sat in winter; 15 Jan to 15 Feb. English spoken.

MASSEUBE 32140 Gers **RN 129 Map 21-B2/3**
♀ ⊗ **LE RELAIS CHEZ YVETTE** (N° RR JUN 12 898) (Mme Yvette **Beyries**) ☎ 62-66-02-14 Closed Sun; 15 Aug to 1 Sept.

M

MATHIEU 14920 Calvados **RD 7 Map 4-B2**
Y ⊗ **RELAIS LA COTE DE NACRE** (N° RR OCT 26 068) (M. Marc **Bedeau de l'Écochère**) 4, rue Auguste-Fresnel ☎ 31-44-10-17 Full-board 150F per night. Evening meals.

MAUBEUGE 59600 Nord **RN 2 Map 6-A3**
Y ⊗ ⌂ **AUX ARCADES Chez Ginette** (N° RR AVR 25 522) (M. Claude **Spittel**) 260, route de Mons ☎ 27-64-60-94 ⊷ 8 Closed Sun afternoon. Full-board 140–180F per night. Coaches welcome (rest. seats 45). Evening meals until 2am (midnight Mon).
Y ⊗ **AUX ROUTIERS** (N° RR NOV 23 009) (Mme Jeanine **Bla**) 21, ave de la Gare ☎ 27-64-82-98 Closed Sun.
Y ⊗ **LE BERLIOZ** (N° RR AVR 26 865) (M. René **Dupont**) 27, ave de la Gare ☎ 27-64-68-79. Closed Sun.

MAUBOURGUET 65700 Htes-Pyr. **Map 21-A2**
Y ⊗ **RELAIS DES AUTOBUS** (N° RR FEV 26 185) (Mme Nicole **Dauba**) 87, place de la Libération ☎ 62-96-38-78 Bar open every day. Restaurant closed Sat evening, Sun. Coaches welcome.

MAUBRANCHES 18390 Cher **Map 13-B1**
Y ⊗ **CHEZ ROMY** SARL Escapade (N° RR MARS 26 482) (Mme Cécile **Dion**) Rte Nle 151 – St Germain du Puy ☎ 48-30-82-07 Closed Sun (bar open). English spoken.

MAURIAC 15200 Cantal **RD 678 Map 17-B2**
Y ⊗ ⌂ **LES ROUTIERS** (N° RR NOV 26 744) (**SARL Laroche-Rongier**) 27, rue St-Mary ☎ 71-68-00-79 ⊷ 9 Closed Fri evening, Sat midday. English spoken.

MAUZE-LE-MIGNON 79210 Deux-Sèvres **RN 11 and 22 Map 15-A1**
Y ⊗ ⌂ **LE RELAIS DU COQ HARDI** (N° RR JUN 22 387) (M. Paul **Bombard**) 41, Grande Rue ☎ 49-26-30-39 ⊷ 10 Closed Sun. Full-board 130–180F per night. Coaches welcome (2 rooms = 230 seats). Evening meals.

MAY-SUR-ORNE 14320 Calv. **RD 562 Map 4-B2**
Y ⊗ ⌂ **L'AMMONITE** (N° RR DEC 26 119) (M. Jean-Claude **Horel**) 2, rue du Canada ☎ 31-79-60-27 ⊷ 7 Closed Sun in winter; 8 days in Feb; 2nd week Aug. Full-board 130–150F. Coaches welcome (rest. seats 90). Evening meals.

MAYENNE 53100 Mayenne **RN 162 and 823-12 Map 8-B1**
Y ⊗ ⌂ **LE RELAIS L'ESCALE** (N° RR JUN 20 742) (M. and Mme **Fortin**) route du Mans 2, rue Colbert ☎ 43-04-19-14 ⊷ 13 Closed Sat afternoon, Sun. Evening meals until 8.30pm.

MAYRES 07330 Ardèche **RN 102 Map 24-A2**
Y ⊗ **LE ROCHER TROUE** (N° RR OCT 25 695) (Mme Colette **Vidil**) Nationale 102 ☎ 75-93-56-68 Closed Sun.

MAZAMET 81200 Tarn **RN 112/118 Map 22-B2**
Voir AUSSILLON-MAZAMET

MAZERES 33210 Gironde **RD 932 Map 20-B1**
♀ ⊗ **LE PASSAGER** (N° RR AVR 18 665) (M. Serge **Garrigues**) route de Pau ☎ 56-63-15-22 Closed Sat, Sun; 3 weeks Aug. Coaches welcome (rest. seats 60). Evening meals. Some English, German, Spanish spoken.

MAZINGARBE 62670 Pas-de-Calais **RN 43 Map 5-A1**
♀ ⊗ **AU RELAIS DES ROUTIERS** (N° RR AVR 20 444) (Mme Geneviève **Marcinkowski**) 85, route Nationale 43 ☎ 21-72-00-09 ⇥ 3 Closed Sun; Aug. Coaches welcome (rest. seats 50). Polish, German spoken.

MEDE (LA) 13220 B.-du-R. **RN 568 Map 24-A/B3**
♀ ⊗ **L'ARC EN CIEL** (N° RR JUL 26 949) (Mme Marie **Courevellis**) 5, avenue Mirabeau ☎ 42-07-04-38 ⇥ 5 Spanish, Greek spoken.

MEES 40990 Landes **RN 124 Map 20-A2**
♀ ⊗ **L'OREE DU BOIS** (N° RR OCT 26 067) (M. Jean-Paul **Gueffier**) Route de Bayonne, Nle 124 ☎ 58-97-57-77 Closed Sun.

MEGEVE 74120 Hte-Savoie **RN 212 Map 19-B2**
♀ ⊗ ⌂ **2 Star NN LE CHALET DES FLEURS** (N° RR JAN 17 730) (M. Georges **Roussel**) route de Sallanches au Pont d'Arbon ☎ 50-21-21-46 ⇥ 27 from 90–180F; breakfast 25F. Closed 15 Sept to 15 Dec; 15 April to 1 Jun. Full-board 190–240F per night. Coaches welcome (rest. seats 84). Evening meals. English spoken. Car park; bar; dogs allowed; recreations (miniature golf, playground). Menus 73–140F. Specialities: *escargots de Bourgogne maison, omelette norvegienne maison, escalope normande garnie.*

MELGVEN 29140 Finistère **Map 7-B1**
♀ ⊗ **KERAMPAOU** (N° RR AVR 23 771) (**SARL Mevellec**) ☎ 98-97-90-18 **Minitel** Closed Sun morning. Video. Coaches welcome. Evening meals. HGV parking. English spoken.

MELLAC 29130 Finistère **Map 7-B2**
♀ ⊗ **LE MARLI** (N° RR AVR 27 267) (M. Rodolphe **Dupart**) Z.A. de Keringant ☎ 98-39-31-97 Closed Sun evening. Meals served until 10.30 pm.

MENIL-BROUT (LES) par DAMIGNY 61250 Orne **RN 12 Map 8-A/B2**
♀ ⊗ ⌂ **LE RELAIS A LA BONNE FRANQUETTE** (N° RR AVR 14 764) (Mme **Castelier**) ☎ 33-27-10-03 ⇥ 12 Auberge rurale Closed Sat, Sun; Aug.

MENNEVAL 27300 Eure **RN 138 Map 4–B3**
♀ ⊗ ⌂ **LES ROUTIERS** (N° RR JUIL 26 944) (M. Michel **Hure**) Bernay ☎ 32-43-16-90 ⇥ 9 Closed Sun; Aug; Feb. English, Yugoslav spoken. Filling station near.

MEOLANS-REVEL 04340 Alpes de Haute-Provence **Map 25-A1**
⊗ **Camping Caravaning Caravaneige RELAIS ROUTIERS DU RIOCLAR** (N° RR JANV 27 140) (SARL Europ Neige et Soleil) ☎ 92-81-10-32 English, Spanish and Italian spoken.

M

MERLINES 19340 Corrèze **RN 89 Map 16-B2**
♈ ⊗ **RELAIS DU COMMERCE** (N° RR FEV 27 186) (Mmes **Rebaix/ Theil**) av. Pierre-Sémard ☎ 55-94-32-31.

MERY-SUR-CHER 18100 Cher **RN 76 Map 13-B1**
♈ ⊗ ⌂ **LE RELAIS BERRY-SOLOGNE** (N° RR NOV 16 762) (M. Claude **Carré**) route de Tours ☎ 48-75-20-34 ⌖ 10 Closed Sat, Sun.

MESGRIGNY 10170 Aube **RN 19** and **CD 373 Map 9-B2/3**
♈ ⊗ **LA BELLE ÉTOILE** (N° RR DEC 26 772) (M. Jean-Claude **Pinol**) Méry-sur-Seine ☎ 25-21-15-70 Closed Sun; public holidays.

MESNIL-DURAND 14140 Calvados **RD 579 Map 4-B2**
♈ ⊗ **LE RELAIS DE LA FORCE** (N° RR JUL 23 881) (M. Roger **Cardonnel**) Les Forges Mézières ☎ 31-63-52-79 Closed Mon; Sept. German spoken.

MESSIA-SUR-SORNE 39570 Jura **RN 83 Map 19-A1**
♈ ⊗ **LA CHARMILLE** (N° RR JANV 22 618) (M. Patrick **Vaucher**) 570, route de Lyon Lons-le-Saunier ☎ 84-47-10-55 Closed Sun afternoon. Coaches welcome (rest. seats 45). Evening meals until midnight. English spoken.

MEURSAULT 21190 Côte-d'Or **RN 74 Map 13-B3**
♈ ⊗ **A LA GOUTTE D'OR** (N° RR SEPT 26 673) (M. Gérald **Garnier**) 11, rue Charles-Giraud ☎ 80-21-60-56 Closed Tue evening. English, Spanish spoken.

MEYLIEU 42210 Loire **RN 82 Map 18-B2**
♈ ⊗ **LES OMBRELLES** (N° RR SEPT 26 661) (M. Christian **Chadrin**) Montrond-Les-Bains ☎ 77-54-52-44 Closed Sun. English spoken.

MEZE 34140 Hérault **RN 113 Map 23 A/B2**
♈ ⊗ **LE MARSEILLAIS** (N° RR NOV 26 109) (M. Willie **Rennie**) 8, avenue de Montpellier ☎ 67-48-81-29 Closed Mon. Coaches welcome (rest. seats 80). Evening meals. English spoken.
♈ ⊗ **LA VITARELLE 11** (N° RR 27 261) (M. Daniel **Garcia**) ☎ 67-43-81-29 ⌖ 35 Closed Sun evening. English, Spanish and Italian spoken. Evening meals served until 10 pm.

MEZEL 04270 Alpes-de-Haute-Provence **RD 207 Map 25-A2**
♈ ⊗ ⌂ **1 Star NN LE RELAIS DE LA PLACE** (N° RR JUL 22 884) (Mme Christiane **Sarracanie**) Place Victor-Arnoux ☎ 92-35-51-05 ⌖ 15 Closed Mon (except Jul, Aug; Sept); Feb. Full-board 135F per night. Coaches welcome (rest. seats 100). Evening meals.

MÉZÉRAIT 01660 Ain **RN 79 Map 18-B1**
♈ ⊗ **RELAIS DE MÉZÉRAIT** (N° RR NOV 27 111) (M. Alain **Darbon**) Les Pigots ☎ 74-30-25-87 Closed Sat.

MÉZIÈRES-EN-DROUAIS 28500 E.-et-L. **Voir MARSAUCEUX**

M

MEZIERES-SUR-ISSOIRE 87330 Haute-Vienne **RN 151 Bis Maps 15-B2 and 16-B1**
 ♀ ⊗ **LE RELAIS DES VOYAGEURS ET DES ROUTIERS** (N° RR MAR 25 341) (Mme Odette **Daganaud**) ☎ 55-68-34-47 ⊷ 5.

MIGENNES 89400 Yonne **RN 6 Maps 9-B2 and 13-A2**
 ♀ ⊗ ⌂ **RELAIS ROUTIER D'EPINEAU-LES-VOVES** (N° RR JUL 22 864) (M. Ahmed **Betroune**) 2, route de Chambey ☎ 86-73-20-45 ⊷ 11 German, Arabic spoken.

MIGNIERES 45490 Loiret **RD 94 Map 9-B2**
 ♀ ⊗ ⌂ **RELAIS DE MIGNIERES** (N° RR AVR 25 916) (Mme Liliane **Francart**) Allee de la Gare ☎ 38-87-82-06 **Minitel** ⊷ 7 Closed Sun; 15 Dec–10 Jan. Evening meals.

MIGNIERES 28000 Eure-et-Loir **RN 10 Map 8-B3 see CHARTRES**

MILLANCAY 41210 L.-et-C. **Map 13-A1**
 ♀ ⊗ **LA TAVERNE SOLOGNOTE** (N° RR NOV 26 382) (Mme Martine **Batalie**) route d'Orléanes ☎ 54-96-65-38 Closed Mon.

MILLAU 12100 Aveyron **RN 9 Map 23-A1**
 ♀ ⊗ **LES TILLEULS** (N° RR DEC 26 406) (M. Jean **Vernhet**) 17, avenue Martel ☎ 65-60-43-98 Closed Sun afternoon.

MIMIZAN 40200 Landes **RN 626 Map 20-A2**
 ♀ ⊗ ⌂ **RELAIS DUCOURT** (N° RR MARS 26 475) (Mme Françoise **Bricard**) 20, avenue de la Plage ☎ 58-82-42-37 **Minitel** ⊷ 35 Closed Sun off season. Full-board 155–170F per night. Coaches welcome (rest. seats 80). Evening meals.
 ♀ ⊗ **LE RABA** (N° RR JUIN 27 311) (M. Stéphane **Noorkhan**) 28, avenue de la Plage ☎ 58-09-18-60 ⊷ 3 English spoken open 24 hours.

MIONNAY 01390 Ain **RN 83 Map 2-A2**
 ♀ ⊗ **LE RELAIS BRESSAN** (N° RR MAI 26 550) (Mme Monique **Millet** and Christian **Desmaris**) St-André-de-Corcy ☎ 78-91-82-22 Closed Sat.

MIRABEAU 84120 Vaucluse **RN 96 Map 24-B3**
 ♀ ⊗ ⌂ **LOU BOUMIAN** (N° RR JANV 26 138) (M. Marcel **Souliol**) Quartier de la Gare ☎ 90-77-04-50 ⊷ 5 Closed Sun. Coaches welcome (rest. seats 80). Evening meals until 10pm.

MIRAMAS 13140 B.-du-R. **RN 569 Map 24-A3**
 ♀ ⊗ **LE RELAIS** (N° RR DEC 25 762) (Mme **Bouvier**) 72, avenue Charles de Gaulle ☎ 90-58-05-89 **Minitel** Closed Sun. Coaches welcome (rest. seats 90). Evening meals.

MIRAMONT-DE-GUYENNE 47800 Lot-et-Garonne **CD 933 Map 21-B1**
 ♀ ⊗ ⌂ **2 star NN L'ÉTAPE DES ROUTIERS** (N° RR NOV 27 097) (Mme Raymonde **Rodes**) Route de Paris **Saint-Pardoux-Isaac** ☎ 53-93-20-76 Closed Sat. Spanish and Italian spoken.

M

MIRANDOL 81190 Tarn **RN 88 Map 22-B1**
☺ ⦻ **RELAIS DE LA PLAINE** (N° RR OCT 27 049) (Mme Marie-Ange **Feral**) **Les Farguettes** ☏ 63-76-65-89 Closed Sat lunchtime.

MITRY-LE-NEUF 77290 Seine-et-Marne **RD 212 Map 1-A3**
☺ ⦻ **LE CHALET NORMAND** (N° RR SEP 15 779) (Mme Maryse **Merle**) 15, avenue de Berry ☏ 64-27-79-23 Closed Mon.

MITRY-MORY 77290 S.-&-M. **Map 1-A3**
☺ ⦻ **LE RELAIS DE MITRY** (N° RR FEV 27 197) (Mme Josiane **Thyphonnet**) 3, rue Paul-Vallant-Couturier ☏ 64-27-11-61 Closed Sat, Sun.

MODANE 73500 Savoie **RN 6 Map 19-B3**
☺ ⦻ **LA CROIX DU SUD** (N° RR JUL 26 599) (M. Bernard **Mestrallet**) La Proz ☏ 79-05-34-47 Closed Sun; Aug. Italian spoken.

MOIDIEU-DETOURBE 38440 Isère **RD 502 Map 2-B2**
☺ ⦻ **CHEZ DÉDÉ** (N° RR OCT 26 079) (M. André **Seigle**) St-Jean-de-Bournay ☏ 74-58-13-02 Closed Sat, Sun midday; 15 to 30 Aug; 10 days at Christmas/New Year. Evening meals.

MOIRANS 38430 Isère **RN 85 Maps 18-B3, 19-A3 and 24-B1**
☺ ⦻ 🏠 **LE VIADUC** (N° RR AOU 23 906) (Mme Marthe **Bonnet-Gamard**) 4, route de Grenoble ☏ 76-35-31-01 — 5 Closed Sat, Sun. Evening meals.

MOISSAC 82200 T.-et-G. **RD 127 Maps 21-B2 and 22-A1**
☺ ⦻ 🏠 **1 Star NN LE RELAIS AUVERGNAT** (N° RR AOU 15 344) (M. Jacques **Ginisty**) 31, boulevard Camille-Delthil place du Palais ☏ 63-04-02-58 or 63-04-93-02 — 7 Closed Sun evening; 20 Dec to 5 Jan. Full-board 150–180F per night. Coaches welcome (rest. seats 40). Meals served until 11.30pm. Menus 45–70F. Specialities: *Magret et confit de canard, Cassoulet*. Spanish spoken.

MOISY 41160 L.-&-C. **RD 924 Map 12-A3**
☺ ⦻ **AUX DÉLICES DU PALAIS** SARL Auberge gastronomique de la Vallée du Loir (N° RR MARS 27 205) (Mme Michèle **Normand**) Dle 924 Bourg de Moisy ☏ 54-82-62-40 Closed Tues and Feb. English and German spoken.

MOLINET 03510 Allier **RN 79 Map 16-A3**
☺ ⦻ **LES ARCADES** (N° RR AVR 25 876) (Mme Anne-Marie **Fongarnand**) Moulins ☏ 85-53-47-51 Closed Sat afternoon.

MOLOMPIZE 15500 Cantal **RN 588 Map 17-A3**
☺ ⦻ 🏠 **LE RELAIS DU CENTRE** (N° RR AVR 18 067) (Mme Marie-Louise **Filliat**) ☏ 71-73-61-97 — 12 Closed Sat, Sun; part of Nov. Full-board 130–160F per night. Coaches welcome (rest. seats 30). Evening meals.

MONASTIER (LE) 48100 Lozère known locally as LES AJUSTONS **RN 9 Map 17-B3 and 23-A1**
☺ ⦻ 🏠 **1 star NN LE RELAIS DES AJUSTONS** (N° RR MAR 20 128)

(M. Guy **Gibelin**) crossroads of Nationales 9 and 88 ☎ 66-32-70-35 ⊷ 27 Closed Sat, Sun in winter; 18 Dec–18 Jan. Full-board 130–170F per night. Coaches welcome (rest. seats 80).

MONBEQUI 82170 T.-Et-G. **RN 113**
♈ ⊗ **RELAIS D'AQUITAINE** (N° RR SEPT 26 319) (M. Yvan **Rochas**) Rte 113 ☎ 63-65-53-62 Closed Sat, Sun; public holidays; 15 days at Christmas.

MONDAVEZAN 31220 Hte-Garonne **RN 117 Map 21-B3**
♈ ⊗ ⌂ **LA FERMIERE** (N° RR MARS 26 488) (Mme Alexine **Ferrage**) rte Nle 117 ☎ 61-97-01-52 ⊷ 16 Closed Sun.

MONDOUBLEAU 41170 Loir-et-Cher **Map 8-B3**
♈ ⊗ ⌂ **LE RELAIS DE LA GARE** (N° RR MAI 23 297) (M. Gérard **Lucas**) 6, rue de la Gare ☎ 54-80-90-59 ⊷ 6 Closed Sat; Aug. Evening meals.

MONESTIER DE CLERMONT 38650 Isère **RN 75 situé à 30 km au sud de Grenoble Map 19-A3 et 24-B1**
♈ ⊗ **REST DU NORD** (N° RR JUN 26 905) (M. Michel **Capogna**) 44, Gran-de-Rue ☎ 76-34-03-75 Closed Sun.

MONETEAU 89470 Yonne **RD 84 Map 13-A2/3**
♈ ⊗ ⌂ **AU RENDEZ-VOUS DES PECHEURS** (N° RR AVR 22 751) (M. R. **Gaufillet**) ☎ 86-40-63-32 ⊷ 6 Coaches welcome (rest. seats 128). Evening meals. Spanish spoken.

MONLET près d'ALLEGRE 43270 Haute-Loire **RD 13 Map 17-A3**
♈ ⊗ ⌂ **1 Star NN LE ROULIS** (N° RR FEV 20 650) (M. Pierre **Marec**) ☎ 71-00-73-54 ⊷ 10 from 60–98F, breakfast 17,50F. Full-board 160F per night. Coaches welcome (rest. seats 50). Closed Mon. Car park; bar; dogs allowed; recreations (*pétanque*). Places to visit: Richard's Windmill (Ambert), Châteaux, Lakes, Forests. English spoken.

MONNAI 61470 Orne **RN 138 Map 8-A2**
♈ ⊗ ⌂ **LE RELAIS DU CHEVAL BAI** (N° RR JAN 7 428) (M. Gilbert **Roussel**) Nationale 138 ☎ 33-39-42-00 ⊷ 6 Open 24 hours (except Sat, Sun). Closed Sun; 15 Dec–15 Jan. Coaches welcome (rest. seats 90). Evening meals until 9.30pm.

MONNAIE 37380 Indre-et-Loire
♈ ⊗ **LA BONNE ÉTAPE** (N° RR NOV 26 722) (M. Marc **Rouxel**) 67, rue Nle ☎ 47-56-10-64 Closed Tue afternoon.
♈ ⊗ **L'ARCHE DE TOURAINE** (M. Pascal **Humblet**) Autoroute A10 ☎ 47-56-15-49 Open 24 hours. Self-service restaurant.

MONT-A-LA-QUESNE par BRIX 50820 Manche **RN 13 Map 4-A1**
♈ ⊗ **LE CLOS NORMAND** (N° RR SEPT 26 628) (Mme **Germain**) ☎ 33-41-94-35

MONTANDON 25190 Doubs **Map 10-A3**
♈ ⊗ ⌂ **LE GRAND CLOS** (N° RR DEC 26 418) (Mme Martine

M

Montandon continued
Lepeme) Saint-Hippolyte ☎ 81-96-51-12 ⊷ 5 German spoken.

MONTAREN 30800 Gard **RN 981 Map 24-A2**
♟ ⊗ 🏠 **LES ROUTIERS CHEZ RÉGINE** (N° RR NOV 26 101) (Mme Régine **Hangard**) Rte d'Alès ☎ 66-22-25-26.

MONTARGIS 54200 Loiret **RN 60 and 7 Map 9-B2**
♟ ⊗ 🏠 **PARIS MONTARGIS** (N° RR NOV 26107) (SARL Paris-Montargis, Mme **Pradet-Papon**) 221, rue Émile-Mengin ☎ 38-85-63-04 Point phone 38-93-91-58 ⊷ 10 Closed Sun. Evening meals. English spoken.

MONTARGIS see FONTENAY-SUR-LOING

MONTAUBAN 82000 T.-et-G. **RN 20 Map 22-A1**
♟ ⊗ **LE RELAIS DE FONNEUVE** (N° RR DEC 23 585) (Mme Agnès **Salles**) Fonneuve ☎ 63-03-14-68 Closed Sat evening, Sun.

MONTAUBAN-DE-BRETAGNE 35360 Ille-et-Vilaine **RN 12 and 164 bis Map 7-B3**
♟ ⊗ 🏠 **2 Star NN HOTEL DE FRANCE** (N° RR AOU 7 884) (M. Gabriel **Le Métayer**) 34, rue du Gl-de-Gaulle ☎ 99-06-40-19 ⊷ 13 Closed Mon low season; 20 Dec to 20 Jan; 15 days in Oct. Full-board 200–280F per night. Coaches welcome (rest. seats 80). Evening meals until 10.00pm. English, Spanish, some German spoken. Menus 62–120F. Specialities: Seafood, *coq au muscadet far breton.*
♟ ⊗ 🏠 **2 star NN LE RELAIS DE LA HUCHERAIS** (N° SEPT 27 032) (M. Alain **Meheust**) ☎ 99-06-54-31 ⊷ 14 Closed Sun. English spoken. Evening meals served until 10 pm. Dogs allowed, TV, bar and lounge.

MONTAUDIN 53220 Mayenne **RN 799 Map 8-B1**
♟ ⊗ 🏠 **HÔTEL DE PARIS** (N° RR MAI 21 111) (M. Daniel **Doudard**) ☎ 43-05-30-79 English spoken.

MONTAUROUX 83440 Var **RN 562 Map 25-B2**
♟ ⊗ 🏠 **2 Stars NN RELAIS DU LAC** (N° RR NOV 26 110) (M. **Hernandez**) RN 563 ☎ 94-76-43-65 ⊷ 37 Full-board 121-231F per night. Coaches welcome (rest. seats 250). Evening meals. English, Spanish spoken.

MONTBARD 21500 Côte-d'Or **RN 5 Map 13-A3**
♟ ⊗ 🏠 **LE VOLTAIRE** (N° RR JUL 21 574) (M. Louis **Piquet**) 5, rue François-Debussy ☎ 80-89-42-21 ⊷ 10 Closed Sun; 15 Jul–15 Aug. Evening meals.

MONTBENOIT 25650 Doubs **Map 14-B3**
♟ ⊗ 🏠 **RELAIS DES VOYAGEURS** (N° RR JANV 26 152) (M. Pierre **Magnin-Feysot**) Place de l'Abbaye ☎ 81-38-10-85 ⊷ 6 Closed Tue afternoon to Wed morning; 1–10 Nov. Full-board 100–138F. Coaches welcome (rest. seats 100). Evening meals.

M

MONTBOUCHER 23400 Creuse **CD 941 Map 16-A2**
♀ ⊗ **LA BERGERIE** (N° RR DEC 26 760) (Mme Brigitte **Belz**) Bourganeuf ☎ 55-64-20-18 Closed Mon; Jan.

MONTBRISON 42600 Loire **RN 496 Map 18-A2**
♀ ⊗ ⌂ **LE RELAIS DE LA GARE** (N° RR JAN 20 369) (M. Jean-Pierre **Gacon**) 2, place de la Gare ☎ 77-58-30-33 ⌐ 8 Closed Sun; Aug. Evening meals.
see also ST-ROMAIN-LE-PUY.

MONTCHANIN-LES-MINES 71210 S.-et-L. **RN 74 Map 18-A1**
♀ ⊗ **LE RELAIS DE BOURGOGNE** (N° RR JUL 17 329) (Mme Jannine **Labrosse**) 149, avenue de la République ☎ 85-78-12-67 Closed Sun; Aug.

MONT-DAUPHIN 05600 Hautes-Alpes **RN 94 Maps 19-B3 and 25-A1**
♀ ⊗ ⌂ **1 Star NN LE RELAIS DE LA GARE** (N° RR JUN 10 820
⌐ (Mme Francine **Lacour**) ☎ 92-45-03-08 ⌐ 24 Closed Sat 1 May to 30 June, 1 Sept to 25 Dec. Full-board 181F per night. Coaches welcome. Evening meals. English spoken.

MONT-DE-MARSAN 40000 Landes **RN 132 Map 20-B2**
♀ ⊗ ⌂ **BAR DES SPORTS** (N° RR FEV 24 508) (Mme Josiane **Ledoux**) Place des Arènes (Stanislas Baron) ☎ 58-75-05-08 ⌐ 20 Spanish spoken.

MONTDIDIER 80500 Somme **RN 30 and 35 Maps 3-A3 and 5-B3**
♀ ⊗ ⌂ **LE RELAIS DU MOUTON D'OR** (N° RR AVR 19 734) (M. Christian **Parmentier**) 10, boulevard Debeney ☎ 22-78-03-43 ⌐ 5 Closed Sun; 1–21 Aug; 24–31 Dec. Coaches welcome (rest. seats 70). Evening meals.

MONT-DORE (LE) 63240 P.-de-D. **RN 496 Map 17-A2**
♀ ⊗ ⌂ **CHEZ ROLANDE** (N° RR JUN 25 009) (Mme Rolande **Gravière**) 78, avenue de La Bourboule ☎ 73-65-03-60 ⌐ 15.

MONTEBOURG 50310 Manche **RN 13 Map 4-B1**
♀ ⊗ **AUBERGE DES ROUTIERS – CHEZ LE CHAROLAIS** (N° RR SEP 25 649) (M. Serge **Charenton**) 19, place Albert Pélerin ☎ 33-41-14-67 **Minitel** ⌐ 4.

MONTECH 82700 T.-et-G. **RN 128 Map 22-A1**
♀ ⊗ **LE RELAIS DE L'AVENUE** (N° RR AVR 21 515) (M. Georges **Taupiac**) 7, boulevard Lagal ☎ 63-64-72-26 Closed Sun; public holidays; 20 Dec to 5 Jan; 15 days in Aug. Coaches welcome (rest. seats 60). Evening meals from May to September inclusive.

MONTÉLIMAR 26200 Drôme **Autoroute A7 Map 24-A2**
♀ ⊗ **SODEXAS RELAIS P.L.M.** (M. **Arletti**) Aire de Service de Montélimar ☎ 75-46-60-00 Open 24 hours. Self-service café and restaurant. Showers, TV, shop.

MONTEREAU 77130 Seine-et-Marne **RN 1 Map 9-B2**
♀ ⊗ **LES ROUTIERS** (N° RR SEP 25 644) (M. Claude **Spinato**) RN 105 ☎ 64-32-44-93 Closed Sun; Jul.

M

MONTFAVET 84140 Vauclse **RN 100 and A7 Map 24-A2**
♀ ⊗ ⌂ **1 Star NN LE RELAIS DE BONPAS** (N° RR JUN 21 138) (M. Alain **Laugier**) locally Pont de Bonpas RN 7 ☎ 90-23-07-01 ⊷ 13 Coaches welcome (rest. seats 110). Evening meals. English spoken.

MONTFIQUET 14490 Calvados **RD 572 Map 4-B1**
♀ ⊗ **RELAIS DE LA FORET – Chez Nicole** (N° RR MAI 25 427) (M. Bernard **Tallendier**) locally L'Embranchement ☎ 31-21-68-74 English, Spanish spoken.

MONTFORT 04600 Alpes de Hte-Provence **RN 96**
♀ ⊗ **LE RELAIS DE MONTFORT** (N° RR JANV 26 131) (M. Bernard **Florent**) RN 96, St-Aubant ☎ 92-64-11-91 Coaches welcome (rest. seats 120). English spoken. Meals until 10.00pm.

MONTGENÈVRE 05100 Htes-Alpes **RN 94 Map 19-B3**
♀ ⊗ **LE TRANSALPIN** (N° RR JUN 22 385) (Mme Yvette Silvestre) ☎ 92-21-92-87 Closed Sat afternoon, Sun; 15 Aug to 15 Sept. Coaches welcome (rest. seats 60). Evening meals.

MONTHLERY 91300 Essonne **RN 20 Map 1-B2**
♀ ⊗ ⌂ **1 Star NN LE SOLOGNE** (N° RR MAI 25 933) (M. Jacques **Cheron**) 65, rte d'Orléans ☎ 69-01-00-98 ⊷ 7 Closed Sun. Evening meals until 9.00pm.

MONTILS (LES) 41120 Loir-et-Cher **RN 764 Map 12-A3**
♀ ⊗ **LES DEUX ROUES** (N° RR MAI 23 299) (M. Jean-Pierre **Levaux**) 28, rue du Bel-Air ☎ 54-44-02-40 Closed Sun. Coaches welcome (rest. seats 80). Evening meals.

MONTLUÇON 03380 Allier **RN 145 Map 16-A2**
♀ ⊗ **LE RELAIS DES MARRONNIERS** (N° RR AVR 20 440) (M. **Coulon**) Lamaids ☎ 70-51-81-50 Closed 2nd and 3rd weeks of Sept.

MONTMARAULT 03390 Allier **RN 145 Map 16-A2**
♀ ⊗ **LE RELAIS DE L'UNION** (N° RR AVR 24 932) (Mme Monique **Desbordes**) 2, Rte de Montluçon ☎ 70-07-60-05 Closed 1 to 15 Sept. Coaches welcome (rest. seats 120). Evening meals.
CLOSE #
♀ ⊗ **LE CHALET** (N° RR FEV 26 815) (M. Alain **Vassort**) 18, boulevard Tourret ☎ 70-07-60-23 Closed Sun in winter, Aug. English spoken.
♀ ⊗ **LE RALLYE** (N° RR DEC 27 131) (M. Jacques **Boulard** et Mme Martine **Ruefroy**) 4, route de Montluçon ☎ 70-07-33-29.

MONTMARTIN-SUR-MER 50590 Manche **RD 20 Maps 4-B1 and 8-A1**
♀ ⊗ ⌂ **2 Stars NN HOTELLERIE DU BON VIEUX TEMPS** (N° RR JUIN 26 257) (M. Érick **Bourbonnais**) ☎ 33-47-54-55 **Minitel** ⊷ 21 from 94–170F, breakfast 17F, telephone in room. Full-board 210–300F. Coaches welcome (rest. seats 120). Evening meals. English spoken. Car park; dogs allowed; bar.

M

MONTMAURIN 31350 Hte-Garonne **Map 21-B3**
♈ ⊗ **LE RELAIS COUPE-GORGE** (N° RR MAI 19 336) (M. Pierre **Favre**) Rte de Montréjeau ☎ 61-88-16-63 Closed Tue. Spanish spoken.

MONTMELIAN 73800 Savoie **RN 6 Map 19-A2**
♈ ⊗ **LE GRAND SCHLEM** (N° RR JANV 27 158) (SARL Le Grand Schlem) RN6 ☎ 79-65-23-63 ou 84-30-82 English, Spanish and Italian spoken. Open 24 hours.

MONTMIRAIL 51210 Marne **RN 33 Map 9-A2**
♈ ⊗ ⌂ **RALLYE-ROUTIER** (N° RR SEP 24 352) (Mme Michèle **Baye**) 4, avenue Charles-de-Gaulle ☎ 26-42-23-93 ⇥ 9 Closed Sun. Full-board 150–180F per night. Evening meals. Some English spoken.

MONTMIRAT 30260 Gard **RN 110 Map 23-B2**
♈ ⊗ ⌂ **LE CASTELAS** (N° RR JUL 25 500) (Mme Chantal **Martinez**) Rte Nationale 10 ☎ 66-77-81-33 Closed Sat; Christmas to New Year. Coaches welcome (rest. seats 65 Sundays only). Evening meals. Spanish spoken. Menus 48–59F. Specialities: *Bourride sétoises, moules farcies, gardiane de taurraux.*

MONTMOREAU 16190 Charente **RN 674 Map 15-B2/3**
♈ ⊗ **LE RELAIS DES ROUTIERS** (N° RR AVR 12 793) (Mme Ernestine **Ferrier**) Route d'Angoulême 3 ☎ 45-60-21-17 ⇥ 15. Evening meals.

MONTOIRE-SUR-LE-LOIR 41800 L.-&-C. **Map 12-A3**
♈ ⊗ **À LA DESCENTE DU PERCHE** (N° RR MAI 27 281) (M. François **Detalle**) 2, rue du Docteur Schweitzer ☎ 54-85-21-39 Closed Sun pm. Evening meals served until 8.30 pm.

MONTPELLIER-FABRÈGUES 34690 Hérault **LA LANGUEDOCIEN-NE A9 Map 23-B2**
♈ ⊗ **L'ARCHE** Aire de Service de Fabrègues 2 sens Passerelle ☎ 67-85-15-06 Open 24 hours. Self-service restaurant. Shop selling cigarettes, newspapers.

MONTPEYROUX see LA VITARELLE 12210 Aveyron

MONTPEZAT-de-QUERCY 82270 T.-et-G. **RN 20 Map 22-A1**
♈ ⊗ ⌂ **1 Star NN LE RELAIS DE L'ETAPE QUERCY** (N° RR JUN 21 121) (M. Maurice **Courpet**) La Madeleine Route Nationale 20 ☎ 63-02-07-58 ⇥ 8 + annexe 6 rooms. Closed Sat low season; Sept.

MONTPINCHON 50210 Manche **RD 73 Map 8-A1**
♈ ⊗ **BAR DES AMIS** (N° RR AOU 25 080) (M. Gérard **Marie**) Tobacconist. **Cerisy la Salle** ☎ 33-46-94-00.

MONTPON 24700 Dordogne **RN 89 Map 15-B3**
♈ ⊗ **LAS DAVALDAS DE MÉNESPLET** (N° RR MAR 23 717) (M. René **Duvillard**) ☎ 53-81-83-67 ⇥ 12 Coaches welcome (rest. seats 50). Evening meals.
♈ ⊗ ⌂ **CHEZ MARTINE** (N° RR SEPT 26 992) (Mme Martine

M

Montpon continued
Bouchet) 27, rue Jean-Moulin ☎ 53-80-32-45 ⏤ 11 Filling stations near.

MONTREAL 11290 Aude **see CARCASSONNE**

MONTREAL 11290 Aude **RD 119 Map 22-B2**
♆ ⊗ **LE MALEPERE** (N° RR OCt 25 696) (M. Gabriel **François**) Les Giscarels ☎ 68-76-29-43 ⏤ 3 Closed Mon evening. Full-board 190-340F per night. Evening meals. Spanish, English spoken.

MONTREDON-CORBIÈRES 11100 Aude **RN 113 Map 23-A2/3**
♆ ⊗ **LE STÉPHANOIS** (N° RR MAI 26 246) (Mme **Simon**) RN 113 ☎ 68-42-08-41 ⏤ 7 Closed Sun. Full-board 220–250F per night. Coaches welcome (rest. seats 100). Evening meals. English, some Spanish, Italian spoken.
♆ ⊗ 🏠 **LA CAILLE QUI CHANTE** (N° RR MAI 27 272) (M. Jacques **Gillet**) La Plaine ☎ 68-42-04-36 ⏤ 20 Closed Sun low season. German, Spanish and Italian spoken.

MONTREUIL-SOUS-BOIS 93100 Seine-St-Denis **Map 1-A3**
♆ ⊗ **LE RELAIS DES ROUTIERS** (N° RR NOV 11 914; (Mmes **Sol** and **Puech**) 70, rue de Lagny ☎ 42-87-04-71.

MONTRIEUX-NAVEIL 41100 L.-et-C. **RD 5 Map 12-A3**
♆ ⊗ **RELAIS ROUTIERS** (N° RR JUL 22 429) (M. René **Houdouin**) 17, rue de Montrieux ☎ 54-77-13-98 Closed Sun.

MONT-SAINT-MICHEL 50116 Manche **RN 776 Maps 7-A3 and 8-A1**
♆ ⊗ 🏠 **LES CAMPINGS DU MONT-SAINT-MICHEL S.A.R.L.** Hôtel **Vert Restaurant La Rôtisserie Campsite 2 Stars NN** (N° RR AVR 15 191) (M. Philippe **François**) La Caserne ☎ 33-60-09-33 ⏤ 83 Closed 15 Nov to 15 Mar. Coaches welcome, 2 large restaurants seat 480. Evening meals until 9pm. English, German spoken.

MONT-SOUS-VAUDREY 39380 Jura **RD 471 Map 14-A3**
♆ ⊗ 🏠 **CHEZ COLETTE – RESTAURANT DU CENTRE** (N° RR JUN 24 259) (M. Maurice **Creusot**) Rue Jules-Grévy ☎ 84-71-71-94 ⏤ 5 Closed Sun evening, Mon all day; 15 May to 30 May; 20 October to 11 Nov. Half-board 120F, Full-board 160F per night. Coaches welcome (rest. seats 50). Evening meals until 10pm.

MORAINVILLIERS par ORGEVAL 78630 Yvelines **A 13 Map 1-A2**
♆ ⊗ **RESTOP DE MORAINVILLIERS** (M. Jean-Paul **Delarme**) ☎ 39-75-92-25 Self-service open 11.00am to 10.00pm. Showers, television, shop.

MORANCE 69480 Rhône **Map 2-A1**
♆ ⊗ 🏠 **REST DE LA MAIRIE** (N° RR JUL 26 274) (Mme Ginette **Roy**) Le Bourg ☎ 78-43-60-82 ⏤ 5 Closed Sat; Jan. Coaches welcome (rest. seats 70). Evening meals until 9pm.

M

MOREAC 56500 Morbihan **RN 24 Map 7-B2**
⚲ ⊗ **LE RELAIS DU BARDERFF** (N° RR FEV 26 453) (M. Jean **Lamour**) Z.I. Le Barderff ☎ 97-60-18-60 Open 24 hours. Closed Sun.

MOREILLES 85450 Vendée **Map 11-A1**
⚲ ⊗ ⌂ **AU CHEVAL BLANC** (N° RR JUL 26 288) (M. Claude **Balitrand**) Le Bourg ☎ 51-56-11-02 ⇌ 5 Closed end of December. Full-board 125-160F per night. Coaches welcome (rest. seats 55). Evening meals.

MOREUIL 80110 Somme **Map 5-A/B3**
⚲ ⊗ **LE CENDRIER** (N° RR SEPT 26 037) (M. Erik **Deraeve**) 79, rue du Cardinal-Mercier ☎ 22-09-70-64.

MORIÈRES-LES-AVIGNON 84310 Vaucluse **A 7 Map 24-A3**
⚲ ⊗ **RESTOP MORIÈRES** (M. Eric **Muller**) Autoroute A7 ☎ (90) 22-59-68 Self-service restaurant open 6.00am to 10.00pm. Television.

MORLINCOURT 60400 Oise **Map 6-A1**
⚲ ⊗ **LE RELAIS DU PORT** (N° RR AVR 24 553) (M. Francis **Collinet**) 201), rue d'Orroire ☎ 44-44-01-88 Closed Sun.

MORNAS 84420 Vaucluse **Autoroute A-7 Map 24-A2**
⚲ ⊗ **Cafè-Route** (N° RR RA-8) (M. Pierre **Mess**) ☎ 90-37-03-09 Direction Paris/Province Open 24 hours. Self-service restaurant. English, German, Spanish, Italian spoken. Shop.
⛽ **Antar Service Station RELAIS DE L'ATOME** (N° RR JUI 25 061) (M. Jean-Pierre **Flanquart**) Autoroute A-7 ☎ 90-37-02-07 English, German, Spanish spoken. Open 24 hours.
⚲ ⊗ **LE RELAIS DE LA CASCADE** (N° RR NOV 25 183) (M. Jean **Bretagnolle**) RN 7 ☎ 90-37-02-67 Closed Sat, Sun. German spoken.

MORNAY-SUR-ALLIER 18600 Cher **RN 76 Map 13-B2**
⚲ ⊗ ⌂ **LE RELAIS DE LA ROUTE** (N° RR DEC 15 044) (Mlle Jacqueline **Chevrot**) ☎ 48-74-53-54 ⇌ 5 Open 24 hours. Closed Sat (3pm), Sun. Evening meals. German, English spoken.

MORTAGNE-AU-PERCHE 61400 Orne **RN 12 Map 8-A2/3**
⚲ ⊗ ⌂ **1 Star HOTEL DES VOYAGEURS** (N° RR FEV 25 798) (Mme Cassimira **Blochel**) 60, fbg St-Éloi ☎ 33-25-25-46 ⇌ 10 Closed Sun evening, Mon evening; 20 Dec to 15 Jan. Full-board 190F. Coaches welcome (rest. seats 110). Evening meals served until 9pm.

MORTAGNE-SUR-SÈVRE 85290 Vendée **RN 160 Maps 11-B3 and 12-B1**
⚲ ⊗ **LE RELAIS DE LA GARE** (N° RR AOU 26 299) (M. Jean-Luc **Arrouet**) 52, route de Cholet ☎ 51-65-11-56 Closed Sat evening, Sun; Aug.

MORTRÉE 61500 Orne **RN 158 Map 8-A2**
⚲ ⊗ **LE POINT DU JOUR** (N° RR JUIN 25 948) (M. Jacques **Montier**)

M

Mortrée continued
Grande-Rue ☎ 33-35-35-22 Closed Sat, Sun. Coaches welcome (rest. seats 220). Evening meals.

MOSLES 14400 Calvados **RN 13 Map 4-B2**
♈ ⊗ **RELAIS DE LA POSTE** (N° RR AVR 26 518) (M. Martial **Becker**) RN 13 ☎ 31-92-40-05 Closed Sun. English spoken.

MOUCHARD 39330 Jura **RN 72 Map 14-B3**
♈ ⊗ ⌂ **SARL LA TONNELLE** (N° RR AOUT 26 303) (M. Bernard **Miller**) **Pagnoz** ☎ 84-37-81-17 **Minitel** ⊸ 11 Closed Sat evening, Sun; Aug. Coaches welcome (rest. seats 70). Evening meals.

MOUEN 14790 Calvados **RN 175 Map 4-B2**
♈ ⊗ ⌂ **LA BRUYÈRE** (N° RR JAN 20 973) (Mme **Lacroix**) Route Nationale ☎ 31-80-96-77 ⊸ 5.

MOULEYDIER 24520 Dordogne **Map 21-B2**
♈ ⊗ **RELAIS DU BARRAGE** (N° RR JUIN 27 309) (M. Patrick **Delmas**) Tuilières ☎ 53-23-20-55 Closed Sun. English, German and Spanish spoken. Evening meals served until 11 pm.

MOULINEAUX 76530 Seine-Maritime **RD 3 Map 3-A1**
♈ ⊗ ⌂ **HOTEL ROBERT LE DIABLE** Tobacconist, magazines (N° RR MAR 22 718) (M. Gilbert **Duroy**) Grand Couronne ☎ 35-23-81-17 ⊸ 10 Closed Sun; 20 Dec to 17 Jan. Coaches welcome (rest. seats 60). Evening meals.

MOULINS 03000 Allier **RN 7 Map 16-A3**
♈ ⊗ **LE RELAIS DES TROIS RUBANS** (N° RR AOU 7 841) (M. Pierre **Molinie**) 1, route de Paris ☎ 70-44-08-51 Closed Sun afternoon.

MOULINS-DES-MALADES par ORCHAMPS 39700 Jura **RN 73 Map 14-A5/B3**
♈ ⊗ **AU RENDEZ-VOUS DE LA MARINE** (N° RR MAI 6 142) (Mlle **Bullet**) 73, route Nationale ☎ 84-71-32-10 Closed Sat 4.00pm to Sun 11.00am; 25 Jul to 23 Aug.

MOULISME 86500 Vienne **RN 147 Map 15-B1**
♈ ⊗ ⌂ **1 Star NN LA TABLE OUVERTE** (N° RR AVR 22 752) (**S.A.R.L. Gransagne-Baudet**) Route Nationale Montmorillon ☎ 49-91-90-68 ⊸ 7 from 58,50 to 96,50F, breakfast 16F. Access for disabled. Closed Sat afternoon, Sun afternoon (except Aug). Car park 5,500m². Coaches welcome (rest. seats 75). Evening meals; bar; dogs allowed.

MOUSQUETTE 81120 Tarn **RN 112 Map 22-B2**
♈ ⊗ ⌂ **2 Stars NN AUBERGE DU SANGLIER** (N° RR JUN 24 985) (Mme Maria **Daures**) Denat/Réalmont ☎ 63-45-50-80 **Minitel** ⊸ 24 English, Spanish spoken.

MOUZEUIL 85370 Vendée **RN 148 Map 11-A1**
♈ ⊗ ⌂ **CENTRAL ROUTIER** (N° RR JUN 21 961) (M. Jean-Marie **Guilbaud**) Le Bourg Place de l'Église ☎ 51-30-72-44 ⊸ 8 Full-

board 130F per night. Coaches welcome (rest. seats 300). Evening meals.

MOUZON 08210 Ardennes **RN 964 Map 6-A3**
Y ⊗ **LA MARINE** (N° RR JUL 26 612) (Mme Danielle **Hisette**) 6, rue du Château ☎ 24-26-19-90 Closed Wed; beginning Sept. Coaches welcome (rest. seats 45). Evening meals.

MOYON 50860 Manche **CD 999 Map 8-A1**
Y ⊗ **CARREFOUR PARIS SUPER ROUTIERS** (N° RR NOV 27 091) (M. Pierre **Borau**) Carrefour Paris-Moyon ☎ 33-05-59-74 Closed Sun Portuguese, English and Spanish spoken.

MUR-DE-SOLOGNE 41230 L.-et-C. **RD 765 Map 12-A3**
Y ⊗ ⌂ **LA CROIX BLANCHE** (N° RR OCT 26 683) (M. Philippe **Gaugry**) rue de Blois ☎ 54-83-81-11 ⇥ 22 English spoken.

MUREAUX (LES) 78130 Yvelines **RD 14 Maps 1-A1 and 3-B2**
Y ⊗ ⌂ **LE RELAIS ICI ON COUPE LA SOIF** (N° RR JUL 12 328) (Mme **Compagnon**) 102, avenue du Maréchal Foch ☎ 34-74-05-04 ⇥ 7 Closed Sun; Aug.
Y ⊗ **CAFÉ D'ARMOR** (N° RR OCT 26 700) (Mme Germaine **Dolais**) 29, rue J.-Jaurès ☎ 34-74-04-95 Closed Wed. English spoken.

MURON 17630 Charente-Maritime **Map 11-B1**
Y ⊗ ⌂ **LE RELAIS** (N° RR SEPT 26 632) (M. Albert **Arnaud**) rue de la Libération ☎ 46-27-78-41 ⇥ 5.

MUY (LE) 83490 Var **RN 7 Map 25-A2**
Y ⊗ **LA CHAUMIÈRE** (N° RR AOUT 26 625) (M. Louis **Fogola**) 7, quartier de la Gare ☎ 94-45-10-81 ⇥ 7.

MYENNES 58440 Nievre **RN 7 Map 13-A2**
Y ⊗ **LE RANCH** (N° RR JAN 22 151) (Mme Marie-Marcelle **Barres**) ☎ 86-28-00-98.

N

NAINTRÉ Lieu-dit LES BARRES 86530 Vienne **RN 10 Map 15-B1**
Y ⊗ **LA HALTE** (N° RR NOV 20 892) (M. and Mme **Henni-Houas**) Nationale 10 ☎ 49-90-09-69 **Minitel** Situated on exit Sud de Châtellerault from Autoroute Aquitaine. Closed Sat, Sun. Coaches welcome (rest. seats 150). Evening meals. English, Arabic, Spanish, German spoken.

NANCY 54000 M.-et-M. **RN 4 Maps 10-A2 and 14-B1**
Y ⊗ ⌂ **LE RELAIS DU PORT** (N° RR FEV 18 314) (M. Claude **Dopp**) ⇥ 5, rue Henri-Bazin ☎ 83-35-49-85 ⇥ 9 Closed Sat, Sun; Aug. English, German spoken.

N

Nancy continued
♀ ⊗ **RELAIS VICTOR** (N° RR SEPT 29 641) (M. Jean-Marie **Hecht**) 7, rue Victor ☎ 83-35-49-85 ⊶ 9 Closed Sat, Sun. Evening meals.

NANTERRE 92000 Hauts-de-Seine **Porte Maillot Map 1-A2**
♀ ⊗ **AU PETIT ROSE** (N° RR MAI 25 931) (Mme Jasmina **Houguenague**) 108, av. Jules-Quentin ☎ 47-21-13-99 Closed Sat, Sun. English spoken.

NANTES 44000 L.-Atl. **RN 43 Maps 11-A/B2 and 12-B1**
♀ ⊗ **LA BOUGRIÈRE** (N° RR OCT 23 491) (M. Pierre **Pertue**) rue du Pavillon-Ste-Luce ☎ 40-25-60-84 Closed Sat, Sun (except for coaches, banquets). Aug; Christmas to New Year. Coaches welcome (rest. seats 200). English, Spanish spoken.
♀ ⊗ ⌂ **L'ANCRE D'OR** (N° RR AOUT 26 295) (M. Serge **Desmortiers**) 55, boulevard Gustave Roch ☎ 40-35-39-30 ⊶ 5 Closed Sat afternoon, Sun; 15 Aug to 7 Sept. Evening meals (except Sat).
♀ ⊗ **CAFÉ DE L'AVENIR** (N° RR SEPT 26 043) (Mme Vivaine **Baron**) 1, rue de la Pompe ☎ 40-43-46-03 Closed Sun. Coaches welcome (rest. seats 50). Evening meals until 9.30pm.
☕ **Total Service Station LE RELAIS DE LA DIVATTE** (N° RR MAR 24 143) (S.A.R.L. Joseph **Guichet**) 226, Bd de la Loire ☎ 40-06-01-44 Basse-Goulaine. Closed alternate Sun.
☕ **BP Service Station RELAIS DE LA MAISON BLANCHE** (N° RR MAR 24 144) (Mme Anne **Bouloux**) RN 23 Le Cellier ☎ 40-25-54-07.
♀ ⊗ **CAFÉ DU HAVRE** (N° RR MARS 26 850) (Mme Betty **Guichard**) 4, rue d L'Hermitage ☎ 40-73-29-19 Closed Sat evening, Sun; 15 days Aug. HGV parking (15 vehicles).
♀ ⊗ **LES TILLEULS** (N° RR JANV 26 784) (Mme Marie-Thérèse **Poirier**) 9, rue de la Petite Baratte ☎ 40-49-68-29 ⊶ 13 Closed Sat, Sun; Aug.

NANTHIAT see CHAMBORET 87140 Hte-Vienne

NARBONNE 11100 Aude **RN 9 Map 23-A3**
♀ ⊗ ⌂ **LE NOVELTY** (N° RR JAN 10 223) (MM. Claude and Louis **Strazzera**) 33, avenue des Pyrénées ☎ 68-42-24-28 ⊶ 18 Full-board. Coaches welcome (rest. seats 250). Evening meals until 10pm. English, Arabic, Spanish, Italian spoken.
♀ ⊗ ⌂ **1 Star NN LE RELAIS DES 2 MERS** (N° RR JAN 23 601) (M. **Mattei**) ☎ 68-41-00-21 ⊶ 39 Italian spoken.
♀ ⊗ **LA TOUPINE** (N° RR NOV 27 112) (M. Yannick **Canessa**) 3, route de Coursan ☎ 68-65-11-01 ⊶ 4 English and Spanish spoken.

NASSANDRES 27550 Eure **RN 13 Map 4-B3**
♀ ⊗ **LE PARIS CAEN/CHERBOURG INTERNATIONAL** (N° RR OCT 26 686) (M. Patrice **Boutel**) SARL Le Paris Caen/Cherbourg 11, Route Nationale 13 ☎ 32-45-00-26 Closed Sat, Sun. Reopens Sun 10pm–1am.

NAVILLY 71650 S.-et-L. **RN 83 Bis Map 14-A3**
♀ ⊗ ⌂ **AU BOIS DE BOULOGNE** (N° RR FEV 10 347) (M. **Grapinet**) ☎ 85-49-10-40 ⊶ 3 Closed Wed; Jan.

N

NÉGRONDES 24460 Dordogne
Y ⊗ **RESTO-ROUTE LA FRINGALE** (N° RR SEPT 26 332) (Mme **Mouret**, M. **Leriche**) Les Riviers ☎ 53-55-24-11 English, Italian spoken.

NEMOURS 77140 S.-et-M. **Autoroute A6 Map 9-B2**
Y ⊗ **RESTOP DE NEMOURS** (M. **Claude Poirier**) Aire de Darvault ☎ 64-28-11-97 Open 24 hours. Self-service restaurant. Showers, TV, shop.

NERE 17510 Charente-Mar **RD 133 Map 15-A2**
Y ⊗ **LES ROUTIERS** (N° RR JUN 23 828) (Mme Monique **Metois**) route d'Aulnay-les-Égaux ☎ 46-33-00-30.

NERONDES 18350 Cher **CD 976 Map 13-B2**
Y ⊗ 🏠 **1 Star NN LE RELAIS DU LION D'OR** (N° RR MAR 9 436) (M. René **Boutillon**) place de la Mairie ☎ 48-74-87-81 ⊷ 14 from 90–140F, breakfast 17F, telephone in room. Closed Sun afternoon; public holiday afternoons; 15 Dec to 13 Jan; third week in Sept. Evening meals. Car park; bar.

NEUFBOURG (LE) 50140 Manche **RN 177 Map 8-A1**
Y ⊗ **LES ROUTIERS** (N° RR AOUT 26 025) (Mme Françoise **Hamel**) 13, rue de Vire ☎ 33-59-00-59 ⊷ 4.

NEUFCHATEL-EN-SAOSNOIS 72600 Sarthe **RN 155 Map 8-B2**
Y ⊗ **Tobacconist CHEZ CHRISTIANE** (N° RR AOU 18 500) (Mme Christiane **Chapellier**) ☎ 43-97-74-10 ⊷ 15 Closed 15 days in Aug. Full-board 180–200F per night. Evening meals until 10pm.

NEUILLY-LES-DIJON 21800 Côte-d'Or **RN 5 Map 14-A3**
Y ⊗ 🏠 **LE RELAIS DES ROUTIERS** (N° RR OCT 15 395) (M. **Manzoni**) 5, Route Nationale ☎ 80-23-01-93 ⊷ 8.

NEUSSARGUES 15170 Cantal **RN 122 Map 17-A2**
Y ⊗ **LE SPORTING BAR** (N° RR AVR 25 875) (Mme Jeannine **Terrisse**) rue des Écoles ☎ 71-20-53-92 Closed Sun; 15 days Jul, Aug. Evening meals.

NEUVE-LYRE (LA) Hameau de CHAGNY 27330 Eure **RN 830 Map 8-A3**
Y ⊗ **LE RELAIS DES AMIS** (N° RR AVR 21 047) (M. Jean-Claude **Guyot**) Hameau de Chagny ☎ 32-08-67-23 Closed Tue; 15 to 30 Aug.

NEUVIC 24190 Dordogne **Map 15-B3**
Y ⊗ **RELAIS LE REPAIRE** (N° RR AVR 27 265) (M. Jacky **Blanchard**) le But ☎ 53-81-63-05.

NEUVILLE-AU-PLAIN 50480 Manche **RN 13 Map 4-B1**
Y ⊗ **LA RENCONTRE** (N° RR AOU 25 079) (M. Jean-Pierre **Alix**) Ste Mère Eglise ☎ 33-41-31-46 Closed Sat/Sun; Aug. English spoken.

NEUVY 41250 Loir-et-Cher **RD 18 and 923**
Y ⊗ 🏠 **LA CHEMINÉE** (N° RR JUL 26 613) (M. Philippe **Masclet**)

N

Neuvy continued
Bracieux ☎ 54-46-42-70 ◀ 9. Closed Wed in winter; 15 to 30 Sept; 15 Feb to 15 Mar.

NEUVY-EN-BEAUCE 28310 E.-et-L. **A10 Map 9-B1**
  ⚲ **BP Service Station RELAIS VAL NEUVY** (N° RR JUL 550000088) (M. Lucien **Blanchard**) A10 ☎ 37-99-91-75 Open 24 hours. English spoken.

NEUVY-SAINT-SÉPULCRE 36230 Indre **RD 927 Map 16-A1**
  ♟ ⊗ ⌂ **LA CHARRETTE** (N° RR FEV 26 454) (M. Nicholas **Pavlice-vic**) 21, place du Champ-de-Foire ☎ 54-30-84-77 ◀ 7 Italian, Yugoslavian, Polish, Czechoslavakian, Russian, English spoken.

NEUVY-SAUTOUR 89570 Yonne **RN 77 Map 9-B2**
  ♟ ⊗ **AU BON COIN Chez Gérard et Annie** (N° RR JUL 26 292) (M. Gérard **Charpignon**) route de Troyes ☎ 86-56-35-52 **Minitel** Closed Sat afternoon, Sun. Coaches welcome (rest. seats 40). Evening meals until 9.30pm.

NEVERS 58000 Nievre **RN 7 Map 13-B2**
  ♟ ⊗ ⌂ **HOTEL NIVERNAIS** (N° RR SeP 23 481) (M. Marcel **George**) 106, route de Lyon-Plagny ☎ 86-37-58-32 ◀ 6 English, Spanish, Italian spoken.
  ♟ ⊗ ⌂ **HOTEL DU LION D'OR** (N° RR OCT 26 682) (M. Thierry **Petillot**) 13, faubourg de Lyon ☎ 86-37-55-48 ◀ 4 Closed Wed. Some English spoken.

NEVERS 58000 Nievre **see PLAGNY**

NICE 06000 Alpes-Marit. **RN 7 Map 25-B2**
  ♟ ⊗ **VENGA VENGA DA MIREILLE** (N° RR MAR 24 883) (M. André **Echampe**) 11, Bld Pierre Sémard ☎ 93-89-58-56 Closed Sun; Aug. Coaches welcome (rest. seats 42). Evening meals (except Fri to Sun, public holidays). Italian spoken.

NICOLE 47190 L.-et-G. **RN 113 Map 21-A/B1**
  ♟ ⊗ ⌂ **LE PLAISANCE** (N° RR JUN 24 615) (M. Bernard **Lambert**) Rte Nle 113 Aiguillon ☎ 53-79-64-07 ◀ 6 Closed Sat; 15 Aug–15 Sept. Coaches welcome (rest. seats 100). Evening meals until 10.00pm.

NIEPPE 59850 Nord **RN 42 Map 5-A1**
  ♟ ⊗ **LE RELAIS DE L'HARMONIE** (N° RR JUL 23 379) (M. Patrick **Hecquet**) 127, rue d'Armentières ☎ 20-77-69-02 Closed Mon; Aug.

NIEUL-LE-DOLENT 85430 Vendée **RD 36 Map 11-B3**
  ♟ ⊗ **CHEZ JACQUES** (N° RR MAR 23 210) (M. Jacques **Pinel**) 8, rue de Lattre-de-Tassigny between la Roche-sur-Yon and les Sables-d'Olonne ☎ 51-07-93-71 Closed Sun. Coaches welcome (rest. seats 40). HGV parking (2000m^2). Evening meals.

NIMES 30000 Gard **Map 23-B2**

⊗   **Sté L'AVONAGE** (N° RR NOV 26 099) (Mme Martine **Finiels**) Rte de Generac, Domaine de la Bastide ☎ 66-38-06-99 Closed Sun low season. Coaches welcome (rest. seats 70). Evening meals. English, Spanish spoken.

NIORT 79000 Deux-Sèvres **RN 150 Map 15-A1**

♈ ⊗ **LE BON ACCUEIL** (N° RR OCT 24 743) (Mme Thérèse **Denibaud**) 424, av. St-Jean-d'Angély ☎ 49-79-27-60 Closed Sat, Sun; from 1 Nov to Easter; 15 Jul–15 Aug. Coaches welcome (rest. seats 70, breakfast only). Evening meals until 10.30pm.

NOAILLES 19600 Corrèze **RN 20 Map 17-A1**

♈ ⊗ 🏠 **RELAIS D'ATAN** (N° RR JUL 26 606) (Mme Josiane **Berthelot**) Fontrouvée ☎ 55-85-85-76 Italian, Spanish, Portuguese spoken.

NOCLE-MAULAIX (LA) 58250 Nièvre **RD 3 Map 16-A3**

♈ ⊗ **LE RELAIS DE LA POSTE** (N° RR JAN 17 715) (M. Marcel **Senotier**) ☎ 86-30-80-32 Closed Mon; 1 to 21 Sept. Evening meals.

LA NOË POULAIN 27560 Eure **CD 810 Map 4-B3**

♈ ⊗ **CHEZ MANU ET JOJO** (N° RR NOV 27 088) (Mme Josiane **Langin**) Lieurey ☎ 35-57-90-35 Closed Sat and July/August.

NOGENT-LE-PHAYE 28630 Eure-et-Loire **RN 10 Map 8-B3**

♈ ⊗ **RELAIS DU MOULIN ROUGE** (N° RR NOV 26 716) (M. Christian **Bru**) Le Moulin Rouge ☎ 37-31-62-68 Closed Sat, Sun; Aug.

NOGENT-LE-ROTROU 28400 E.-et-L. **RN 23 Map 8-B3**

🏆   **Total Service Station LE RELAIS DE SULLY** (N° RR SEP 25 629) (M. Claude **Lepretre**) RN 23 ☎ 37-52-45-27.

NOHANT-EN-GOUT 18390 Cher **Map 13-B2**

♈ ⊗ **RELAIS DU BERRY** (N° RR AVR 27 251) (SARL Ligot) ☎ 48-30-42-90 German, English, Spanish and Italian spoken.

♈ ⊗ **LA GRANDE HALTE** (N° RR AVR 27 250) (M. Gérard **Lesimple**) ☎ 48-30-42-07 Closed Feb. English and Spanish spoken.

NOISY-LE-SEC 93130 Seine-St-Denis **Map 1-A3**

♈ ⊗ **LE CAPITOL** (N° RR OCT 25 711) (M. Claude **Magre**) 2, rue Jean-Jaurès ☎ 48-44-59-03 Closed Sun; Aug. Spanish, Portuguese spoken.

NOLAY 21340 Côte-d'Or **RD 73 Map 13-B3**

♈ ⊗ 🏠 **2 Star NN LE RELAIS DU CHEVREUIL** (N° RR AOU 20 799) (Mme Rachelle **Suissa**) place de l'Hôtel de Ville ☎ 80-21-71-89 ⊷ 14 Closed Wed in low season; Dec. English, Spanish spoken.

NONANT-LE-PIN 61240 Orne **RN 26 Map 8-A2**

♈ ⊗ **LE RELAIS DES HARAS** (N° RR MAR 25 345) (M. Jacques **Lampin**) Grand-Rue ☎ 33-39-93-35 **Minitel** Closed Sun. Coaches welcome (rest. seats 35). Evening meals until 10pm.

N

NOTRE-DAME-DE-GRAVENCHON 76330 Seine-Marit. **RD 428 Map 4-B3**

♟ ⊗ **LE COUP D'FREIN** (N° RR AVR 21 897) (Mme Marie-Josée **David**) rue Claude-Bernard ☎ 35-94-61-35.

NOUZONVILLE 08700 Ardennes **RD 1 Map 6-A2**

♟ ⊗ 🏠 **LE RELAIS DE LA PLACE** (N° RR SEP 21 243) (Mme Annie **Boquillon**) 15, place Gambetta ☎ 24-53-80-43 ⊷ 6 Closed Sun; Christmas Day to 1 Jan. Full-board available. Evening meals.

NOVES 13550 B.-du-R. **RN 7 Map 24-A3**

⊗ **RELAIS DE LA BASSAQUE** (N° RR SEPT 26 325) (M. Joseph **Masi**) Route Nationale 7 ☎ 90-94-26-84 Closed Sun. Italian spoken.

NOVION-PORCIEN 08270 Ardennes **RN 985 Map 6-A2**

♟ ⊗ **LE FRANCO-BELGE – LE RELAIS DES ROUTIERS** (N° RR AVR 17 499) (Mme Simone **Boniface**) place de la Gare ☎ 24-23-20-06 ⊷ 2 Evening meals.

NOYAL-SUR-VILAINE 35530 I.-et-V. **Map 8-B1**

♟ ⊗ 🏠 **LE RELAIS 35** (N° RR JUL 26 290) (M. Jean **Monnerais**) 20, rue du Gal-de-Gaulle ☎ 99-00-51-20 ⊷ 12 Closed Sat 4.00pm to Sun evening. Coaches welcome (rest. seats 80). Evening meals until 1am. English spoken.

NOYANT-LA-PLAINE 49700 M.-et-L. **Map 12-B2**

♟ ⊗ 🏠 **L'ÉTAPE** (N° RR FEVR 25 821) (M. Michel **Eono**) RD 761 ☎ 41-59-30-40 ⊷ 7. Closed Sun. Coaches welcome (rest. seats 80). Evening meals.

NOYARET 38360 Isère **RN 532 Maps 19-A3 and 24-B1**

♟ ⊗ 🏠**AU BON ACCUEIL DES ROUTIERS** (N° RR FEVR 25 815))M. Jean-Claude **Compe**) rue de la Gare Le Maupas ☎ 76-53-95-61 ⊷ 11 Closed Sun evening. Coaches welcome (rest. seats 100). Evening meals. Italian, German, Spanish spoken.

NOYON 60400 Oise **Map 3-A3 6-A/B1**

♟ ⊗ **LE BELLEVUE** (N° RR OCT 27 074) (Mme Mariette **Deucornetz**). 1, avenue Jean Jaurès ☎ 44-44-19-56 Closed Sun pm and July. Dutch spoken.

NUITS-SAINT-GEORGES 21700 Côte-d'Or **RN 74 Map 14-A3**

♟ ⊗ 🏠 **2 Stars NN HOTEL DES CULTIVATEURS** (N° RR JUN 1 894) (MM. **Villemagne Père et Fils**) 12, rue du Gl-de-Gaulle ☎ 80-61-10-41 ⊷ 15 Closed Sun; 15 Dec to 15 Jan. Coaches welcome (rest. seats 60). Evening meals. English spoken.

OCTEVILLE 50130 Manche **RD 3 and 900 Map 4-A1**
♀ ⊗ **LE VENT D'AMONT** (N° RR MAI 26 885) (M. Jacky **Travers**) 1,
rue Jules Ferry ☎ 33-51-16-16 Closed Mon after lunch. Private car
park (2,200m²). English spoken. Filling station near.

OFFWILLER 67340 Bas-Rhin **RD 28 Map 10-B1**
♀ ⊗ ⌂ **AUBERGE DU LION D'OR** (N° RR NOV 26 729) (M. Henri
Pfeiffer) 22, rue de la Libération ☎ 88-89-30-50 Closed Wed.
German spoken.

OGEVILLER 54450 M.-et-M. **RN 4 Map 10-A2**
♀ ⊗ **RELAIS DE LA VERDURETTE** (N° RR MAI 26 537) (Mme Lydie
Martin) 22, route de Strasbourg ☎ 83-72-24-65 Closed Sat, Sun.
Evening meals.

OISSEAU-LE-PETIT 72830 Sarthe **N 138 Map 8-B2**
♀ ⊗ **HOTEL DE L'ESPERANCE** (N° RR SEP 21 653) (Mme **Besnard**)
☎ 33-26-81-97 ⊸ 4 Closed Sat from Oct–Apr. Coaches welcome
(rest. seats 60). Evening meals.

OLEMPS 12510 Aveyron **Map 22-B1**
♀ ⊗ ⌂ **1 star NN RELAIS DU PAS** (N° RR JUIN 27300) (M. Jean-Marc
Mayrand) RD 994 Le Pas Druelle ☎ 65-69-39-11 ⊸ 8 80 to 100F.
English and Spanish spoken. Evening meals.

OLLIERES-SUR-EYRIEUX (LES) 07360 Ardèche **RN 103 Map 24-A1**
♀ ⊗ **LE RELAIS DU SIECLE** (N° RR JUN 21 114) (Mme Jacqueline
Loulier) ☎ 75-65-20-42 ⊸ 4 Closed Sat, Sun. Full-board 175F per
night. Evening meals.

OLORON-SAINTE-MARIE 64400 Pyrénées-Atl. **RN 134 Map 20-B3**
♀ ⊗ ⌂ **LE TERMINUS** (N° RR JUL 26 603) (Mme Jeanne **Debonne**)
place de la gare ☎ 59-39-01-72 ⊸ 14. 60 to 85F. Breakfast 11F.
Coaches welcome (rest. seats 150). Evening meals until midnight. Lourdes only 40km away.

OMONVILLE par BACQUEVILLE-EN-CAUX 76730 Seine-Maritime
RN 27 Map 4-A3
♀ ⊗ **A L'ARRET DES TOURISTES** (N° RR MAR 15 566) (Mme Colette
Devingt) ☎ 35-83-20-78 Closed Sat, Sun.

ORANGE 84100 Vaucluse **RN 7 Map 24-A2**
♀ ⊗ **LE MOULIN A VENT** (N° RR JUN 25 031) (M. Henri **Garcia**)
Pont de l'Aigue ☎ 90-34-02-41 Spanish, Italian spoken.

ORBEC 14290 Calvados **RD 31 Map 8-A2**
♀ ⊗ **LE RELAIS DES ROUTIERS** (N° RR JUN 20 760) (Mme Marie-
Claude **Morel**) 37, rue de Bernay ☎ 31-32-70-70 Closed Sun;
Aug.

ORGENOY par PONTHIERRY 77310 Seine-et-Marne **RN 7 Map 9-B1**
♀ ⊗ ⌂ **LE RELAIS DU RHINS** (N° RR OCT 14 982) (M. **Saint-Jean**) ☎
60-65-71-01 ⊸ 8 Closed Sat evening, Sun; Aug; Christmas to New
Year. Evening meals.

O

ORGEVAL see MORAINVILLIERS

ORGON 13660 B.-du-R. **RN 7 Maps 24-A3 and B3**
♡ ⊗ **LE BELLEVUE** (N° RR MARS 26 201) (M. Eugène **Giraud**) Quartier Paradou ☎ 90-73-00-24 Evening meals. English, German, Dutch spoken.
♡ ⊗ **AU BEC FIN** (N° RR JUIL 26 948) (M. Michel **Toesca**) RN 7 ☎ 90-73-00-49 Closed Sun. Private car park (6000m²). English, Italian, Spanish spoken. Filling station open 24 hours.
♡ ⊗ ⌂ **RELAIS DES RUMADES** (N° RR AVR 27 256) (M. Jean **Etcheverry**) ☎ 90-73-00-81 ⊷ 11 100 to 150F. German and English spoken. Evening meals served until midnight.

ORLEANS 45100 Loiret **RN 20 and D 951 Map 13-A1**
♡ ⊗ ⌂ **RELAIS DU PARC** (N° RR JUN 24 994) (M. Claude **Gibert**) 45, rue du Parc ☎ 38-53-34-13 ⊷ 9 Closed Sat, Sun. Coaches welcome (3 dining rooms = 106 seats). Evening meals.
♡ ⊗ ⌂ **LE RELAIS DES QUATRE MARCHES** (N° RR DEC 16 327) (M. Pierre **Guyot**) 163, route de Saint-Mesmin ☎ 38-66-31-12 ⊷ 9 Closed Sat, Sun; Aug. Evening meals.
⚓ **Total Service Station LE RELAIS DE LA RETREVE** (N° RR MAI 25 433) Autoroute A10 Gidy Fleury-les-Aubrais ☎ 38-91-30-20 Open 24 hours.

ORLEANS-SARAN 45400 Loiret **Autoroute Aquitaine A10 Map 13-A1**
♡ ⊗ **RELAIS DU VAL DE LOIRE** (N° RR RA-10) (M. Loïc **Brasseur**) Aire de Service de Gidy Saran ☎ 38-73-30-20 Self-service restaurant open 6.00am to midnight. English, German, Spanish spoken. Telex 780959.

ORNANS 25290 Doubs **RD 67 Map 14-B3**
♡ ⊗ ⌂ **1 Star NN HÔTEL LE PROGRES** (N° RR AOU 20 800) (M. **Perriot-Comte**) 11, rue Jacques-Gervais ☎ 81-62-16-79 ⊷ 15 from 125–140F, breakfast 18–20F, telephone, WC in room. Closed Sun evening in winter. Bar; dogs allowed; recreations (fishing, shooting, canoeing, swimming, tennis). Places to visit: Loue Valley, Museums. Menus 50–160F. Specialities: Trout, *Terrine maison, Escargot maison*.

OSNY 95520 Val-d'Oise **RN 15 Maps 1-A2 and 3-B2**
♡ ⊗ ⌂ **LE RELAIS DE LA DEMI-LIEUE** (N° RR FEV 18 012) (Mme **Massari**) route de Gisors ☎ 30-30-15-12 Closed Sat, Sun; Aug.

OUISTREHAM 14150 Calvados **RD 514 Map 4-B2**
♡ ⊗ **AU COIN DU PORT** (N° RR AVR 26 237) (M. Patrick **Bourdon**) 90, avenue Michel-Cableu ☎ 31-97-15-22 Closed Sun; Coaches welcome (rest. seats 60). Evening meals. English, Spanish spoken.

OURVILLE-EN-CAUX 76450 Seine-Maritime **Map 4-A3**
♡ ⊗ ⌂ **BAR DE LA PLACE** (N° RR MAI 25 924) (M. Jean-Pierre **Pouchet**) Place Jean-Picard ☎ 35-27-60-01 ⊷ 10 Closed Aug.

O

Full-board 120–140F per night. Coaches welcome (rest. seats 45). Evening meals.

OUZOUER-LE-MARCHE 41240 L.-et-C. **RN 157 Maps 8-B3 and 12-A3**

♀ ⊗ ⌂ **LA HALTE BEAUCERONNE** (N° RR NOV 11 912) (M. Marcel **Malaquin**) 18, place de l'Eglise RN 157 ☎ 54-82-41-26 ⇥ 5 from 62–105F, breakfast 18,50–19,50F Closed Tue; 15 to 30 Jan; 15 to 29 Jul. Coaches welcome (rest. seats 60 breakfast only). Evening meals served to hotel guests only. Car park; amusements (pin ball etc). Places to visit: Châteaux, Chambord, Orleans.

OZON 65190 Htes-Pyr **RN 117 Map 21-A3**

♀ ⊗ **AUBERGE DU PETIT ROBINSON** (N° RR FEV 25 810) (M. Jean-Roger **Labarde**) Rte de Toulouse ☎ 62-35-70-01 Open 24 hrs. Coaches welcome (rest. seats 70). Evening meals. English, Italian, Spanish spoken.

OZOURT par MONTFORT 40380 Landes **RD 32 Map 20-B2**

♀ ⊗ **AUBERGE DU ROUTIER** (N° RR JUL 23 859) (M. Alain **Deschamps**) ☎ 58-98-65-98 Closd Tue 2.00pm to 6.30pm.

P

PACAUDIÈRE (LA) 42310 Loire **Map 16-B3**

♀ ⊗ **LE RELAIS DU LAC** (N° RR MARS 27 210) (M. Marcel **Vernay**) RN 7 ☎ 77-64-36-08 ⇥ 4.

PACÉ par ALENÇON 61000 Orne **RN 12 Map 8-B2**

♀ ⊗ **LE RELAIS DES ROUTIERS Tobacconist** (N° RR SEPT 12 434) (M. Marcel **Bruneau**) 12, route de Bretagne (7 km from Alençon) ☎ 33-27-70-69 Closed Sat afternoon, Sun afternoon; Sun during winter; closed Feb. Coaches welcome (rest. seats 70). Evening meals.

PAIMPOL 22500 Côte-du-Nord **Map 7-A2**

♀ ⊗ **LE TRISKEL** (N° RR SEPT 26 649) (M. Daniel **Hello**) 15, av. Chateaubriand ☎ 96-20-82-72 Closed Sat afternoon, Sun. English spoken.

PAJAY 38260 Isère **RD 73 Map 18-B3**

♀ ⊗ ⌂ **LE RELAIS DE MA PETITE AUBERGE** (N° RR JUL 19 435) ⇥ (Mme Huguette **Vivier**) La Côte-Saint-André ☎ 74-54-26-06 ⇥ 7 Closed Sept. Full-board 130–160F per night. Coaches welcome (rest. seats 58). English, some German spoken.

PALLICE (LA) Charente-Marit. **RN 22 Map 11-B1 see ROCHELLE (LA)**

P

PANTIN 93500 Seine-St-Denis Porte de Pantin **RN 3 Map 1-A/2-3**

♀ ⊗ **RESTODERM** SARL (N° RR JUN 25 026) (M. **Demougin**) 110, bis avenue du Général Lecierc ☎ 48-44-75-84 Closed Sat, Sun; public holidays. Coaches welcome (rest. seats 280 + 40).

♀ ⊗ **EUROPE TABAC SABRIE** (N° RR AVR 23 220) (M. Georges **Sabrie**) 203, avenue Jean-Lolive ☎ 48-45-03-17 Closed Sun. German, English, Spanish, Italian spoken. Evening meals.

♀ ⊗ **MONIA NADJET** (N° RR JUN 26 566) (M. José **Riestra-Materno**) 14, av. du Cimetière Parisien ☎ 48-46-80-32 Closed Sun. Arabic, Spanish, Italian, Portuguese spoken.

PARAY-SOUS-BRIAILLES see CHAZEUIL 03500 Allier

PARIGNÉ 35133 Ille-et-Vilaine **CD 19 ET 108 Map 8-A/B1**

♀ ⊗ **FRANK'ELLE** (N° RR OCT 27 066) (M. Franck **Rousset**) 12, rue de la Mairie ☎ 99-97-22-90 Closed Mon pm.

PARIGNE-LE-POLLIN 72330 Sarthe **RN 23 Map 12-A2**

♀ ⊗ **LE RELAIS FLEURI** (N° RR JAN 26 145) (Mme Jacqueline **Bouchevereau SARL NB RESTAURATION**) La Chesnay RN 23 ☎ 43-87-81-41 Closed Sat afternoon, Sun. English spoken.

PARIS 75008

♀ ⊗ **LE RELAIS CHEZ LEON** (N° RR JAN 23 789) (Mme **Grange**) 5, rue de l'Isly ☎ 43-87-42-77 Closed Sun, Aug.

PARIS 75012

♀ ⊗ **CHEZ MADJID** (N° RR JANV 27 146) (M. Madjid **Blaidi**) 8, rue du Charolais ☎ 43-43-63-86 Closed Sat and July. Friday's Special couscous.

PARIS 75013

♀ ⊗ 🏠 **AU RENDEZ-VOUS DES ROUTIERS Chez Smail** (N° RR JUL 22 881) (M. Naït **Mohand**) 117, quai de la Gare ☎ 45-84-57-06 ⇥ 24 Arabic spoken. Evening meals.

♀ ⊗ **LE RELAIS CHEZ MOMO** (N° RR OCT 25 062) (Mme Ghylaine **Varin**) 127, quai de la Gare ☎ 45-85-23-42 Closed Sun. Evening meals until midnight.

PARIS 75016

♀ ⊗ **A LA RENOMMEE D'AUTEUIL** (N° RR AVR 23 219) (M. Francis **Zanoletti**) 21, rue Gros ☎ 45-27-49-33 Closed Sat, Sun; Jul.

PARIS 75018

♀ ⊗ **LE RELAIS DES ROUTIERS** (N° RR OCT 15 413) (M. Bernard **Dubreuil**) 50 bis, rue Marx-Dormoy ☎ 46-07-93-80 Closed Sun; Evening meals.

PARIS 75019

♀ ⊗ **CHEZ MICHELE** (N° RR MAI 22 354) (M. Guy **Garnier**) 243, rue de Crimée ☎ 46-07-56-23 Closed Sun.

PARIS 75020
♀ ⊗ **ETOILE DE LISBONNE** (N° RR AOU 25 522) (M. Manuel **Duarte**) 139, bld. Davout ☎ 43-61-04-80 Closed Aug. Spanish, Portuguese spoken.

PARON 89100 Yonne **RN 60 Map 9-B2**
♀ ⊗ **LE RELAIS DE ST-BOND** (N° RR MARS 25 835) (M. Daniel **Millard**) 32, avenue Jean-Jaurès ☎ 86-95-41-41 Closed Sun. Evening meals.

PAU 64000 Pyr.-Atl. **RN 117/134 Maps 20-B3 and 21-A3**
♀ ⊗ **RELAIS BELLEVUE** (N° RR MAR 23 204) (Mme **Lorry**) **Belair par Buziet** ☎ 59-21-76-03 ◣ 6 Closed Sat, Christmas. Some Spanish spoken.
♀ ⊗ ⌂ **1 Star NN HOTEL DU BOIS LOUIS** (N° RR SEPT 23 482) (M. **Bareille**) 18, avenue Gaston-Lacoste ☎ 59-27-34-98 ◣ 10 Closed Sun.
♀ ⊗ **LE RELAIS DE L'INDUSTRIE** (N° RR MAI 23 801) (Mme Yveline **Sala**) avenue Larregain quartier Montauba **Lons** ☎ 59-32-07-57 Closed Sat, Sun. Coaches welcome (2 dining rooms = 230 seats). Italian, German, some English spoken.

PAUILLAC 33250 Gironde **RD 2 Maps 15-A3 and 20-A1**
♀ ⊗ ⌂ **LE YACHTING** (N° RR JAN 26 136) (Mme Louisette **Puyfour-cat**) 12, Port de Plaisance ☎ 56-59-06-43 ◣ 16 (single rooms use of shower, for bearers of 'Les Routiers card, 100F). Closed Sat in winter. Coaches welcome (rest. seats 100). Evening meals.
♀ ⊗ ⌂ **LA TORCHE** (N° RR NOV 27 099) (Mme Maryse **Tisinger)** 2, quai A. Depichon ☎ 56-59-19-20 ◣ 5 Closed Sun pm low season and Jan. English spoken.

PAULHAGUET 43230 Haute-Loire **RN 102 Map 17-A3**
♀ ⊗ ⌂ **LE COQ HARDI** (N° RR MAR 22 715) (Mme Marie-Louise **Meyronneine**) La Chomette ☎ 71-76-62-29.
♀ ⊗ ⌂ **LES TILLEULS** (N° RR DEC 23 560) (M. Gilbert **Vigouroux**) Saint-Georges-d'Aurac ☎ 71-77-50-75 ◣ 6 Closed Sat evening; Sun. Evening meals until 9pm.

PAULHAN 34230 Hérault **Map 23-A2**
♀ ⊗ **LE CASTEL FLEURI** (N° RR JUL 25 057) (M. Bernard **Belan**) 11, avenue de la Gare ☎ 67-25-01-23 Public car park; filling station (8am–8.30pm) near. English, Italian spoken.

PAVILLONS-SOUS-BOIS (LES) 93320 Seine-St-Denis **RN 3 Map 1-A3**
♀ ⊗ **CAFÉ DU STADE** (N° RR JUL 23 368) (M. Jean-Pierre **Georgelin**)
⊶ 31, rue A.-France ☎ 48-48-10-98.
⊶

PEAGE (LE) (Commune de SERAZEREUX par CHATEAUNEUF-EN-THYMERAIS) 28210 Eure-et-Loir **RN 154 Map 8-A3**
♀ ⊗ **AU BON ACCUEIL** (N° RR FEV 16 440) (Mme Paule **Fourni-quet**) Le Péage ☎ 37-38-32-49 Closed Sat, Sun; Aug. Evening meals served.

P

PEDERNEC 22540 C. du N. **Map 7-A2**
♀ ⊗ **RELAIS DE MAUDEZ** (N° RR JUL 26 614) (M. Denis **Dutillet**) ☎ 96-45-31-28 Closed Sun.

PELLEVOISIN 36500 Indre **RD 11 Map 12-B3**
♀ ⊗ ⌂ **LES ROUTIERS DE LA POSTE CHEZ BABETTE** (N° RR MARS 28 837) (Mme Elisabeth **Petit**) 30, rue Jean-Giraudoux ☎ 54-39-03-78 ⊸ 4 Closed Mon evening and October. Full board from 150 to 175F. Coaches welcome (rest. seats 70). Evening meals. English spoken.

PERCEY 89360 Yonne **CD 905 Maps 13-A2 and 9 B2/3**
♀ ⊗ ⌂ **1 Star NN L'AUBERGE DES PECHEURS** (N° RR JANV 26 424) (M. Paul **Kohl**) RN 5 ☎ 86-43-21-62 ⊸ 19 from 80–160F, breakfast 18–26F, telephone. Car park; bar; dogs allowed; recreations (fishing in canal and river), places to visit: Fosse d'Ione, Chablis vineyards. Closed Sun afternoon.

PERCY 50410 Manche **RD 999 Map 8-A1**
♀ ⊗ **LE RELAIS DE LA GARE** (N° RR OCT 24 704) (M. Bernard **Guillotte**) ☎ 33-61-20-96 **Minitel** ⊸ 4 Closed Sun; 1 to 13 Aug inl. Full-board 130F per night. Evening meals until 10pm.

PERIGNY 03120 Allier **RN 7 Map 16-A/B3**
♀ ⊗ ⌂ **LE RELAIS DE PERIGNY** (N° RR OCT 26 702) (M. René **Laniel**) ☎ 70-99-84-57 ⊸ 4 Closed Sat, Sun.

♀ ⊗ **AUBERGE FLEURIE** (N° RR JUN 26 926) (Mme Patricia **Milius**) Lapalisse ☎ 70-99-81-23 Closed Sun. German, English, Spanish, Italian spoken. Filling station (24 hrs) 5km distant.

PERIGUEUX 24000 Dordogne **RN 89 Map 15-B3**
♀ ⊗ **RELAIS BIBY** (N° RR MAR 21 821) (M. Jean-Pierre **Mazarguil**) 202 bis, route d'Angoulême ☎ 53-53-47-46 Closed Sun, Mon.
♀ ⊗ **LES ROUTIERS CHEZ ODETTE** (N° RR SEPT 27 025) (Mme Odette **Lecoq**) 129, avenue du Maréchal Juin ☎ 53-08-64-11 Closed Sun. Open 5am to 10pm.

PERN 46170 Lot **Map 22-A1**
♀ ⊗ **LE RELAIS DES CIGALES** (N° RR JUL 24 640) (M. Claude **Touron SARL**) Route Nationale 20 **Castelnau-Montratier** ☎ 65-31-97-49 Closed Sun.

PERONNE 80200 Somme **RN 17 Maps 5-B3 and 6-A1**
♀ ⊗ ⌂ **CHEZ BÉATRICE** (N° RR SEPT 26 320) (M. Serge **Seilier**) 61, route de Paris ☎ 22-84-10-82 ⊸ 6 Closed Sun; 2nd fortnight Aug; Easter week. Full-board 140F per night. Coaches welcome (rest. seats 25). Meals served until 9.30pm. German, English spoken.

PERONNE-ASSEVILLERS 80200 Somme **Autoroute A1 Maps 5-A3 and 6-A1**
♀ ⊗ **ACCOR L'ARCHE** (M. Aimé **Henry**) Aire de Service d'Asservilliers Province/Paris direction ☎ 22-85-20-35 Telex 140828

Open 24 hours. Self-service restaurant. Shop, TV, Showers. English, German spoken.

PERPIGNAN 66000 Pyrénées-Orientales **Map 23-A3**
⌂ **LA CHAUMIÈRE** (N° RR FEV 26807) (M. Michel **Mallet**) ZL St. Charles ☎ 68-56-57-69 Closed Sat evening, Sun; Aug.
⊗ **POLYGONE NORD** (N° RR MAI 27 290) (M. Claude **Lacaze**) 10, rue Beau de Rochas ☎ 68-61-46-74 Closed Sat and Sun.

PERRUSSON 37600 I.-et-L. **RN 143 Map 12-B3**
♈ ⊗ ⌂ **LE RELAIS DES ROUTIERS** (N° RR JUN 16 590) (M. Kleber **Lanchais**) 3, rue de l'Indre ☎ 47-59-04-34 ⊷ 8 Closed Sun evening; Aug. Holds the Relais Diplôme D'Honneur. Full-board 140F per night. Coaches welcome (rest. seats 120). Evening meals.

PERTHES 52100 Haute-Marne **RN 4 Map 9-A3**
♈ ⊗ ⌂ **LE COMMERCE** (N° RR JAN 26 141) (Mme Gilberte **Douard**) Rte Nle ☎ 25-56-41-79 ⊷ 18 Closed Sat, Sun open 24 hrs. Evening meals.

PERTUIS (LE) 43200 Haute-Loire **RN 88 Map 18-A3**
♈ ⊗ ⌂ **LE RELAIS DU COL** (N° RR SEP 17 888) (Mme Odile **Rioufrait**) ☎ 71-57-60-06 ⊷ 12 Closed Sat; 1 to 15 Sept. Coaches welcome (rest. seats 100). Meals served until 11pm.

PERTUIS 84120 Vaucluse **Map 24-B3**
♈ ⊗ **LE VICTOR HUGO** (N° RR AVR 26 233) (Mme Ghislaine **Pelisson**) 143 Bld Victor Hugo ☎ 90-79-12-29 Closed Sun; 20 days Aug. Coaches welcome (rest. seats 50). Evening meals. Italian, Spanish, English spoken.

PERUSE (LA) 16270 Charente **Map 15-B2**
♈ ⊗ **RESTAURANT LES ROUTIERS** (N° RR JANV 26780) (Mme Guylaine **Griffon**) Roumazières-Loubert ☎ 45-71-11-73 Closed Sun afternoon; Sept.

PETIT-FOSSARD (LE) 77130 S.-et-M. **RN 5 Map 9-B2**
♈ ⊗ ⌂ **LE RELAIS DU PETIT-FOSSARD** (N° RR OCT 20 572) (M. Jean **Guillard**) ☎ 64-32-03-28 and 432-17-47 ⊷ 6 Closed Sat afternoon, Sun; Aug; holidays. Evening meals until 11pm.

PETIT-REDERCHING 57410 Moselle **RN 410 Map 10-B1**
♈ ⊗ **REST DE LA GARE** (N° RR OCT 8 908) (M. Bernard **Vogel**) 6, rue de Strasbourg ☎ 87-09-81-09 **Minitel** Closed Sat; 15 Jul–15 Aug. Evening meals.

PETITE-BOISSIERE (LA) 79700 Deux-Sèvres **RN 148 bis Maps 11-B3 and 12-B1**
♈ ⊗ **Tobacconist LE RELAIS DES ROUTIERS** (N° RR JUL 23 858) (M. Jean-Michel **Charrier**) Grande Rue ☎ 49-81-42-72 Closed Mon afternoon.

PETITES (LES) LOGES see REIMS

P

PETIVILLE 14390 Calvados **RD 513 Map 4-B2**
♀ ⊗ **LE COLOMBIER** (N° RR NOV 26 103) (M. Gèrard **Baudel**)
Cabourg ☎ 31-78-00-67 Closed Sun; Sept.

PEYRIAC-DE-MER 11440 Aude **RN 9 Map 23-A3**
♀ ⊗ **RELAIS PORTE DES CORBIÈRES** (N° RR NOV 27 109) ☎ 68-48-
30-88 Closed Sun. English and German spoken.

PEZOU FONTAINE 41100 L.-et-C. **RN 10 Map 12-A3**
♀ ⊗ ⌂ **RELAIS D'ARGENTEUIL** (N° RR JAN 26 142) (M. Pierre
Hauville) RN 10 ☎ 54-23-42-47 ⊶ 5 Closed Sun. Evening meals.

PEZOU 41100 L.-&-C. **RN 10**
♀ ⊗ **L'ÉTAPE** (N° RR MARS 27 214) (M. Claude **Chève**) RN 10 ☎ 54-
23-42-85 Closed Sat pm and Sun.

PHILIPPSBOURG 57230 Moselle **RN 62 Map 10-B1 see BITCHE**

PIA 6380 Pyr. Orientales **Map 23-A3**
♀ ⊗ **AU P'TIT NICE** (N° RR OCT 26 398) (M. Jean Louis **Leone**) Km5
RN 9 ☎ 68-61-05-70 Closed Sat, Sun. Spanish, Italian, Arabic
spoken. Evening meals.

PIACE 72170 Sarthe **RN 138 Map 8-B2**
♀ ⊗ **LES DEUX RENARDS** (N° RR SEPT 27 004) (M. Jérôme **Brilliet**)
Le Bourg ☎ 43-97-02-16. Closed Sat afternoon, Sun. Filling station
at 4km.

PIAN MEDOC (LE) 33290 Gironde **RD 1 Map 15-A3**
♀ ⊗ **LE CHAMPETRE** (N° RR FEV 26 176) (Mme Arlette **Decons**)
Chabanau ☎ 56-72-04-72 Closed Sat, Sun. English, Yugoslavian,
Spanish spoken.

PICAUVILLE 56360 Manche **see PONT-L'ABBE**

PIERREFITTE 93380 Seine-St-Denis **Map 1-A3**
♀ ⊗ **LE NORMANDIE** (N° RR JUN 24 982) (Mme **Vidal**) 105 av.
Galliéni ☎ 48-26-55-62 Closed Sun; 2nd fortnight July. Evening
meals. Some English, Spanish spoken.
♀ ⊗ **AU RENDEZ-VOUS DES ROUTIERS** (N° RR JUN 26 571) (Mme
Aicha **Habj**) 71, ave Lénine ☎ 48-26-53-59 Closed Sun; Aug.
Coaches welcome (rest. seats 80). Evening meals. Arabic spo-
ken.

PIERREFITTE-NESTALAS 65260 Hautes-Pyr. **RN 21 Map 21-A3**
♀ ⊗ ⌂ **LE RELAIS DE BEL-AIR** (N° RR JUN 21 131) (M. Raymond
Bellocq) 5, rue Lavoisier ☎ 62-97-75-22 ⊶ 12 Closed 15 Sep–15
Oct. Full-board 145F per night. Evening meals. Spanish spoken.

PIERREFITTE-RONAI 61160 Orne **RN 158 Map 8-A2**
♀ ⊗ **LE PIERREFITTE** (N° RR JANV 27 143) (M. Yves **Delaunay**)
Trun ☎ 33-35-95-06 Closed Tues.

P

PIERREFITTE-SUR-LOIRE 03470 Allier
♀ ⊗ **AU CAFÉ DE LA MAIRIE** (N° RR JUIL 27 322) (M. Daniel **Monnier**) Place de l'Église ☎ 70-47-00-87 Closed Wed pm low season and Jan. Evening meals served until 11pm.

PIERRELATTE 26700 Drôme **RN 7 Map 24-A2**
⊗ **RESTAURANT DU TRICASTIN** (N° RR OCT 25 722) (M. François **Spagna**) RN 7 ☎ 75-96-34-11 Italian, Portuguese, German, Spanish spoken.

PIEUX (LES) 50340 Manche **RD 904 and 265 Map 4-A/B1**
♀ ⊗ **T'CHEU P'TIT LOUIS** (N° RR MAR 23 687) (M. Louis **Mabire**) 17, rue Centrale ☎ 33-52-43-18.

PIN MORIES-LE-MONASTIER Lieu-dit LES AJUSTONS 48100 Lozère **RN 9 Map 17-B3 et 23-A1**
♀ ⊗ ⌂ **1 star NN LES AJUSTONS** (N° RR MAR 20 128) (M. Guy **Gibelin**) Marvejols ☎ 66-32-70-35 Closed Sat/Sun and 15/12 to 15/1. Evening meals served until 9pm.

PINOLS 43200 Haute-Loire **RN 590 Map 17-A3**
♀ ⊗ ⌂ **HÔTEL DES VOYAGEURS** (N° RR JUL 19 853) (Mme **Cornet**) 71-74-11-42 ➡ 9 Full-board 150–160F per night. Coaches welcome (rest. seats 40). Meals until 9pm.

PIOLENC 84420 Vaucluse **Autoroute A7 Map 24-A2**
♀ ⊗ **LE COMMERCE** (N° RR NOV 25 182) (M. Roger **Sambucini**) place Cours Corsin ☎ 90-37-60-14 Closed Wed; Nov. Coaches welcome (rest. seats 60). English spoken.

PIPRIAC 35550 I.-et-V. **RD 777 Map 7-B3**
♀ ⊗ ⌂ **1 Star NN LE RELAIS DE LA TOUR D'AUVERGNE** (N° RR NOV 22 093) (M. Michel **Gérard**) 7, rue de l'Avenir ☎ 99-34-41-34 ➡ 10 Closed Mon (except lunchtime); Feb. Full-board 170–220F per night. Coaches welcome (rest. seats 40). Evening meals.

PISSOS 40410 Landes **RD 43 and 20 Map 20-B1**
♀ ⊗ **HÔTEL DU COMMERCE** (N° RR MAR 24 533) (M. Jean-Jacques **Mondat**) **Au Bourg** ☎ 58-07-70-16 ➡ 10 Closed Fri; Jan; end Oct. Full-board 145F per night. Coaches welcome (rest. seats 60).Evening meals.

PITHIVIERS 45300 Loiret **RN 51 Map 9-B1**
♀ ⊗ **HÔTEL DU POINT DU JOUR** (N° RR MAI 21 528) (Mme Marie-Claude **Rivière**) 4, faubourg d'Orléans ☎ 38-30-01-76 ➡ 3 Closed Mon; Open 8am–midnight.
♀ ⊗ **LE RELAIS** (N° RR JUN 23 339) (M. Christian **Pellerin**) route d'Etampes ☎ 38-39-71-70 Closed Sat; Aug.

PLAGNY 58000 Nièvre **Map 13-B2**
⊗ **LE RELAIS DE PLAGNY** (N° RR JAN 25 267) (M. Maurice **Chet**) 108, route de Lyon **Nevers** ☎ 86-57-51-51 ➡ 3 Closed Sun; 1 week at Christmas; 15 days in Aug.

P

PLAINE-SAINT-DENIS 93210 Seine-Saint-Denis **RN 1 Porte de la Chapelle Map 1-A2**

♀ ⊗ **LE RELAIS DE LA PLAINE** (N° RR OCT 25 127) (M. Amar **Kejat**) 138, avenue du Président-Wilson ☎ 48-20-02-31 Closed Sun. Arabic, Spanish spoken.

♀ ⊗ **LE CRISTAL** (N° RR AVR 25 366) (M. André **Leconte**) 101, av. du Président-Wilson ☎ 42-03-77-78 Closed Sun. English spoken.

LA PLAINE see SAINT-DENIS

PLAISANCE-DU-GERS 32160 Gers **RN 646 Map 12-A2**

♀ ⊗ ⌂ **LA PERGOLA** (N° RR OCT 14 040) (Mme Christiane **Lagisquet**) 11, allée des Ormeaux ☎ 62-69-30-22 ⇌ 10 Closed 24 Dec–3 Jan. Full-board 145F per night. Coaches welcome (rest. seats 50). Evening meals until 11pm.

PLAINTEL 22940 C.-du-N. **Map 7-A2**

♀ ⊗ ⌂ **A LA DESCENTE DES CHAOS** (N° RR AOU 25 616) (M. Jean-Claude **Bonenfant**) gare de Plaintel ☎ 96-32-16-05 ⇌ 8 Closed Tue afternoon, Sun afternoon; Aug. English spoken.

♀ ⊗ **LE SÉBASTOPOL** (N° RR MARS 26 474) (Mme Colette **Helary**) route de Sébastopol ☎ 96-52-15-74 Closed Sun; Aug. Coaches welcome (rest. seats c.100). Evening meals. English, German spoken.

PLEUMEUR-GAUTIER 22740 Côtes-du-Nord **CD 33 Map 7-A2**

♀ ⊗ ⌂ **LA VIELLE AUBERGE** (N° RR NOV 27 087) (M. Jean-François **Querou**) Le Bourg ☎ 96-20-13-35 ⇌ 5 Closed Aug.

PLENÉE JUGON 22640 Côtes-du-Nord **RN 12 Map 7-A3**

♀ ⊗ **LES GARENNES** (N° RR SEPT 27 007) (M. Jean **Elings**) **Lieu dit Les Garennes** ☎ 96-34-52-11 English, Spanish and Dutch spoken.

PLEYBEN 29190 Finistère **RN 787 and Dle 787 Map 7-A2**

♀ ⊗ **HÔTEL DES VOYAGEURS** (N° RR SEPT 26 648) (M. Jean-Yves **Marzin**) 17, Grande Place, Charles de Gaulle ☎ 98-26-61-06 ⇌ 6 Closed Fri evening, Sun; 2nd/3rd week Aug. Coaches welcome (rest. seats 64). Evening meals until 9pm.

PLIVOT 51150 Marne **RD 3 Map 9-A3**

♀ ⊗ **LE JARD** (N° RR JAN 26 156) (M. **Garcia**) 2, rue Maréchal Leclerc ☎ 26-57-68-15 Closed Sun; public holidays; 15 days in Jul; 15 days Dec to Jan. Coaches welcome (rest. seats 60). Special menu available. Evening meals except Mon. English spoken.

PLOERMEL 56800 Morbihan **RN 24 Map 7-B3**

♀ ⊗ ⌂ **LES ROUTIERS** (N° RR DEC 20 052) (Mme Solange **Rio**) route de Rennes ☎ 97-74-00-48 **Minitel** ⇌ 11 Closed Sat; Sept; 1 week at Christmas to New Year. Coaches welcome (rest. seats 150). Evening meals.

PLOMBIERES-LES-BAINS 88370 Vosges **RN 57 Maps 14-B2 and 10-A3**

♀ ⊗ ⌂ **1 Star NN LE RELAIS STRASBOURGEOIS** (N° RR AVR 6 049)

(M. Alain **Robert**) 3, place Beaumarchais ☎ 29-66-00-70 ⊷ 13 Closed Sun 1 Oct to 1 April; Nov. Full-board 148–190F per night. Coaches welcome (rest. seats 80). Evening meals. **Total Service Station** opposite hotel.

PLOMELIN 29000 Finistère **RN 785 Map 7-B1**
♈ ⊗ ⚑ **LE RELAIS DE L'AVANTAGE** (N° RR JUN 10 737) (M. Alain **Le Vergos**) ☎ 98-94-22-06.

PLOUAGAT 22170 C. du N. **RN 12 Quintin exit CD7**
♈ ⊗ **CHEZ PIERRETTE** (N° RR AOUT 26 296) (**SARL Drouin**) ZA de Fournello Sortie Quintin ☎ 96-74-28-13 Closed Sat midday, Sun. Coaches welcome (rest. seats 124), reservations necessary. Evening meals until 1am.

PLOUEDERN 29220 Finistère **RN 12 Map 7-A1**
♈ ⊗ **LE RELAIS KERIEL** (N° RR JUN 24 264) (Mme Marie **Gac**) Keriel - Landerneau ☎ 98-20-82-53 **Minitel** Closed Fri evening; end Sept to beginning Oct for 2 weeks. Coaches welcome (rest. seats 50). Evening meals. English spoken.

PLOUER-SUR-RANCE 22490 Côtes-du-Nord **RD 366 Map 7-A3**
♈ ⊗ **LE BON ACCUEIL CHEZ THEO** (N° RR MARS 26 483) (M. Théo **Yris**) La Gourbanière ☎ 96-86-91-67 Closed Mon afternoon, Aug.

PLOUGOUMELEN 56400 Morbihan **RN 165 Map 11-A1**
♈ ⊗ **LE KENYAH** (N° RR MAI 26 893) (M. Joël **Boriller**), Zone Commerciale du Kenyah ☎ 97-56-25-37 Closed Sun. Public car park. English spoken. Filling station near.

PLOUGUENAST 22150 C.-du-N. **RN 168 Map 7-A2**
♈ ⊗ **LE RELAIS DU SQUARE** (N° RR JUL 20 257) (Mme Sylviane **Lafon-Sagory**) route de Moncontour ☎ 96-28-70-47 ⊷ 2.

PLOUIGNEAU 29234 Finistère **Map 7-A2**
♈ ⊗ **LE RELAIS DES SPORTS** (N° RR JAN 26 151) (M. Paul **Talguen**) 18, rue du 9 Août ☎ 98-67-71-37 Closed Sun (except for banquets); Aug. Coaches welcome (rest. seats 65). Evening meals.

PLOUNEVEZ-MOEDEC 22810 C.-du-N. **RN 12 main road exit D 11 Map 7-A2**
♈ ⊗ ⌂ **AUX ROUTIERS – LE RELAIS DU BEG-AR-C'HRA** (N° RR JAN 3 717) (M. Jean- Marie **Rubeus**) N12 Begarchra exit (D11) ☎ 96-38-61-08 ⊷ 11 (6 deluxe) Closed Sat, Sun; 10 days between 20 Aug–20 Sep. Coaches welcome (rest. seats 140). Evening meals served until midnight. English spoken.

PLOUVENEZ-QUINTIN 22110 C.-du-N. **RN 790 Map 7-A/B2**
♈ ⊗ **LE RELAIS DES ROUTIERS** (N° RR MAR 14 273) (Mme **Martin**) place de'Eglise ☎ 96-24-54-05 Closed Sat; 15 Aug to 1 Sept.

PLOURAY 56770 Morbihan **Map 7-B2**
♈ ⊗ **LE RELAIS DES SPORTS** (N° RR JUL 24 642) (M. Léandre **Le Lain**) 2, rue de l'Ellé ☎ 97-23-90-18 Closed Sun. Evening meals.

P

POITIERS 86000 Vienne **RN 10 Map 15-B1**
♀ ⊗ **LE RELAIS DES DOUVES** (N° RR OCT 20 854) (Mme **Gremillon**) 2, avenue de la Libération ☎ 49-37-80-04 ⇔ 5 Coaches welcome (rest. seats 50). Evening meals. English, German spoken.

POIX TERRON 08430 Ardennes **Map 6-A2**
♀ ⊗ **LE GODILLOT** (N° RR OCT 26 080) (M. José **Michel**) 26, Place de la Gare ☎ 24-35-61-46 ⇔ 3 (1 double room) Closed Sat, Sun. Coaches welcome. Evening meals.

POMMEVIC 82400 T.-et-G. **RN 113 Map 21-B2**
♀ ⊗ ⌂ **A LA BONNE AUBERGE** (N° RR OCT 12 514) (M. Pierre
⊡ **Hume**) Route Nationale ☎ 63-39-56-69 ⇔ 7 Closed Sat evening 2 weeks in Nov. Full-board 150–180F per night. Coaches welcome (rest. seats 120). Evening meals.

PONS 17800 Charente-Maritime **Map 15-A2**
♀ ⊗ **RESTO-GRILL CHARENTOTEL** Autoroute A10 Aire de Saint-Léger ☎ 46-94-25-30.

PONT-A-LA-QUESNE see CHERBOURG 50820 Manche.

PONT-A-MOUSSON see LOISY 54700 M.-et-M. **Autoroute A31 Map 14-B1**
⚑ **Les Routiers Total Service Station LE RELAIS DE L'OBRION** (N° RR AVR 22 779) Loisy ☎ 83-81-03-85 Open 24 hours. English, German, Italian spoken.
⚑ **Les Routiers Elf Service Station LE RELAIS DE LOISY** (N° RR JUL 22 883) (M. **Bouilhac**) Aire de service de Loisy ⇔ 83-81-17-00 Open 24 hours. English, German spoken.
⊗ **TOURNEBRIDE** (MM **Joël** Frères) Autoroute A31 ☎ 83-81-18-89 Self-service restaurant with TV.

PONT-L'ABBE PICAUVILLE 50360 Manche **Map 4-B1**
♀ ⊗ ⌂ **HOTEL DES VOYAGEURS** (N° RR MAR 24 886) (Mme Fabienne **Françoise**) 43, rue de Périer ☎ 33-41-00-59 ⇔ 9 Closed Sun 1st Sep–Easter. Evening meals. English spoken.

PONT-D'AIN 01160 AIN **Map 18-B2**
♀ ⊗ **CRISNO** (N° RR NOV 26 731) (M. Christian **Sanchez**) 56, rue St-Exupéry ☎ 74-39-01-22.

PONTANEVAUX 71570 Saône-et-Loire **RN 6 Map 18-B1**
♀ ⊗ **Station-service CHEZ ALAMO** (N° RR MAI 27 279) (Mme Lydia **Paris**) ☎ 85-36-71-18 Closed Sat and Sun. Italian spoken. Evening meals.

PONTARLIER 25300 Doubs **Map 14-B3**
♀ ⊗ **CAFÉ DE LA LIBERTÉ** (N° RR SEPT 27 029) (Mmes Michèle **Besand** et Martine **Petit**) 36, rue de Salins ☎ 81-39-01-68 Closed Sun and 15/8 to 5/9.

P

PONT-D'ASPACH 68520 Haut-Rhin **Map 10-B3**
- ⚑ **Total Service Station LE RELAIS DE DIEFMATTEN** (N° RR
  SEP 24 688) Autoroute A36 Burnhaupt-le-Bas ☎ 89-48-74-00
  German, English spoken.

PONT-AUDEMER 27500 Eure **RN 180 Map 4-B3**
- ♈ ⊗ **RELAIS DE ST-PAUL** (N° RR JUL 26 286) (M. Claude **Virfollet**)
  Les Saulniers Route de St-Paul ☎ 32-41-16-17 Closed Sun; 1st
  fortnight Aug. Evening meals.
- ♈ ⊗ **AU RENDEZ-VOUS DES CHAUFFEURS** (N° RR JUN 25 439) (M.
  Renaud **Pierrel**) 4, rue Notre-Dame-du-Pré ☎ 32-41-04-36 Clo-
  sed Sun.
- ♈ ⊗ **RELAIS DU BOULANGARD** (N° RR AVR 23 230) (M. Francis
  Égret) Corveville-sur-Riscle ☎ 32-57-01-27.

PONTAULT-COMBAULT 77340 S.-et-M.) RN Map 1-B3
- ♈ ⊗ ⌂ **SARL LE RELAIS DU PAVÉ** (N° RR DEC 27 115) (M. José
  Da Silva) 9, route de Paris ☎ 60-28-00-21 Closed Sun and Aug.

PONT-AVEN 29123 Finistère **RN 783 Map 7-B1**
- ♈ ⊗ ⌂ **CHEZ MELANIE ET MONIQUE** (N° RR OCT 17 916) (M.
  ⌑ Bertrand **Le Goc**) Croissant-Kergoz ☎ 98-06-03-09 ⊸ 7 Closed
  Mon in Summer, Sept. Evening meals only Jun to Aug.

PONTCHARRA 38530 Isère **RN 90 Map 19-A2**
- ♈ ⊗ **LE RELAIS DU PONT DE LA GACHE** (N° RR AVR 25 357) (M.
  Jean-Pierre **Rubatat**) RN 90 **La GACHE** ☎ 76-97-30-08 Closed
  Sat; 15–30 Aug; 15 days at Christmas. Coaches welcome. Evening
  meals. English, Italian spoken. HGV parking.

PONTCHATEAU 44160 Loire-Atl. **RN 165 Map 11-A2**
- ♈ ⊗ ⌂ **LE RELAIS DE BEAULIEU** (N° RR AOU 7 869) (SARL
  Louisette **Praud**) ☎ 40-01-60-58 ⊸ 15 Coaches welcome (rest.
  seats 70 + café, annexe). Evening meals until midnight. Menus
  from 42,30–140F. Specialities: Eels in cider, grilled salmon with
  ⌑ butter, prawns à la Beaulieu. English spoken.
- ♈ ⊗ ⌂ **1 Star NN L'AUBERGE DU CALVAIRE** (N° RR NOV 20 885)
  ⌑ (Mme **Couvrand**) 6, route de la Brière 4km from centre of
  Pontchâteau on Herbignac road. Le Calvaire ☎ 40-01-61-65 ⊸ 12
  Full-board 160–188F per night. Coaches welcome (rest. seats 60).
  Evening meals.

PONTET (LE) 84130 Vaucluse **RN 7 Map 24-A3**
- ♈ ⊗ **LA CROIX VERTE** (N° RR DEC 24 439) (M. Guy **Prat**) route de
  Lyon ☎ 90-86-39-56 Closed Sun. Coaches welcome (rest. seats
  240).

PONT-CHRETIEN-CHABENET 36800 Indre **RN 727 Map 16-A1**
- ♈ ⊗ **LE RELAIS DE BOUZANNE** (N° RR OCT 24 000) (M. Gilbert
  Boileau) 15, rue Principale ☎ 54-25-81-54 Closed Wed afternoon;
  10 to 25 Aug. Evening meals.
- ♈ ⊗ **AUBERGE DU PONT** (N° RR JUIN 27 302) (Mme Yvelisé
  Lardeau) 46, rue Nationale ☎ 54-25-81-03 Closed Thurs and 15th
  to 30th Sept. Evening meals.

P

PONT GLENIC 23380 Creuse **see GLENIC**

PONT-DE-CHERUY 38230 Isere **RD 517 and 18 Map 2-A2**
♀ ⊗ **RELAIS CHEZ ZEPI** (N° RR AVR 26 490) (SARL **Delaur**) 30, rue
Giffard ☎ 78-32-20-02 ⇥ 30 Closed Sun. Coaches welcome at
weekend. Meals served until 10pm. English spoken.

PONT-DE-MENAT 63500 Puy-de-Dôme **RN 144 Map 16-B2**
♀ ⊗ ⌂ **LE RELAIS CHEZ ROGER** (N° RR JUN 13 786) (Mme
⌁ Marie **Pinel**) ☎ 73-85-50-17 ⇥ 8 Closed Wed evening, Jan. Full-
board 150–160F. Coaches welcome (rest. seats 60). Menus 55–
70F and more. Specialities *Jambon d'Auvergne, potée auverg-
nate,* trout.

PONT-DE-NERS 30190 Gard **RN 106 Map 23-B1**
♀ ⊗ **LE TAHURE** (N° RR OCT 26 713) (M. Georges **Apostolakis**)
Boucoiran **St-Chaptes** ☎ 66-83-58-45 Closed Sun off season.

PONT-EN-ROYAN
Voir SAINT-JUST-DE-CLAIX 38680 Isère

PONT-DES-SABLES 47200 Lot-et-Garonne **Map 21-A1**
♀ ⊗ **LE MARINIER** (N° RR JUN 24 991) (M. **Flores**) **Soussans -
Marmande** Toll exit ☎ 53-93-60-37 Closed Sat, Sun. Evening
meals. English, Italian, German, Spanish spoken.

PONT-DES-BEIGNERS 45530 Loiret **RN 60 Map 13-A1**
♀ ⊗ **LE RELAIS DU PONT DES BEIGNERS** (N° RR JUL 17 581) (M.
Jean-Pierre **Gueru**) ☎ 38-59-47-72 **Minitel** Closed Sat afternoon,
Sun; mid Aug to mid Sept. Evening meals.

PONTGIBAUD 63230 Puy-de-Dôme **RN 141 Map 16-B2**
♀ ⊗ ⌂ **LE RELAIS DES VOYAGEURS** (N° RR NOV 15 448) (M.
Sardier) avenue de Verdun ☎ 73-88-70-35 ⇥ 16 Closed Nov.
Full-board 135–140F per night. Coaches welcome (rest. seats 60).
Evening meals.

PONT-HÉBERT 50880 Manche **RN 174 Map 4-A1**
♀ ⊗ ⌂ **LE MADRILÉNE** (N° RR FEV 27 185) (Mme Marie-Thérèse
Hamet) Quartier du Pont-la-Meauffe ☎ 33-56-44-18 ⇥ 6

PONTHIERRY 77310 S.-et-M. **RN 7 Map 8-B1**
♀ ⊗ **LE RELAIS DES TROIS MARCHES** (N° RR DEC 24 054) (Mme
Odette **Pothier**) 7, rue de la Saussale ☎ 60-65-77-67 Closed Sun,
Aug.

PONTIGNY 89230 Yonne **RN 77 Map 13-A2**
♀ ⊗ ⌂ **RELAIS DE PONTIGNY** (N° RR AOUT 26 619) (Mme Carole
Leducq) 9, rue Paul-Desjardins ☎ 86-47-42-83 ⇥ 8 Closed Sun.
English, German, Italian spoken.

PONT-L'EVEQUE 71400 S.-et-L. **see AUTUN**

P

PONTOISE 95300 Val-d'Oise **RN 14 Maps 1-A2 and 9-A1**
♀ ⊗ **LE RELAIS DE LA POSTE** (N° RR JAN 24 810) (M. Jean-Marie
⊷ **Hofmann**) 68, rue Pierre-Butin ☎ 30-32-47-72 Closed Sun; Aug.
English, Spanish, German spoken.

PONTORSON 50170 Manche **RN 176 Map 8-A1**
♀ ⊗ ⌂ **LE FAMILY** (N° RR OCT 25 157) (Mme Antoinette **Hardel**) 4,
rue de Rennes ☎ 33-60-00-21 **Minitel** ⬩ 12 Full-board 120F per
night. Coaches welcome (rest. seats 60). Evening meals.

PONTORSON see SACEY

PONT-REMY 80580 Somme **Map 5-A3**
♀ ⊗ **LE CONTINENTAL** (N° RR JUL 25 480) (Mme Ginette **Therasse**)
SARL 10, rue Robert-Bordeux ☎ 22-27-12-89 Closed Mon; Aug.

PONT-ROYAL 08300 Ardennes **Map 6-B2**
♀ ⊗ **LE RELAIS PONT-ROYAL** (N° RR AVR 24 561) (M. Yves
Detruiseux) **Chatelet-sur-Retourne** ☎ 24-23-13-27 Closed Mon
evening. Evening meals.

PONT-ROYAL 13370 B.-du-R. **RN 7 Map 24-B3**
♀ ⊗ ⌂ **1 Star NN LE RELAIS PROVENÇAL** (N° RR AVR 15 614)
(Mmes **Audibert and Arnadi**) ☎ 90-57-40-64 ⬩ 10 Closed Wed;
Jan.

PONTS-ET-MARAIS 76260 S.-Marit **RD 1015 Bis Map 4-A2**
♀ ⊗ **LA FERME NIÇOISE** (N° RR JAN 26 777) (M. Patrick **Nalais**)
route de Gamache ☎ 35-86-50-37 Closed Sun.

PORT-A-BINSON 51700 Marne **Map 9-A2**
♀ ⊗ ⌂ **LE RELAIS DE LA GARE** (N° RR OCT 26 363) (Mme Nadine
Negri) 22, rue du Gl-Leclerc ☎ 26-58-30-41 ⬩ 5 Closed Sun. Full-
board 120–130F per night. Coaches welcome (rest. seats 60).
Evening meals.

PORT-SAINT-LOUIS-DU-RHONE 13230 Bouches-du-Rhône **Map 24-
A3**
♀ ⊗ ⌂ **1 Star NN REST. DES OUVRIERS HOTEL LAZZERI** (N° RR
JUL 26 953) (Messrs. Dominique and Pierre **Garcia**) 59 and 64,
⊷ rue Jean-Jaurès ☎ 42-86-01-28 ⬩ 23 (7 with own bath) from 110–
160F, breakfast 20F. Bar; dogs allowed. Places to visit: Camar-
gue, Arles, Les Saintes-Maries.

POULIGNY-NOTRE-DAME 36160 Indre **RD 940 Map 16-A2**
♀ ⊗ ⌂ **LA CHAUME BLANCHE** (N° RR JUN 23 308) (M. René
Pilorget) ☎ 54-30-21-43 ⬩ 7 Full-board from 190F per night.
Coaches welcome (rest. seats 45). English spoken.

POUSSAN 34140 Herault **RN 113 Map 23-B2**
♀ ⊗ **LE LANDRY** (N° RR DEC 25 236) (M. Joseph **Siauvaud**) ☎ 67-78-
24-74 Shops. Closed Sat afternoon, Sun. Spanish spoken.
♀ ⊗ **LE CHALET CHEZ CASTOR 05** (N° RR JUL 26 280) (M. Jean
Plawczyk) La Moulière ☎67-78-83-29 **Minitel** Closed Sat even-

P

Poussan continued

⌐ ing, Sun from midday; Christmas to New Years Day. Coaches welcome (rest. seats 120). Evening meals until midnight. Polish spoken.

POUSSAY 88500 Vosges **RN 413 Map 10-A2 and 14-B1**

♀ ⊗ ⌂ **AUBERGE DES PECHEURS** (N° RR NOV 2 282) (M. **Hingray**) ☎ 29-37-07-73 ⊷ 7 Closed Tue; 2 weeks in Dec; 2 weeks in Jun. Evening meals until 9pm.

POUZIN (LE) 07250 Ardèche **RN 86 Map 24-A1**

♀ ⊗ ⌂ **1 star NN ROUTIERS** (N° RR AVR 21 048) (Mme Juliette **Vialatte**) 64, rue Olivier-de-Serres ☎ 75-63-83-45 ⊷ 5 Closed Sun; 15 days Aug; 15 days Sept. Evening meals.

POZIERES 80300 Somme **RN 29 Map 5-B3**

♀ ⊗ **LE RELAIS DES ROUTIERS** (N° RR SEP 24 345) (Mme Josiane **Brihier**) Route Nationale ☎ 22-75-23-05.

PRESSAC 86460 Vienne **RN 148 Map 15-B2**

♀ ⊗ **LE RELAIS** (N° RR MAI 25 409) (Mme Francine **Bouyer**) Place de l'Église Mauprevoir ☎ 49-48-56-99 Closed Sat; Aug. Coaches welcome (rest. seats 60). Evening meals.

PREZ-SOUS-LAFAUCHE 52700 Hte-Marne **Map 14-A1**

♀ ⊗ **LES 3 VALLEES** (N° RR AVR 24 550) (Mme Eliane **Trommens-chlager**) ☎ 25-31-57-84 Closed Aug. Coaches welcome (rest. seats 140). Evening meals. Open 24 hrs.

PRIMAUBE (LA) 12450 Aveyron **RN 88 Map 22-B1**

♀ ⊗ **LES ROUTIERS** (N° RR MAI 26 534) (**Castanie Frères**) 3, avenue de Rodez ☎ 65-71-40-31 Closed Sun.

PRIVAS 07000 Ardèche **RN 104 Map 24-A1**

♀ ⊗ **LA RENAISSANCE** (N° RR MAR 21 437) (M. **Monteil**) 4, place du Champ-de-Mars ☎ 75-64-21-60 Closed Sun, Aug.

PROSNES 51400 Marne **RD 31 Map 6-B2**

♀ ⊗ **LE RELAIS CONSTANTINE** (N° RR NOV 14 593) (M. René **Roselet**) Constantine Route Nationale ☎ 26-61-70-70 **Minitel** Closed Sat, Sun; 15 to 31 Aug. Coaches welcome (rest. seats 150). Evening meals until 10pm.

PROVILLE-LEZ-CAMBRAI see CAMBRAI 59400 Nord **RN 17 Map 6-A1 and 5-B3**

PROVINS 77160 S.-et-M. **RN 19 Map 9-A/B2**

♀ ⊗ ⌂ **LE RELAIS DE LA CURE D'AIR** (N° RR NOV 3 083) (M. ⌐ **Amroun**) 54, avenue du Général-de-Gaulle ☎ 64-00-03-21 ⊷ 8 Closed Fri; Jul; Aug.

PROYART 80121 Somme **RN 29 Map 5-B3**

♀ ⊗ ⌂ **LA RAPERIE** (N° RR MAI 19 350) (Mme Odete **Mourier**)

🍴 Route Nationale La Raperie ☎ 22-85-37-30 🍴 8 Closed Sat afternoon; 23 Dec to 10 Jan. German, Italian, Spanish spoken.

PRUNAY-LE-GILLON see FRAINVILLE 28360 Eure-et-Loir **RN 154 and RD 28 Maps 8-B3 and 9-B3**
🍷 ⊗ **LE RELAIS DE LA GERBE D'OR** (N° RR MAI 14 347) (M. Charles **Miklos**) 10, rue du Pavillion ☎ 37-25-72-38 Closed Sun in winter; Feb. Coaches welcome (rest. seats 40). Evening meals. English spoken.

PUCH D'AGENAIS 47160 Lot-et-Garonne **A62 Map 21-A1**
⛽ **Mobil Oil Service Station AIRE DU QUEYRAN** (N° RR MAI 24 949) (M. René **Garcia**) Autoroute A62 (Nord) ☎ 53-79-48-92 **Damazan** Open 24 hours. Spanish, English spoken.

PUGET-THENIERS 06260 Alpes-Maritime **Map 25-B2**
🍷 ⊗ **LE RELAIS PUGETOIS EUROPA 202** (N° RR JUL 24 648) (M. Jean-Claude **Daviot**) SARL Route Nationale 202 ☎ 93-05-01-42/ 05-01-67 German spoken.

PUGNAC 33710 Gironde **RN 137 Map 15-A3**
🍷 ⊗ **LE RELAIS DU FASSIER - LE GRILLON** (N° RR DEC 22 117) (M. Rémi **Pitois**) ☎ 56-68-80-76 Lafosse. Closed Sun; Sept. Coaches welcome (rest. seats 100).

PUISSERGUIER 34620 Hérault **Map 23-A2**
🍷 ⊗ 🏠 **CAFÉ DE LA BOURSE** (N° RR NOV 27 108) (M. Joseph **Maya**) Place de la République ☎ 67-93-74-31 🍴 20.

PUJAUT 30131 Gard **RN 580 Map 24-A2**
🍷 ⊗ **CHEZ ODETTE** (N° RR DEC 25 765) (Mme Odette **Quinquemelle**) Les Gravières ☎ 90-25-19-70 Closed Sun. Evening meals until midnight.

PUTOT-EN-AUGE 14430 Calvados **RN 175 Map 4-B2**
🍷 ⊗ 🏠 **LE DAUPHIN** (N° RR NOV 25 733) (M. Jacques **Ribourg**) ☎ 31-79-20-29 **Minitel** 🍴 6 Closed Sun low season; 15 Dec to 15 Jan. Full-board 155–195F per night. Evening meals until 11.00pm. German spoken.

PUY (LE) 43000 Haute-Loire **Maps 17-A3 and 18-A3**
🍷 ⊗ **LA TAVERNE** (N° RR JUN 10 835) (M. René **Rolland**) 50, boulevard Carnot ☎ 71-09-35-16 🍴 10 furnished. Coaches welcome (rest. seats 50). Evening meals.
🍷 ⊗ 🏠 **1 star NN LA VERVEINE** (N° RR FEV 24 844) (M. Gaston **Mathieu**) 6, place Cadelade ☎ 71-02-00-77 et 02-14-66 **Minitel** ☎ 30 Closed 15/12 to 15/1. Full board 230–260F per night. Coaches welcome. (1 room, 100 covers). Evening meals.

PUYDROUARD par FORGES 17290 Aigrefeuille - Charente- Maritime **Map 11-B1**
🍷 ⊗ **CHEZ NÉNÉ** (N° RR SEPT 26 630) (M. **Bourieau**) ☎ 46-35-07-83 **Minitel** Closed Sun afternoon. Coaches welcome (rest. seats 80). Evening meals until 10pm. English spoken.

P

PUY-MAURY Commune de CONDAT-EN-COMBRAILLES 63380 P.-de-D. **RN 141 and RD 108 Map 16-B2**
♓ ⊗ **LE RELAIS CHEZ LUCETTE** (N° RR JAN 19631) (Mme Lucette **Condon**) ☎ 73-79-00-40 Closed 2nd fortnight Aug. Coaches welcome. Evening meals until 10.30pm.

PUYRICARD 'LA PETITE-CALADE' 13540 B.-du-R. **RN7 Map 24-B3**
♓ ⊗ ⌂ **LE TOURANGEAU** (N° RR MAI 21 533) (Mme Danielle **Roccia**) Nationale 7 ☎ 42-21-60-65 ⊷ 13 Closed Sun; Aug. Italian spoken.

Q

QUAEDYPRE 59380 Nord **CD 9 16 Map 5-A/B2**
♓ ⊗ **AUBERGE DU BON COIN - CHEZ L'GITAN** (N° RR JAN 21 368) (M. Pierre **Lammin**) CD 916 ☎ 28-68-76-94 Closed Mon; Aug. Coaches welcome (rest. seats 550). English spoken.

QUETTREVILLE-SUR-SIENNE 50660 Manche **Map 8-A1**
♓ ⊗ **BAR RESTAURANT DE L'ARRIVÉE** (N° RR NOV 27 106) (M. Jean-Louis **Guillon**) La Gare ☎ 33-47-62-00 Closed Sun. English and Italian spoken.

QUEVEN 56330 Morbihan **RD 6 Map 7-B2**
♓ ⊗ ⌂ **LE RELAIS DE LA MAIRIE** (N° RR JUL 17 317) (Mme Yvonne **Le Gallic**) rue Principale ☎ 97-05-07-50 ⊷ 8 Evening meals.

QUIMPER 29000 Finistère **RN 165 Map 7-B1**
♓ ⊗ **LE TRUCK** (N° RR JANV 27 165) (M. Jacques **Le Grand**) 96, avenue de la Libération ☎ 98-90-32-14 Closed Sun. English spoken.

QUINCY-SOUS-SEMART 91480 Essonnes
♓ ⊗ **A LA BONNE TABLE** (N° RR JANV 27 170) (M. Pierre **Walter**) 3, av. Henri-Chasles ☎ 699-00-93-81 Closed Sun.

QUINTIN 22800 C.-du-N. **St-Brieux/Quimper Map 7-A2**
♓ ⊗ **RELAIS JACOB** (N° RR SEPT 26 032) (M. Pierre **Jacob**) Zl St Brandan ☎ 96-74-88-19 Closed Sat afternoon, Sun.

R

RACHECOURT-SUR-MARNE 52170 Haute-Marne **RN 67 Map 14-A1**
Ⴤ ⊗ **L'AURORE** (N° RR DEC 26 413) (M. **Narat**) avenue de Belgique
☎ 25-04-41-58 ◄ 4 Closed Mon; Aug. Coaches welcome (rest.
seats 36).

RAHON 25430 Doubs **RD 31 Map 14-B3**
Ⴤ ⊗ ⌂ **1 Star NN AUBERGE DU CHATEAU** (N° RR OCT 25 725) (M.
Jean-Louis **Angelot**) ☎ 81-86-82-27 ◄ 9 Closed Sat. Full-board
120–135F. Coaches welcome (rest. seats 60). Evening meals.

RANES 61150 Orne **RN 916 Map 8-A2**
Ⴤ ⊗ **LE RELAIS DU PARC** (N° RR JUL 17 316) (M. Rogé **Cantin**) ☎
33-39-73-85 ◄ 5 Closed Sun (in winter); Sept. Full-board 160–
200F per night. Coaches welcome (rest. seats 150). Evening
meals until 8.30pm.

RASSATS (LES) par BRIE 16590 Charente **RN 141 Map 15-B2**
Ⴤ ⊗ **L'AUBERGE DES ROUTIERS** (N° RR NOV 19 204) (SARL **Doré
and Son**) ☎ 45-65-90-24 Closed Sun; Aug. Evening meals until
midnight.

RAVOIRE (LA) 73490 Savoie **RN 6 and CD 21 Map 19-A2**
Ⴤ ⊗ **LA PETITE TARENTAISE** (N° RR JUN 26 269) (Mme Maryse
Favre) Rte Nle 6 ☎ 79-72-94-27 Closed Sun low season. Private
carpark 1200m^2. Coaches welcome (rest. seats 92). Evening
meals.
Ⴤ ⊗ **CHEZ COLETTE** (N° RR MARS 26 470) (Mme Colette **Michaud**)
route d'Apremont VRU Chambéry exit 1 ☎ 79-33-35-07 **Minitel**
Closed Sun. Showers. Full-board 160–250F per night. (2 star
restaurant 100m from hotel). Coaches welcome (rest. seats 100).
Evening meals until 10pm. English, German, Italian, Spanish,
Portuguese spoken.

REALMONT 81120 Tarn **RN 112 Map 22-B2**
Ⴤ ⊗ **BAR RESTAURANT LES ALLÉES** (N° RR JUN 26 913) (M. Didier
Amalvy) 27, boulevard Armengaud ☎ 63-55-52-72 Closed Sun.
Filling station near.

REBENACQ 64260 Pyrénées-Atlantiques **Map 20-B3**
Ⴤ ⊗ **CHEZ PALU** (N° RR DEC 24 776) (M. Alain **Palu**) RD 134 ☎ 59-
21-74-11 Closed Sun. Coaches welcome (rest. seats 40). Evening
meals until 10pm.

REDESSAN 30129 Gard **RD 999 Map 24-A3**
Ⴤ ⊗ **LE RELAIS DU CANARD** (N° RR JUN 26 577) (M. Thierry
Lafont) ☎ 66-20-22-02 Closed Sun. Spanish spoken.

REDON 35600 I.-et-V. **Map 11-A2**
Ⴤ ⊗ ⌂ **1 Star NN LE RELAIS** (N° RR FEV 26 172) (M. Noël **François**
SARL) Rte de Rennes ☎ 99-71-46-54 **Minitel** ◄ 18 Full-board 98–
160F per night. Coaches welcome (rest. seats 120). Evening
meals. English spoken.

R

REFFANNES 79420 Deux-Sèvres **RD 938 Map 15-A1**
☺ ⊗ **LE CHEVAL BLANC** (N° RR SEPT 26 033) (M. **Chevaller**) ☏ 49-64-25-18 Evening meals.
☺ ⊗ ⌂ **HÔTEL DU COMMERCE** (N° RR JUL 26 005) (M. René **Chiron**) ☏ 49-70-22-08 ⎄ 10.

REGUISHEIM 68890 Haut-Rhin **RN 422 Map 10-B3**
☺ ⊗ ⌂ **SARL A L'ANGE** (N° RR JUN 19 085) (M. Raymond **Bertrand**) 90, Grande-Rue ☏ 89-81-12-66 ⎄ 5 Closed Sun; Aug. German spoken. Evening meals.

REIMS see also BEAUMONT-SUR-VESLE 51100 Marne **RN 31-51 and CD 75 Map 6-B1/2**

REIMS 51400 Marne **Autoroute A4 Maps 6-B1 and 2**
☺ ⊗ **RESTOP DE REIMS** (M. Patrice **Jezequel**) Aire de Service de Reims Champagne Les Petites Loges par Mourmelon-le-Grand ☏ 26-61-63-57 Self-service restaurant open 6.00am to 10.00pm. Showers, TV, Shop.

RELLECQ-KERHUON 29219 Finistère **RN 165 and D 205 Map 7-A1**
☺ ⊗ ⌂ **LE LONGCHAMPS** (N° RR MARS 26 203) (M. Jacky **Alinc**) 2, rue Jules-Ferry ☏ 98-28-26-55 ⎄ 9 Closed Sat, Sun. Evening meals. Weekdays only.

REMIREMONT 88200 Vosges **Voir SAINT-NABORD**

REMOULINS 30210 Gard **RN 86 Map 24-A3**
☺ ⊗ ⌂ **AUBERGE DES PLATANES** (N° RR NOV 24 421) (M. Gérard **Reynaud**) Castillon-du-Gard-les-Croisées ☏ 66-37-10-69 ⎄ 10 Closed Sat evening, Sun; Jan. Full-board 220–255F per night. Coaches welcome (rest. seats 55). Evening meals. English, Spanish spoken. Menus 50–100F. Specialities: *Rouille d'encornets carmagueuse, potée du pêcheur aux fruits der mer* (made to order).

RENAC 35660 1.-et V. **RD 177**
☺ ⊗ **BEAUREGARD** (N° RR FEV 27 192) (Mme Marie-Annick **Bonno**) ☏ 99-72-07-83 Closed Mon and 10 days in Feb.

RENESCURE 59173 Nord **RN 344 Map 5-A1**
☺ ⊗ **LE RELAIS DE LA CLEF DES CHAMPS** (N° RR JAN 15 505) (Mme Marlène **Lamiaux**) Route Nationale 42 ☏ 28-49-81-12 Evening meals.

REVIN 08500 Ardennes **RN 388 Map 6-A2**
☺ ⊗ **LE RELAIS DES ROUTIERS** (N° RR JAN 17 985) (M. **Mahut**) 4, rue Voltaire ☏ 24-40-12-91 ⎄ 4.

REYERSVILLER 57230 Moselle **Map 10-B1**
☺ ⊗ **LE RELAIS DE LA SCHWANGERBACH** (N° RR AVR 24 924) (Mme Marie-Christine **Huet**) 63, route de Lemberg ☏ 87-96-10-72 Closed Wed; Oct. German spoken.

R

REYRIEUX 01600 Ain
♀ ⊗ **BAR RESTAURANT DE LA GARE** (N° RR MAI 27 271) (Mme Yvonne **Oritz**) ☎ 74-00-12-00 Closed last week of August. English and Spanish spoken.

RHODES 36170 Indre **RN 20 Map 16-A1**
♀ ⊗ **LE RELAIS ROUTIERS DE RHODES** (N° RR AVR 25 375) (M. Jean-Pierre **Perez**) Mouhet-Rhodes ☎ 54-47-65-26 **Minitel** Closed Sat afternoon, Sun; Aug. Evening meals until 10.30pm.

RIAILLE 44440 Loire-Atlantique **Map 11-A3**
♀ ⊗ **AU RENDEZ-VOUS DES PECHEURS** (N° RR AVR 26 528) (M. Joël **Aspot**) 7, rue de Bretagne ☎ 40-97-80-95 Closed Wed afternoon. Coaches welcome (rest. seats 60). Evening meals.

RIBAUTE-LES-TAVERNES 30720 Gard **RN 110 Map 23-B1**
♀ ⊗ ⌂ **LE VIEUX MOULIN** (N° RR JUN 26920) (Mmes **Coste** and **Riminucci** ☎ 66-83-07-94 ⊷ 5 Closed Tue; Mon evening; Sept–June. English, Spanish, Italian spoken. Filling station near.

RIBAY (LE) 53240 Mayenne **RN 12 Map 8-B1**
♀ ⊗ ⌂ **LE LION D'OR** (N° RR JUN 23 351) (Mme Simone **Reboux**) Le Bourg ☎ 43-03-90-27 ⊷ 7 Closed 20 Dec–2 Jan. Full-board 140–180F per night. Coaches welcome (rest. seats 80). Evening meals. English spoken.

RIBERAC 24600 Dordogne **RN 708/710 Map 15-B3**
♀ Snack **LAKANAL LES ROUTIERS** (N° RR FEV 20 395) (Mme **Angelier**) 1, avenue Lakanal ☎ 53-90-04-77 Closed Thur; Jun or Sept for 20 days.
♀ ⊗ ⌂ **CAFE DU COMMERCE** (N° RR MAR 23 172) (M. Paul **Ratineau**) **La Borie** Villetoureix ☎ 53-90-05-24 ⊷ 9 Closed Sun except high season. Full-board 120F per night. Evening meals.

RICAMARIE (LA) 42150 Loire **RN 88 Map 2-B1**
♀ ⊗ **AU RELAIS SYMPA RICAMONDOIS** (N° RR SEPT 27 008) (M. Franck **Bonnaire**) 5 bis, rue de la Libération ☎ 77-57-89-31 Closed Mon pm. Open 7.30am to midnight. English and German spoken.

RICHEVILLE 27420 Eure **RN 14 Map 3-B1**
♀ ⊗ **LE RELAIS DES GLYCINES** (N° RR AOU 21 192) (M. Serge **Gaultier**) Route Nationale 14 ☎ 32-55-61-05 ⊷ 1 Closed Sun afternoon.
♀ ⊗ **LE RESTOROUTE LE BALTO** (N° RR FEV 27 173) (M. Pierre **Sadok**) RN 14 ☎ 32-27-10-55 Closed Sun. English spoken.

RIEUMES 31370 Haute-Garonne **Map 22-A2**
♀ ⊗ ⌂ **LES PALMIERS** (N° RR AVR 26 524) (M. Jean-Claude **Gilibert**) 13, place du Foirail ☎ 61-91-81-01 ⊷ 7 Closed Sun evening; Feb. Half-board 90F, full-board 130F per night. Coaches welcome (2 dining rooms = 105 seats). Evening meals until 9pm. German, English, Italian spoken.

R

RIEUPEYROUX 12240 Aveyron **RD 905 Map 22-B1**
♀ ⊗ ⌂ **1 Star NN CHEZ PASCAL Tobacconist** (N° RR OCT 23 965)
(M. Claude **Bou**) rue de l'Hom ☎ 65-65-51-13 ⊷ 15 Closed Sun
evening low season; 1 to 15 Oct. Full-board 120–130F per night.
Coaches welcome (rest. seats 60). Evening meals.

RIEUTORT- DE RANDON 48700 Lozère **CD 1 Map 17-B3**
♀ ⊗ **RELAIS DE LA POSTE** (N° RR JUL 26 611) (Mme Simone
Magne) Place de la Poste ☎ 66-47-34-67.

RILLIEUX-LA-PAPE 69140 Rhône **Map 2-A2**
♀ ⊗ **RELAIS DU BUGEY** (N° RR FEV 26 455) (M. Alain **Rebout**) 1270,
avenue Victor Hugo ☎ 78-88-09-60 **Minitel** Closed Sat, Sun; 15
Jul to 15 Aug. Coaches welcome (rest. seats 50).

RIOM 63200 P.-de-D. **RN 9 Map 16-B3**
♀ ⊗ **LE CANTALOU** (N° RR MAI 24 939) (M. Jean-Louis **Tholonias**)
12, avenue de Clermont ☎ 73-38-03-68 Closed Sun; 15 days Aug;
1 week Christmas. Coaches welcome (2 dining rooms = 50
seats). English spoken.
♀ ⊗ **AU STAND** (N° RR OCT 25 680) (Mme **Dassaud-Riquier**) 24,
avenue de Clermont ☎ 73-38-04-06.

RIOTORD 43200 Haute-Loire **RD 503 Map 18-A3**
♀ ⊗ **BAR RESTAURANT DES CHASSEURS** (N° RR MARS 26 824)
(Mme Dominique **Arnaud**) route de Dunières ☎ 71-75-31-40
Closed Mon afternoon. Filling station at 3 kms.

RIS/PUY GUILLAUME 63290 Puy-de-Dôme **Map 16-B3**
♀ ⊗ **HOTEL DE LA GARE** (N° RR JUN 25 008) (M. Jean-Louis **Robin**)
Route Nationale 106 (D 906) ☎ 73-94-61-61 Closed Sat.

RISCLE 32400 Gers **RD 135 Map 21-A2**
♀ ⊗ ⌂ **1 Star NN LE RELAIS DE L'AUBERGE** (N° RR DEC 21 307)
(Mme **Portes**) place de la Mairie ☎ 62-69-70-49 ⊷ 10 (with WC)
from 65–80F, breakfast 15–18F. Closed Sun; Oct. Full-board 140F
per night. Coaches welcome (rest. seats 100). Car park; bar;
dogs allowed. Places to visit: Cave de Saint-Mont, Tour de
Termes d'Armagnec, Foie gras cannery.

RIVES-SUR-FURE 38140 Isère **RN 85 Map 24-B1**
♀ ⊗ **BAR DES SPORTS** (N° RR JUL 26 019) (M. Michel **Le Guyader**)
315, rue du Plan ☎ 76-91-04-37 **Minitel** Closed Sun; 15 to 31 Dec.
Evening meals.

RIVIERE-DE-CORPS (LA) 10300 Aube **RN 60 Map 9-B3**
♀ ⊗ **LA QUEUE DE LA POELE** (N° RR MAI 25 404) (M. Gaby
Barbier) RN 60 Sens road, Troyes exit ☎ 25-74-47-94 Closed Sun
evening.

RIVIERE-SAINT-SAUVEUR (LA) 14560 Calvados **RN 180 Map 4-B2**
♀ ⊗ **AUX OISEAUX DE MER** (N° RR AVR 21 501) (M. Daniel
Frabois) Lieu-dit Le Poudreux ☎ 31-89-11-61 ⊷ 4 Closed Sun;
Aug.

R

ROANNE 42300 Loire **RN 7 Map 18-A2**
Y **CHEZ PATRICE ET MARCEL** (N° RR JUN 23 310) (M. Patrice
Comby) 1, place du Champ-de-Foire ☎ 77-71-43-09 Closed Tue
afternoon.
Y ⊗ ⌂ **LE PARIGNY** (N° RR OCT 24 897) SARL (Mme Jeanine
Pamure) LesBas de Rhins Le Coteau sortie sud de Roanne ☎ 77-
62-06-18 Closed Sun and 10th to 20th August.

ROCHE-CHALAIS (LA) 24490 Dordogne **RD 730 Map 15-A3**
Y ⊗ **CAFE DU MIDI** (N° RR AVR 21 884) (Mme Violette **Rawyler**)
⌐ 32, avenue du Stade ☎ 53-91-43-65 English, German spoken.

ROCHECORBON 37210 I.-&-L. **RN 152**
Y ⊗ **RELAIS DES PATYS** (N° RR FEV 27 198) (M. Jean-Marc **Nourry**)
1, rue des Patys ☎ 47-52-61-75 ☎ 4 Closed Sun and Dec. English
and Spanish spoken.

ROCHE-LA-MOLIERE 42290 Loire **Map 18-A2**
Y ⊗ **LE FLORENCE** (N° RR SEPT 26 659) (M. Michel **Bruyas**) 3 rue
des Carrières ☎ 77-90-58-41 Closed Aug.

ROCHEFORT/NENON 39700 Jura **RN 73 Map 14-A3**
⚑ **Total Service Station RELAIS DES POIRIERS** (N° RR OCT
55000005) (M. Daniel **Chaney**) RN 73 ☎ 84-72-40-35 Closed Sun;
9–21 Aug.

ROCHEFORT-SUR-MER 17300 Charent.-Marit **RN 11 Map 11-B1**
Y ⊗ **LE REPOS DES ROUTIERS Tobacconist** (N° RR SEPT 26 650)
(M. Paul **Guillon**) Le Grand Vergeroux Nationale 137 ☎ 46-84-41-
48 Closed Sun.
Y ⊗ **LE DAUPHIN** (N° RR SEPT 26 633) (M. J.-C. **Philibert**) 24, rue
Denfert-Rochereau ☎ 46-99-21-43 Closed Sun afternoon and
evening. English spoken.

ROCHELLE (LA) 17010 Charente-Maritime **Map 11-B1**
Y **DELMAS BAR** (N° RR JAN 24 479) (Mme Jeanine **Francson**) 32,
bd Emile-Delmas ☎ 46-42-60-23 Snacks. Closed Sun; 2nd fortnight Sept.
Y ⊗ ⌂ **LES EMBRUNS** (N° RR JUIL 935) (M. René **Poultier**) 413,
avenue Guiton ☎ 46-42-61-88 or 46-43-69-73 ⊷ 7 Closed Sun; 1
week Christmas. Filling station near.
Y ⊗ **LE TOUT VA MIEUX** (N° RR NOV 27 110) (Mme Josianne
Verdier-Muon) 1, avenue de Colmar ☎ 46-41-10-69.

ROCHELLE-AIGEFEUILLE (LA) 17290 Chte-Mme **RD 939 Map 11-
B1**
Y ⊗ ⌂ **LA CLEF DES CHAMPS** (N° RR AOU 22 911) SO-DI-HO-CP)
(M. **Maurel**) Z.I. des Grands-Champs près de La Rochelle –
Camp de Croix Chapeau ☎ 46-35-64-43 German and English
spoken. Free camping. Coaches welcome (rest. seats 90). Even-
ing meals.

ROCHELLE-PALLICE (LA) 17000 Chte-Mme
Y ⊗ ⌂ **RELAIS OCÉANIC** (N° RR JUL 25 494) (M. Claude **Chauvin**)

R

Rochelle-Pallice continued

    Place du Marché ☎ 46-42-62-37 ⊷ 5 Closed Sat; Aug. Evening meals until 9.30pm.

🍷 ⊗ **CHEZ ANNIE** (N° RR AVR 27 262) (Mme Annie **Bernelas**) Ancien Embarcadère de l'Ile de Ré ☎ 46-42-53-61 Closed Sun. Evening meals served until 11pm.

ROCHEMAURE 07400 Ardèche **RN 86 Map 24-A2**

🍷 ⊗ **LE RELAIS DE LA CONDAMINE** (N° RR NOV 14 069) (Mme Josiane **Sicoit**) ☎ 75-52-96-26 Closed Sun; 15 to 31 Aug. Coaches welcome (rest. seats 50).

ROCHE-SUR-YON 85000 Vendée **RN 137 Map 11-B2/3**

🍷 ⊗ 🏠 **2 Stars NN LE SULLY** (N° RR OCT 22 072 (Mme Natalie **Bohy**) boulevard Sully ☎ 51-37-18-21 and 51-37-54-02 **Minitel** ⊷ 34 from 120–160F, breakfast 18F. Full-board 180–250F per night. Coaches welcome (rest. seats 50). Evening meals until midnight. English, Spanish spoken. Car park; bar; dogs allowed, recreations (skating, swimming). Places to visit: Haras, museum, dam at Papon.

🍷 ⊗ **LE MOULIN DE LA BERGERIE** (N° RR JUN 22 375) (S.N.C. **Mothais**) Aizenay Carrefour de la Grolle Nationale 60 Rte La Roche/Les Sables - Rte de Landeronde - Venansault ☎ 51-40-36-94 Closed 1 to 20 Jan.

ROCHETAILLÉE par LE BOURG-D'OISANS 38520 Isère **RN 91 and RD 526 Map 19-A3**

🍷 ⊗ 🏠 **1 Star NN HOTEL BELLEDONNE** (N° RR OCT 22 965) (Mme Mireille **Esposito**) ☎ 76-80-07-04 ⊷ 25 Closed weekends low-season. Full-board 160F per night. Coaches welcome (rest. seats 100). Evening meals. Some English spoken.

ROCHE-VINEUSE 71960 S.-et-L. **RN 79 Map 18-B1**

🍷 ⊗ **CHEZ FRANCE** (N° RR SEP 25 115) (Mme France **Brouillon**) Place du Chaucher ☎ 85-37-71-51 **Minitel** Closed Sat afternoon, Sun; Aug. Coaches welcome (rest. seats 50). Evening meals.

ROCROI 08230 Ardennes **RN 51 and 377 Map 6-A2**

🍷 🏠 **HÔTEL DE LA GARE** (N° RR JAN 23 633) (SARL **Minucci**) 1, Ave du Gl-Moreau ☎ 24-54-10-32 ☎ 11.

🍷 ⊗ **REST DE LA JEUNESSE** (N° RR FEV 27 177) (M. Jean-Luc **Lecomte**) Rue Royale ☎ 24-54-25-12 Closed Tues after lunch.

RODEZ 12000 Aveyron **RN 88 and 595 Map 22-B1 see also BERTH-OLENE**

🍷 ⊗ 🏠 **LE RELAIS MON BAR** (N° RR NOV 12 569) (M. Henri **Cristol**) 19, avenue Victor-Hugo ☎ 65-68-14-59 **Minitel** ⊷ 10 Closed Sun. Full-board 130–160F per night. Coaches welcome (rest. seats 50). Evening meals.

🍷 ⊗ 🏠 **1 Star NN LA ROCADE** (N° RR AOU 18 491) (M. **Gayraud**) La Roquette RN 88 ☎ 65-67-10-44 and 67-17-12 **Minitel** ⊷ 17 from 65–115F, breakfast 17F, telephone. Open 7.00am to 10.00pm. Closed Fri evening, Sat; 1 to 14 July; 24 December 1988 to 12 Jan 1989. Full-board 150–180F per night. Coaches welcome (rest.

seats 70). Evening meals. Car park; bar; dogs allowed (only in restaurant); garden. Menu 43–100F. Specialities *Confit de Canard, Civet d'oie*.

ROFFIAC 15100 Cantal **RD 926 Map 17-A2**
Y ⊗ **AUBERGE DE LA VALLÉE** (N° RR MAR 23 193) (M. Pierre **Farges**) St. Flour ☎ 71-60-04-50 Closed Sat, Sun; 15–30 Aug.

ROGNAC 13340 B.-du-R. **RN 113 Map 24-B3**
Y ⊗ ⌂ **2 Stars NN CADET ROUSSEL** (N° RR AVR 25 353) (M. Jack **Schiele**) Autoroute exit-Berre ☎ 42-87-00-33 ⊷ 13 from 160–220F, breakfast 18–20F. Closed Sun. Full-board 160–240F per night. Evening meals until 10pm. Some German spoken. Car park; bar; dogs allowed.

ROGNONAS 13870 Bouches-du-Rhône **RN 570 Map 24-A2**
Y ⊗ **LE COMMERCE** (N° RR JUN 26 914) (M. Robert **Giacometti**) avenue de la Libération ☎ 90-94-84-26 ⊷ 4 Filling station near.

ROMAGNY 50140 Manche **Map 8-A1**
Y ⊗ **AUBERGE DES CLOSEAUX** (N° RR OCT 24 717) (M. Bernard **Clouard**) Les Closeaux ☎ 33-59-01-86 Closed Sat; Feb; Aug. Coaches welcome (rest. seats 60). Evening meals.

ROMILLY-SUR-SEINE 10100 Aube **RN 19 Map 9-B2**
Y ⊗ **LA BONNE ÉTAPE** (N° RR MAI 26 249) (M. William **Faroy**) RN 19, St-Hilaire ☎ 25-24-78-04 Closed Sun; Aug. Evening meals until 9pm.

ROMORANTIN-LANTHENAY 41200 L.-et-C. **RN 722/765 Map 13-B1**
Y ⊗ **RELAIS DE L'AVENIR** (N° RR AOU 25 075) (M. Jean-Luc **François**) 44, Avenue de Villefranche ☎ 54-76-14-28 **Minitel** Closed Sat, Sun; Aug. Coaches welcome (rest. seats 60). Evening meals only.
Y ⊗ ⌂ **1 Star NN LES AUBIERS** (N° RR MAR 23 703) (M. Guy **Boivin**) 1, avenue de Blois ☎ 54-76-05-59 ⊷ 20 (2 with bathroom) from 60–120F, breakfast 16F. Coaches welcome (rest. seats 120). Evening meals.

RONCHAMP 70250 Haute-Saône **RN 19 Map 10-A3**
Y ⊗ ⌂ **1 Star NN LE RELAIS DE LA POMME D'OR** (N° RR FEV 18 622) (MM. **Cenci Frères**) Rue Le Corbusier ☎ 84-20-62-12 ⊷ 25 German spoken. Evening meals.

ROQUE-D'ANTHÉRON (LA) 13640 Bouches-du-Rhône **CD 561 et 543 Map 24-B3**
Y ⊗ ⌂ **AU RELAIS FLEURI** (N° RR OCT 27 058) (M. Guy **Auguste**) **Hameau de St. Christophe** ☎ 12-50-20-24 ⊷ 9 English, Italian, German and Spanish spoken.

ROQUEFORT 40120 Landes **Map 21-A2**
Y ⊗ **AUBERGE DE LA DILIGENCE** (N° RR MAI 26 881) (M. Antoine **Cardoso**) Rte de Bordeaux ☎ 58-45-54-94 Open 24 hrs. Portuguese, Spanish, English spoken. Filling station near.

R

ROQUEFORT-DES-CORBIÈRES 11540 Aude **RN 9 Map 23-A3**

♈ ⊗ **LE RELAIS D'EL ROC** (N° RR AVR 22 785) (Mme Geneviève **Droulez**) Motorway exit between Sigean/Leucate. Côtes Roquefort region. ☎ 68-48-20-88 Closed Thurs (except high season). English, German, Spanish, Italian, Dutch spoken.

♈ ⊗ **RELAIS CÔTES DE ROQUEFORT** (N° RR JUL 26 616) (M. Jean-Claude **Mayer**) ☎ 68-42-20-09.

ROQUETTE see RODEZ 12000 Aveyron **RN 595 Map 22-B1**

ROSIÈRES 07260 Ardèche **RD 104 Map 23-B1**

♈ ⊗ ⌂ **1 Star NN LES CÉVENNES** (N° RR AVR 22 783) (Mme Colette **Reynouard**) Joyeuse ☎ 75-39-52-07 ⇥ 14 Full-board 160–170F per night. Coaches welcome (rest. seats 150). Evening meals until 10pm.

ROSOY 89100 Yonne **RN 6 Map 9-B2**

♈ ⊗ ⌂ **LA MAISON BLANCHE** (N° RR JUL 10 864) (M. **Reinhold**) Rte d'Auxerre ☎ 86-97-13-01 ⇥ 12 Open 24 hours. Full-board 145F per night. Coaches welcome (rest. seats 100). Evening meals. Menus 50–110F.

ROSPORDEN 29140 Finistère **RN 165 Map 7-B1**

♈ ⊗ ⌂ **LES ROUTIERS** (N° RR OCT 26 703) (Mme Maryvonne **Michal**) 9 Pont Biais ☎ 98-59-20-40 ⇥ 17 Closed Sun.

ROSTRENEN 22110 Côtes-du-Nord **Map 7-B2**

♈ ⊗ **LE RELAIS DES ROUTIERS** (N° RR MAI 14 345) (M. Corentin **Cerno**) 32, rue Olivier Perrin ☎ 96-29-01-30 **Minitel**.

ROTS 14980 Calvados **RN 13 Map 4-B2**

♈ ⊗ ⌂ **LE RELAIS DU COUP DE POMPE** (N° RR NOV 25 176) (M. Serge **Guizard**) Route de Caen ☎ 31-74-14-19 ⇥ 5 Closed Sun.

ROUANS 44640 Loire-Atlantique **Map 11-A2**

♈ ⊗ ⌂ **LA CHAUSSÉE LE RETZ** (N° RR JUN 26 911) (Mme Claudette **Biton**) La Chaussée le Retz ☎ 40-64-22-23 ⇥ 6 Closed Sats Oct to Whitsun. Filling station 2 km distant.

ROUBAIX 59100 Nord **Map 5-B1**

♈ ⊗ **LE CALAIS** N° RR OCT 27 073) (Mme Josette **Vaze**) 2, quai Calais ☎ 20-26-14-01 Closed Sat pm, Sun and August. German, Dutch and English spoken.

ROUDOUALLEC 56110 Morbihan **RD 1 and 15 Map 7-B1**

♈ ⊗ **LE RELAIS TY KORNN Chez Sylviane** (N° RR DEC 22 598) (Mme Sylviane **Lereste**) ☎ 97-34-50-38 Closed Sun. Evening meals until 9.30pm.

ROUEN 76100 Seine-Marit **RN 13 Bis and RN 14 Map 3-A1**

♈ ⊗ ⌂ **LES PLATANES** (N° RR MARS 26 468) (M. Roger **Sannier**) 57, avenue du Mont-Riboudet ☎ 35-71-01-52 ⇥ 20 Closed Sun; 24 Dec–2 Jan. Evening meals.

♈ ⊗ **LE RELAIS 207 Chez Joële et Patrick** (N° RR JAN 25 277) (M.

Patrick **Clivaz**) 46, quai Cavelier-de-la-Salle ☎ 35-73-18-55 Closed Sat, Sun.

Ⓨ ⊗ **LONDON BAR** (N° RR JAN 25 278) (M. Dominique **Merchi**) 55, quai Cavelier-de-la-Salle ☎ 35-73-03-01 Closed Sat, Sun. Evening meals. English, Arabic spoken.

Ⓨ ⊗ 🏠 **HÔTEL D'ORLÉANS** (N° RR OCT 26 715) (M. Guy **Soligny**) 32, quai Cavelier-de-la-Salle ☎ 35-73-36-99 ⊷ 10 Closed Sat, Sun.

ROUFFIGNAC-DE-SIGOULES 24240 Dordogne
Ⓨ ⊗ **RELAIS LA TAVERNE ALSACIENNE** (N° RR AVR 27 245) (Mme Francine **Thomann**) La Tabaline ☎ 53-58-84-13 German spoken. Evening meals.

ROUFFILLAC-DE-CARLUX 24370 Dordogne **RD 703 Map 17-A1**
Ⓨ ⊗ 🏠 **2 Stars NN AUX POISSONS FRAIS** (N° RR MAR 12 788) (**Cayre and Son**) ☎ 53-29-70-24 ⊷ 20 Closed 1 to 31 Oct. Full-board 210–225F per night. Coaches welcome (rest. seats 150). Evening meals.

ROUGE (LA) see LE THEIL 61260 Orne **RD 11 Map 8-B3**

ROUGEMONTIERS 27350 Eure **RN 180 Map 4-B3**
Ⓨ ⊗ **LE LUDO** (N° RR FEV 24 871) (M. Jean-Clude **Duboc**) ☎ 32-56-85-22 Closed Sat afternoon, Sun; public holidays.

ROUILLAC 16170 Charente **RN 139 Map 15-A2**
Ⓨ ⊗ 🏠 **LA BOULE D'OR SARL** (N° RR AOUT 26 304) (M. Franck **Chiron**) 56, rue Gal-de-Gaulle ☎ 45-96-50-45 ⊷ 9 Closed Fri evening 2.30pm. Full-board 130–140F per night. Coaches welcome (rest. seats 80). Evening meals. English spoken.

ROULANS 25640 Doubs **RN 73 Map 10-A3 and 14-B3**
Ⓨ ⊗ **LE RELAIS DES ROUTIERS** (N° RR AVR 19 331) (M. Émile **Triponney**) ☎ 81-87-51-72 Open 24 hours. Closed Sun.

ROUMAZIÈRES-LOUBERT 16270 Charente **RN 141 Map 15-B2**
Ⓨ ⊗ 🏠 **LE RELAIS DU CENTRE** (N° RR OCT 24 725) (Mme Marcelle **Chaussonnaud**) 25, rue Nationale Place du Marché ☎ 45-71-10-24 ⊷ 8 Closed 26 Dec to 8 Jan.
Ⓨ ⊗ **LES ROUTIERS** (N° RR MAI 25 394) (M. Charly **Rondeau**) 122, route Nationale ☎ 45-71-10-88 Closed Fri after 3.00pm. English, German, Spanish spoken.

ROUSSET 13790 Bouches-du-Rhône **Map 24-B3**
Ⓨ ⊗ **LA CENGLE** (N° RR JUN 24 609) (M. **Hoffmann**) 110 Route Nationale 7 ☎ 42-29-00-40 Closed Fri evening, Sat, Sun. Full-board 150F per night. Coaches welcome (rest. seats 110). Evening meals. Italian spoken.
⛽ **Total Service Station RELAIS DE ROUSSET** A8 ☎ 42-29-01-95.

ROUSSON 30340 Gard **RD 904 Map 23-B1**
Ⓨ ⊗ **RELAIS DU CHÊNE** (N° RR JUN 26 576) (Mme Georgina **Quet**) Pont d'Avène-Salindre ☎ 66-85-65-82 Closed Sun evening. Coaches welcome (rest. seats 55). English spoken.

R

ROUXIÈRE (LA) 44370 Loire-Atlantique **D28, D29 Map 11-A3**
🍷 ⊗ **CAFÉ DES SPORTS** (N° RR MAI 26 898) (M. Raoul **Mahé**) 123, rue de la Croix Bouvier ☎ 40-96-98-12. English spoken. Filling station near.

ROYAN 17600 Chte-Mme **Map 11-B1**
🍷 ⊗ **L'ESPÉRANCE** (N° RR FEV 26 169) (Mme Bernadette **Baisson**) 72, boulevard d'Aquitaine ☎ 46-05-01-02 Coaches welcome (rest. seats 40). Evening meals.
🍷 ⊗ ⌂ **LE SYMPATIC** (N° RR SEPT 26 672) (M. Yves **Boinard**) 30 av de la Libération ☎ 46-05-67-21 🛏 12 Closed Sat afternoon, Sun; Christmas–New Year. Full-board 170–180F per night.

ROYE 70200 Haute-Saône **RN 19 Map 10-A3**
🍷 ⊗ **LE RELAIS DES ROUTIERS** (N° RR AOU 15 771) (Mme Huguette **Kuhn**) 50, rue de la Verrerie ☎ 84-30-06-48 Closed Sun. Car Park. Coaches welcome (rest. seats 25). Evening meals until 9pm.

RUFFEC 16700 Charente **RN 10 Map 15-B2**
🍷 ⊗ **LES ROUTIERS** (N° RR JAN 26 799) (M. Jean-Michel **Lapegue**) 34, avenue Célestin-Sieur ☎ 45-31-04-16 Closed last weekend of month (off-season).

RUFFEC-LE-CHATEAU 36300 Indre **Map 16-A1**
🍷 ⊗ **CHEZ P'TIT JEAN** (N° RR NOV 26 728) (Mme Micheline **Merandon**) Le Bourg ☎ 54-37-70-05 **Minitel** 🛏 6 Closed Sept. Full board 130 to 140F. Coaches welcome (2 restaurants seating 30). Evening meals served until 9pm.

RUNGIS 94150 Val-de-Marne **RN 7 Map 1-B2/3**
🍷 ⊗ **LE GRAND COMPTOIR DE RUNGIS** (N° RR OCT 25 698 (SARL **Sogere**) Place St-Hubert Halles de Rungis ☎ 46-86-29-30 Restaurant with take-away. Closed Sat, Sun. Coaches welcome (rest. seats 200).

RUPT-SUR-MOSELLE 88360 Vosges **Map 10-A3**
🍷 ⊗ **LE P'TIT RESTO** (N° RR NOV 27 086) (M. René **Antoine**) 89 A, rue de Lorraine ☎ 29-34-38-11 Closed Wed low season.

RYE 39230 Jura **Map 14-A3**
🍷 ⊗ **Chez Lucette** (N° RR JUL 24 641) (Mme Lucette **Cambazard**) ☎ 84-48-61-60 Closed Thurs afternoon; 1 to 15 Aug.

S

SAALES 67420 Bas-Rhin **voir COLROY-LA-GRANDE**

SABLES-D'OLONNE (LES) 85100 Vendée **RN 160/149 Map 11-A1**
🍷 🍴 🏠 **AU COQ HARDI** (N° RR MAI 20 453) (Mlle Françoise **Pajot**) 7, avenue Alcide-Gabaret ☎ 51-32-04-62 🛏 8 Closed Sat/Sun; end of Sept/beginning of Oct. Full-board 140–180F per night. Coaches welcome (rest. seats 90).
🍷 🍴 🏠 **LES VOYAGEURS** (N° RR AOU 26 307) (M. Clément **Pacory**) 17, rue de la Bauduère ☎ 51-95-11-49 🛏 11 Closed Sat; end of Dec/beginning of Jan. Evening meals until 9pm.

SABLONNIERES 38460 Isère **RD 522 and 517 Crossroads Map 2-B2**
🍷 🍴 **LE RELAIS DE LA PLACE** (N° RR OCT 24 366) (M. Maurice **Mailler**) Crémieu ☎ 74-92-80-19.

SACEY 50170 Manche **RD 80/D 169 Map 8-A1**
🍷 🍴 🏠 **RELAIS DES VOYAGEURS** (N° RR NOV 25 168) (Mme Marcelle **Belan**) Le Bourg ☎ 33-60-15-11 🛏 8 Full-board 130–160F per night. Coaches welcome (rest. seats 90). Evening meals until 10pm.

SAGY 71580 Saône-et-Loire **Map 18-B1**
🍷 🍴 **LE BLUES GIN'S** (N° RR OCT 27 040) (M. Guy **Moreau**) **Les Bulets** ☎ 85-74--07-03 English spoken.

SAHUNE 26510 Drôme **RN 94 Map 24-B2**
🍷 🍴 🏠 **1 Star NN LE RELAIS DAUPHINE-PROVENCE** (N° RR MAI 16 059) (M. **Aumage**) Route Nationale 94 ☎ 75-27-40-99 **Minitel** 10 Closed Wed, last week of Aug; Christmas/New Year holiday. Full-board 145–150F per night. Coaches welcome (rest. seats 60). Evening meals.

SAILLANS 26340 Drôme **RN 93 Map 24-B1**
🍷 🍴 🏠 **LE NATIONAL** (N° RR SEP 18 179) (Mme Jeannine **Chauvet**) place du Prieuré - Grand-Rue ☎ 75-21-51-33 🛏 6 Closed Tue; Sept. Full-board 140–160F per night. Coaches welcome (rest. seats 35). Evening meals.

SAINT, SAINTE: for compound names beginning with Saint or Sainte, see the end of this section.

SAINTENY 50500 Manche **CD 971 Map 4-B1**
🍷 🍴 **LE RELAIS DES FORGES** (RR NOV 27 092) (Mme Francine **Cousin**) Les Forges Carentan ☎ 33-42-39-36 Closed Tues and last two weeks of August.

SAINTES 17100 Char.-Marit. **RN 137 Map 15-A2**
🍷 🍴 **LE RELAIS DE L'OASIS** (N° RR MAI 14 348) (M. Guy **Fumoleau**) Route de Rochefort ☎ 46-93-07-20 Closed Sat, Sun off season; Aug. Coaches welcome (rest. seats 50). Evening meals. German spoken.

S

SALAISE-SUR-SANNE 38150 Isère **Map 18-B3**
♀ ⊗ **LE RELAIS DE LA SANNE** (N° RR MAR 24 522) (M. Marc **Giraud**) Route Nationale ☎ 74-86-37-91 English, German spoken.

SALAVRE 01270 Ain **RN 83 Map 18-B1**
♀ ⊗ **LE SALAVRE** (N° RR DEC 26 717) (Mme Anick **Grudet**) Coligny ☎ 74-30-15-75 Closed Wed 2.30pm.

SALLE (LA) 71260 Saône-et-Loire **RN 6 Map 18-B1**
♀ ⊗ **RELAIS DU MACONNAIS** (N° RR JUL 26 590) (Mme Valérie **Zorzi**) Lugny ☎ 85-37-51-34 Closed Sat afternoon, Sun; Jan. Italian spoken.

SALOUEL 80480 Somme **RN 29 Map 5-A3**
♀ ⊗ **LE TROU NORMAND** (N° RR MAI 25 938) (M. Jean-Louis **Manot**) 75, route de Rouen ☎ 22-95-53-90 Closed Sun. Coaches welcome (rest. seats 130).

SAMADET 40340 Landes
♀ ⊗ ⌂ **AU PELLE** (N° RR OCT 26 346) (MM **Darolles-Cassou**) Rte d'Hagetmau ☎ 58-79-19-81 ⊷ 6 Full-board 100–200F per night. Coaches welcome. Evening meals. English, Spanish spoken.

SAMMERON 77260 S.-et-M **RN 3 Map 9-A2**
♀ ⊗ **LES CICOGNES** (N° RR OCT 13 153) (Mme **Meteyer**) 73, rue de Metz ☎ 60-22-14-06 Closed Sun.

SANCERGUES 18140 Cher **RN 151 Map 13-B2**
♀ ⊗ ⌂ **LE RELAIS AU BON LABOUREUR** (N° RR JAN 22 148) (Mme Martine **Dubois**) 54, Grande-Rue ☎ 48-72-76-13 ⊷ 6 Full-board 140–150F per night. Closed Tue afternoon; 15 Jun–5 Jul. Coaches welcome (rest. seats 90). German, Italian spoken.
♀ ⊗ **LE RELAIS DU CHEVAL BLANC** (N° RR MAR 16 916) (M. Daniel **Gitton**) 44, Grand-Rue ☎ 48-72-70-38 ⊷ 6 Closed Mon. Full-board 120–150F. Coaches welcome (rest. seats 80). Evening meals cooked to order.

SANCY-LES-PROVINS 77320 S.-et-M. **Map 9-A2**
♀ ⊗ **LE RELAIS DE SANCY** (N° RR JUL 26 955) (M. Michel **Tonnelier**) RN 4 ☎ 64-01-92-07 Closed Sun. English spoken.

SARAN see ORLEANS 45400 Loiret **Autoroute A10 Map 13-A1**

SARCEY 69490 Rhône **2 km from RN 7 Map 2-A1**
♀ ⊗ **LE RELAIS DES ROUTIERS** (N° RR AVR 26 223) (M. Patrick **Parisi**) Place de l'Église ☎ 74-01-20-08 Closed Wed afternoon. Sunday lunch. Evening meals. English spoken.

SARGE-SUR-BRAYE 41170 Loir-et-Cher **Map 12-A3**
♀ ⊗ **LE RELAIS DE MONPLAISIR Tobacconist** (N° RR FEV 25 827) (M. Roger **Monchatre**) Mondoubleau ☎ 54-72-72-21 Closed Sat, Sun; Aug. Evening meals. HGV parking.

S

SARLAT 24200 Dordogne **CD 46/57 Map 17-B1**
♉ ⊗ **RELAIS DE CORDY** (N° RR AOUT 26 982) (Mme Marika **Treillou**) Pré de Cordy ☎ 53-31-19-65 English, Spanish spoken. Filling station near.

SARREGUEMINES 57200 Moselle **RN 74 Map 10-A/B1**
♉ ⊗ ⌂ **AU RELAIS DES ROUTIERS - CHEZ EDMOND** (N° RR SEPT 18 829) (M. Camille **Fasel**) 19, rue du Bac ☎ 87-98-15-39 ⊷ 11 Closed Sun during Jul, Aug. Full-board 150–160F per night. Coaches welcome (rest. seats 60). Evening meals until 9.30pm. German spoken.

SAUCATS 33650 Gironde **RN 651 Map 20-B1**
♉ ⊗ **L'AUBERGE QUI CHANTE** (N° RR SEPT 26 988) (Mme Claire **Dupuis**) Le Bourg ☎ 56-72-23-11 ⊷ 3 Closed Sat from 1 Oct–30 Apr; Nov; Feb. English spoken. Filling station 7 km.

SAUJON 17600 Chte-Marit **Map 11-B1**
♉ ⊗ ⌂ **1 Star NN HÔTEL DE LA GARE** (N° RR OCT 24 404) (M. Michel **Mellot**) 2, rue Clémenceau ☎ 46-02-80-33 ⊷ 12 from 95–140F, breakfast 18–22F, access for disabled. Closed Sun; Christmas to New Year. Full-board 130–170F per night. Coaches welcome (2 rooms; 70/80 seats). Evening meals. Car park; bar; dogs allowed; sports (table tennis, *petanque*, swings). Indoor terrace.

SAULCE 26630 Drôme **RN 7 and RD 26 motorway exit Loriol, Montélimar Nord Map 24-A1**
♉ ⊗ ⌂ **LE DISQUE BLEU** (N° RR OCT 25 134) (M. Jacques **Brillo**) quartier des Blaches à **Cliouscat** ☎ 75-63-00-08 ⊷ 8 Closed Sat afternoon, Sun. Full-board 130–160F per night. Coaches welcome (rest. seats 60). Evening meals.

SAULCE-LES-ALPES (LA) 05110 Hautes-Alpes **RN 85 Map 25-A1**
♉ ⊗ ⌂ **1 Star NN LE RELAIS DE FRANCE** (N° RR SEPT 20 281) (Mme **Ubaud**) ☎ 92-54-20-08 ⊷ 10.

SAULIEU 21210 Cote-d'Or **RN 6 Map 13-B3**
♉ ⊗ ⌂ **LE RELAIS AUX POIDS LOURDS** (N° RR FEV 12 693) (M. **Godet**) 30, rue Courte-Epée ☎ 80-64-19-83 ⊷ 7 Closed Sat, Sun. Evening meals.

SAULNIÈRES 35320 l.-et-V. **RD 777 Map 7-B3**
♉ ⊗ **LA TAVERNE BRETONNE** (N° RR MAI 26 540) (Mme Nicole **Clipet**) Bourg de Saulnières, Bel de Bretagne ☎ 99-44-70-61 Coaches welcome (rest. seats 100).

SAUMUR 49400 Maine-et-Loire **RN 152 Map 12-B2**
♉ ⊗ ⌂ **2 Stars NN HÔTEL DE LA GARE** (N° RR FEV 17 188) (M. Jacques **Gaudicheau**) 16, avenue David-d'Angers ☎ 41-67-34-24 ⊷ 16 from 80–220F, breakfast 18–27F, telephone, access for disabled. Closed 1 Oct to 1 April. View of Loire and castle. Full board 230–345F per night. Coaches welcome (rest. seats 200). Evening meals until 10pm. English, German spoken. Proprietor-

S

Saumur continued

ship passed from father to son since 1919. Member of 'Courtoisie Française'. Car park patrons only, secure; bar; dogs allowed. Menus 28–80F. Specialities: *Cuisse de poulet bonne femme; Rôti à la saumuroise; omelette arc-en-ciel*. Places to visit: Stone circles, châteaux, museums, churches, wine cellars.

SAUQUEVILLE 76550 Seine-Maritime **RN 27 Map 4-A3**
♈ ⊗ ⌂ **LA FALAISE** (N° RR NOV 25 214) (Mme **Levasseur**) **Bas de Tourvilles/Arques** ☎ 35-85-44-77 ⊷ 11 Closed Sun evening. English, Italian, Spanish spoken.

SAUVIAT-SUR-VIGE 87560 Haute-Vienne **RN 141 Map 16-B1**
♈ ⊗ ⌂ **1 Star NN HÔTEL 400 DE LA POSTE** (N° RR AOU 10 941) (M. Pierre **Chassagne**) ☎ 55-75-12 ⊷ 12 (10 with WC) from 75–145F, breakfast 18–30F. Closed Wed; Sept. Full-board 150–180F per night. Coaches welcome (rest. seats 120). Evening meals. Car park; bar; dogs allowed; recreations (fishing, hunting); countryside to explore.

SAUZE-VAUSSAIS 79190 Deux-Sèvres **RN 148 Map 15-A1/2 LES ALLEUDS (Chaignepain)**
♈ ⊗ **LE RELAIS DES ROUTIERS** (N° RR JAN 20 089) (M. Joël **Quintard**) ☎ 49-29-34-61 Closed Sat. Coaches welcome (rest. seats 180). Evening meals until 10pm.

SAVENAY 44260 L.-Atl. **RN 165**
♈ ⊗ **RELAIS 165** (N° FEV 27 193) (M. Claude **BOURGINE**) Le Pas de l'Aulne Prinquiau ☎ 40-56-64-99 Closed Sat/Sun.

SAVERDUN 09700 Ariège **RN 20 Map 22-A2**
♈ ⊗ ⌂ **A LA BONNE AUBERGE** (N° RR AVR 21 880) (Mme **Boutet**) Route Nationale 20 or 73 - rue du Lion-d'Or ☎ 61-69-30-33 ⊷ 6 Closed Mon; Sept. Spanish spoken.

SAVIGNAC 33190 Gironde **Map 21-A1**
⛫ **Total Service Station LE RELAIS DE SAVIGNAC** (N° RR MAI 24 948) (M. Patrick **de Smet**) Aire du Bazadais Autoroute A62 ☎ 56-25-40-93. Open 24 hours. French, Spanish, English, Portuguese, Italian spoken.

SAZILLY 37220 I.-et-L. **RD 760 Map 12-B2**
♈ ⊗ **LE RELAIS DE LA PROMENADE** (N° RR MARS 25 862) (Mme Jocelyne **Bigot**) Le Bourg ☎ 47-58-55-50 Closed Sun. Coaches welcome (rest. seats 80). Evening meals.

SCHWANGERBACH par REYERSVILLER 57230 Moselle **RD 37 Map 10-B1**
♈ ⊗ **LE RELAIS DES ROUTIERS** (N° RR MAR 19 693) (Mme Joséphine **Volb**) ☎ 87-06-00-64 Closed on Thursday and from 1/9 to 1/10.

SCIEZ 74140 Hte-Savoie **RN Map 19-A1**
♈ ⊗ ⌂ **1 star NN LE LEMAN** (N° RR AVR 25 358) (M. Roger **Berthet** Bonnatrait ☎ 50-72-60-04 ⊷ 12 (60–100F; breakfast 16F). Closed

S

Sat in winter; Oct. Full-board 160–180F per night; breakfast 16F. Coaches welcome (rest. seats 70). Evening meals. Parking, bar. Sites to visit: Evian, Genève, mountain walks. English, German spoken.

SCOURY 36300 Indre **RN 151 Map 16-A1**
Y ⊗ ⌂ **LE RELAIS DES ROUTIERS** (N° RR JANV 26 791) (Mme Roselyne **Pilet**) Nationale 151 ☎ 54-37-98-09 Closed Sun evening; 21–31 Aug; 18–31 Dec.

SEAUVE-SUR-SEMENE (LA) 43470 Haute-Loire **RD 500 Map 18-A3**

Y ⊗ **LE RELAIS DE LA GARE** (N° RR DEC 24 448) (Mme Denise **Teissèdre**) 105, avenue de la Semène ☎ 71-61-04-86 Closed Mon; Aug.

SÉBAZAC 12850 Aveyron **CD 904 Map 22-A1**
Y ⊗ **LE LONGCHAMP** (N° RR SEPT 27 033) (Mme Monique **Guilpin**) 56, avenue Tabardelle ☎ 65-74-93-62.

SECONDIGNY 79130 Deux-Sèvres **RN 148 Map 15-A1**
Y ⊗ ⌂ **LE RELAIS DES ROUTIERS** (N° RR JAN 19 615) (M. Noël **Duranceau**) 43, rue de la Vendée ☎ 49-95-61-35 ⊷ 5 Closed Mon; 1st weeks Sep. Coaches welcome (rest. seats 120). Evening meals.

SEDAN 08200 Ardennes **RN 64 Map 6-A2**
Y ⊗ ⌂ **1 star NN LE BELLEVUE** (N° RR FEV 25 294) (M. François **Pochet**) 56, avenue Philippoteaux ☎ 24-27-03-96 ⊷ 14 (80–120F). Closed Sun. Full-board 130–160F; breakfast 16,50–20F. Coaches welcome (rest. seats 30). Evening meals. Parking; bar; dogs permitted; bowling alley. Sites to visit: castles, abbeys, lakes, forests. English spoken.

SEGLIEN 56160 Morbihan **RN 782 Map 7-B2**
Y **LE CAFE DE LA PAIX** (N° RR MAR 20 134) (M. Armand **Bigouin**) ☎ 97-51-23-73 Lann-Blomen.

SEGRE 49500 M.-et-L. **RN 775 Maps 11-A3 and 12 A1**
Y ⊗ ⌂ **LE RELAIS DU COMMERCE** (N° RR DEC 18 576) (M. Emile **Georget**) 1, place de la Gare ☎ 41-92-22-27 ⊷ 10.

SELLES-SAINT-DENIS-SALBRIS 41300 Loir-et-Cher **RN 724 Map 13-A/B1**
Y ⊗ **BAR DES SPORTS** (N° RR MAI 23 813) (M. Robert **Billet**) 2, place du Mail ☎ 54-96-21-38 Closed Tue afternoon; Feb (15 days).

SEMUR-EN-AUXOIS 21140 Côte d'Or **CD 980 Map 13-A3**
Y ⊗ **AUBERGE DES QUINCONCES** (N° RR SEPT 26 985) (M. Daniel **Vilatte**) 58, rue de Paris ☎ 80-97-02-00 English spoken (by 1 staffer). Filling station near.

SENAN 89710 Yonne **RD 955 Map 13-A2**
Y ⊗ ⌂ **HOTEL DE LA CROIX BLANCHE** (N° RR NOV 26 104) (M.

S

Senan continued
Jean-Claude **Lecourt**) 16, rue d'Aillant ☎ 86-63-41-31 ◄ Closed Sun after lunch.

SENAS 13560 B.-du-R. **RN 7 Map 24-B3**
♀ ⊗ **L'ETAPE** (N° RR MARS 21 043) (SNC Veyrier Frères) RN 7 ☎ 90-59-22-81 Closed Sat, Sun; 25 Dec–5 Jan. Evening meals.
♀ ⊗ **LE RESTO GRILL** (N° RR SEPT 26 326) (M. **Degoul**) RN 7 ☎ 90-57-27-82 Closed Sat afternoon, Sun. Evening meals.

SENE 56000 Morbihan **RN 165 Map 11-A1/2**
♀ ⊗ ⌂ **1 Star NN LE POULFANC** (N° RR FEV 16 886) (S.A. **Penru**) route de Vannes ☎ 97-47-47-97 ◄ 45 Closed 23 Dec to 5 Jan. Evening meals until 9.30pm.

SENNECEY-LE-GRAND 71240 S.-et-L. **RN 6 Map 18-B1**
♀ ⊗ **L'ARCHE** (Mme Marie-Claude **Debrune**) Autoroute A6 St Ambreuil ☎ 85-44-20-64 Open 24 hours.
♀ ⊗ **CAFÉ ROUTE** Autoroute A6 ☎ 85-44-21-79 Open 24 hours.

SENS 89100 Yonne **RN 5 Map 9-B2**
♀ ⊗ ⌂ **RELAIS DES TROIS GARES** (N° RR JUL 26 288) (M. Jean **Bouju**) 29 bis, avenue Vauban ☎ 86-65-12-76 ◄ 9 Closed Sat afternoon, Sun; Jul.

SEREILHAC 87620 Haute-Vienne **Map 16-B1**
♀ ⊗ **AUBERGE DES ROUTIERS** (N° RR FEV 24 846) (Mme Denis **Vignaud**) Route Nationale 21 ☎ 55-39-10-46 ◄ 6 Coaches welcome (rest. seats 260). English spoken.

SERIFONTAINE 60590 Oise
♀ ⊗ **CAFÉ DES SPORTS** (N° RR SEPT 27 002) (M. Michel **Decaux**) 20, rue Hacque ☎ 44-84-80-33 Closed Sun. Filling station (7am–9pm) near.

SÉRIGNY 17230 Charente-Maritime
♀ ⊗ **CHEZ JOHAN** (N° RR MAI 27 288) (M. Johan **Mercier**) ☎ 46-01-40-03 Closed Sun. Evening meals.

SERQUIGNY 27470 Eure **Map 4-B3**
♀ ⊗ **LE RELAIS DE LA GARE** (N° RR JAN 24 480) (Mme Huguette **Lebas**) route de Beaumont ☎ 32-44-08-74 Closed Sat, Sun; Aug. English spoken.

SERRES-CASTETS 64160 Pyr.-Atl **Maps 20-B3 and 21-A3**
♀ ⊗ ⌂ **LES ROUTIERS** (N° RR MAR 23 199) (M. Léon **Salis**) ☎ 59-33-91-06 ◄ 4 Closed Sat, Sun; Aug. Evening meals. Spanish spoken.

SERVAS 01240 Ain **RN 83 Map 18-B2**
♀ ⊗ ⌂ **LE RELAIS DU POSTILLON** (N° RR AVR 25 364) (**Lastab-Champier**) ☎ 74-52-79-10 ◄ 5 Closed Tue. Evening meals.

SERVOZ 74310 Haute-Savoie **Map 19-B2**
♀ ⊗ **LE RELAIS DU CHATELARD** (N° RR DEC 25 238) (M. Pierre **Verdier**) Le Châtelard-les-Houches ☎ 50-47-21-62.

SETE 34200 Hérault **RN 108 Map 23-B2**
♀ ⊗ **LE PAVILLON** (N° RR MARS 26 471) (Mme Marie-France **Petitfils**) 23, route de Montpellier ☎ 67-48-62-53 Closed Sat afternoon, Sun. Coaches (rest. seats 64). English spoken.
♀ ⊗ **RESTO ROUTIER LA PENICHE** (N° RR AVR 23 758) (Mme Paquerette **Dupuy**) 1, quai des Moulins ☎ 67-48-64-13 Evening meals.
♀ ⊗ **LA REGENCE** (N° RR DEC 27 116) (M. Noël **Barthe**) 1, quai de la République Place Delille ☎ 67-74-32-92 English, Spanish and Italian spoken.

SEURRE 21250 Côte-d'Or **Map 14-A3**
♀ ⊗ **RELAIS DU CHAMP DE FOIRE** (N° RR JUL 26 580) (M. Jacky **Madesclaire**) 13, place du Champ de Foire ☎ 80-21-03-42 Closed Sun. Coaches welcome (rest. seats 50). Evening meals.

SEXCLES 19430 Corrèze **RN 120 Map 17-A2**
♀ ⊗ ⌂ **AUBERGE DES ROUTIERS** (N° RR JUL 26 597) (M. Claude **Gubert**) Le Mas ☎ 55-28-70-70 ⊨ 10.

SEYCHES 47350 L.-et-G. **RN 133 Map 21-B1**
♀ ⊗ **AU BON ACCUEIL** (N° RR NOV 14 086) (Mme Laliette **Madec**) ☎ 58-93-60-10 ⊨ 4 Closed Sat.

SEYNOD 74600 Haute-Savoie **RN 201 Map 19-A2**
♀ ⊗ ⌂ **1 Star NN LE RELAIS SAINTE-CATHERINE** (N° RR MARS 9 372) (M. Lucien **Zerbola**) 181, route d'Aix ☎ 50-69-00-86 ⊨ 10 from 90–130F, breakfast 18–20F. Closed Sun; Jul (restaurant only). Full-board 150–160F per night. Coaches welcome (rest. seats 120). Evening meals. English spoken. Car park; bar; large dogs not allowed. Places to visit: Annecy.
⛽ **Total Service Station** Autoroute A41 ☎ 50-69-12-11 Credit cards: GR, CB, Diners Club, Eurocard.

SIDEVILLE 50690 Manche **RD 904**
♀ ⊗ **LES ROCHES** (N° RR FEV 27 184) (M. Louis **Galopin**) Hameau Colette ☎ 33-52-02-03

SIDIALLES 18270 Cher
♀ ⊗ **CHEZ MIMI** (N° RR MAI 27 268) (M. Lucien **Le Bellego**) Le Bouquet ☎ 48-56-63-02 Evening meals.

SIGOTTIER 05700 Htes-Alpes **RN 5 Map 24-B2**
♀ ⊗ **PONT LA BARQUE** (N° RR MARS 25 841) (M. and Mme Claude **Faizende**) Serres ☎ 92-67-04-15 Coaches welcome (rest. seats 100). Evening meals until 11pm. Italian spoken.

SILLE-LE-GUILLAUME 72140 Sarthe **CD 37 Map 8-B2**
♀ ⊗ **HÔTEL DE L'OUEST** (N° RR OCT 26 676) (M. Jean-Jacques

S

Sille-le-Guillaume continued

Aubert) RD 304, 8, place de la Gare ☎ 43-20-10-58 Closed Sun evening.

♀ ⊗ **LA COQUE** (N° RR SEPT 27 005) (M. Claude **Rouzier**) 11 Gis, route de Mans, St. Rémy de Sillé ☎ 43-20-11-84 Closed Sun; 15–30 Aug. Filling station (7am–10pm) near.

SISTERON 04200 Alpes-de-Haute-Provence **RN 85 Map 25-A1**

♀ **LE CAFE DES ARCADES** (N° RR MAI 16 570) (SARL – **Bar des Arcades**) place de la République ☎ 92-61-02-52.

SIZUN 29237 Finistère **RD 167 Map 7-A1**

♀ ⊗ ⌂ **1 Star NN HÔTEL DES VOYAGEURS** (N° RR MAR 14 263) (M. Joseph **Corre**) 2, rue de l'Argoat ☎ 98-68-80-35 ⊷ 16 from 70–135F, breakfast 20F. Closed Sat evening (off season); 3 last weeks of Sept. Full-board 137–157F per night. Coaches welcome (rest. seats 300). Evening meals. English spoken. Menus 40–65F. Specialities: *Terrine de lapin, Mousseline de truite, Fruits de mer.*

SOLAIZE 69360 Rhône **Autoroute A7 Map 2-B1**

♀ ⊗ **RESTOP DE SOLAIZE** (M. Jean-Paul **Goupy**) ☎ 78-02-82-63 Self-service restaurant open 11.00am to 10.00pm. Showers.

SOLESMES 59730 Nord **Map 5-B3**

♀ ⊗ ⌂ **HÔTEL DE LA HURE** (N° RR NOV 26 726) (M. **Zurawski**) 2, rue Georges-Clémenceau ☎ 27-37-32-49 ⊷ 17 Closed Fri evening.

SOMMERY 76440 Seine-Maritime **Map 3-A1**

♀ ⊗ **AU BON CIDRE** (N° RR JUN 24 605) (Mme Raymonde **Guillou**) La Cavée **Forges-les-Eaux** ☎ 35-90-57-11 Closed Wed. Yugoslavian spoken.

♀ ⊗ **LE MONTESTRUC** (N° RR MARS 27 208) (M. Jean-Luc **Édet**) La Cavée ☎ 35-90-56-16 Closed Wed pm.

SOMMIERES-DU-CLAIN 86160 Vienne **RD 1 Map 15-B1**

♀ ⊗ ⌂ **LES TROIS PILIERS** (N° RR JUIL 26 937) (M. Martial **Richard**) place de l'Église ☎ 49-87-70-09 ⊷ 5.

SORGUES 84700 Vaucluse **Autoroute A7 and RN 7 Map 24-A2**

♀ ⊗ **RESTOP DE SORGUES** (M. Jean-Jacques **Hurey**) ☎ 90-39-10-72 Self-service restaurant open 11.00am to 10.00pm. TV, Shop.

SORINIERES (LES) 44400 L.-Atl. **RN 137 and 178 Maps 11-A/B2 and 12-B1**

♀ ⊗ ⌂ **LE RELAIS – CHEZ PIERRETTE ET JEAN-LOUIS** (N° RR SEP 24 673) (M. Jean-Louis **Benoît**) 16, rue du Général-de-Gaulle ☎ 40-31-22-91 ⊷ 7 Closed Sat evening, Sun; 15 Dec to 5 Jan. Full-board 150–170F per night. Coaches welcome (3 rooms: 50 seats). Evening meals.

SOUAL 81580 Tarn **RN 126 Map 22-B2**

♀ ⊗ ⌂ **LE MAÏZOU** (N° RR JUN 26 912) (M. Jean-Marie **Lemaire**) 12–

14 Grand-Rue ☎ 63-74-52-24 ⊷ 5 Closed Tue evening. Filling station 100m.

SOUBERAC 16130 Charente **RN 141 Map 15-A2**
♈ ⊗ **AUX CHASSEURS** (N° RR MAI 26 254) (M. Raymond **Joffrion**) Gensacla-Pallue ☎ 45-32-13-80 Closed Sat; Aug. Coaches welcome (rest. seats 90).

SOUCHEZ 62153 P.-de-C. **RN 37 Map 5-A1**
♈ ⊗ **AU RENDEZ-VOUS DES ROUTIERS** (N° RR DEC 20 352) (Mme **Louf**) 5, rue Carnot ☎ 21-45-15-01.

SOUDAN-CHATEAUBRIAND 44110 Loire-Atl. **RN 775 Maps 11-A3 and 12-A1**
♈ ⊗ **CAFE DE LA POSTE** (N° RR SEP 24 321) (M. Claude **Fruchard**) place Tolhouët - place de la Poste ☎ 40-28-62-36 Coaches welcome (2 rooms = 70 seats).

SOUILLAC 46200 Lot **RN 20 Map 17-B1**
♈ ⊗ ⌂ **1 Star NN LE RELAIS DE L'ESCALE** (N° RR JAN 21 758) (M. Jean **Regnères**) 41, avenue Louis-Jean Malvy ☎ 65-37-82-65 ⊷ 18 Closed Mon.

SOULAINES-DHUYS 10200 Aube **RD 960 Map 9-B3**
♈ ⊗ **LE RELAIS DES ROUTIERS** (N° RR 20 866) (M. Guy **Demongeot**) Route Nationale 60 ☎ 25-26-51-10 Evening meals.

SOULGE-SUR-OUETTE 53210 Mayenne **RN 157 Map 8-B1**
♈ ⊗ ⌂ **LA BELLE ÉTOILE** (N° RR OCT 26 710) (M. Gérard **Couillebault**) Le Point du Jour ☎ 43-02-30-18 ⊷ 10.

SOULIGNY par BOUILLY 10320 Aube **RN 77 Map 9-B3**
♈ ⊗ ⌂ **1 Star NN AU RELAIS DE MONTAIGU** (N° RR AVR 18 374) (M. René **Braux**) 300, rue du Martel ☎ 25-40-20-20 ⊷ 13 Coaches welcome (rest. seats 70). Evening meals.

SOUMOULOU 64420 Pyr.-Atl. **RN 117 Map 20-B3**
♈ ⊗ ⌂ **LE RELAIS BEARNAIS** (N° RR FEV 18 644) (Mme Jeanne **Suberbielle**) 5, rue de Platanes ☎ 59-33-60-45 ⊷ 6 Closed Sun afternoon. Full-board 160–180F. Coaches welcome (rest. seats 80). Evening meals.

SOURDEVAL-LA-BARRE 50150 Manche **Map 8-A1**
♈ ⊗ **AU BON ACCUEIL** (N° RR SEP 26 635) (Mme Micheline **Petitpas**) 1, place du Champ-de-Foire ☎ 35-59-62-91 ⊷ 2 Closed Sun. Full-board 100–150F per night. Coaches welcome (3 rooms = 60 seats). Meals served until 1pm.

SOURDEVAL-LES-BOIS 50650 Manche **RN 799 Map 8-A1**
♈ ⊗ **LE RELAIS DES ROUTIERS** (N° RR FEV 20 659) (Mme Colette **Dufour**) Near La Crois ☎ 33-61-77-99.

STEENVOORDE 59114 Nord **AUTOROUTE 25 Map 5-A1**
♈ ⊗ **ACCOR** (M. Michel **Jaminion**) Air de Service de Saint-Laurent

S

Steenvoorde continued

Paris/Province and Province/Paris directions ☎ 28-42-04-67 ⊷
Self-service restaurant open 6.30am to 10.00pm. English, German
spoken. Shop.

STENAY 55700 Meure **D 947 Map 6-B3**

♀ ⊗ **BAR DES SANGLIERS – LA MANGEOIRE** (N° RR MARS 26
841) (M. Daniel **Demaçon**) 1, rue Carnot ☎ 29-80-60-06/29-80-37-
64 ⊷ 7 (4 single) Closed Fri afternoon; 15–31 Aug. German,
English (some) spoken. Filling station 300m.

STRASBOURG 67000 Bas-Rhin **RN 4 Map 10-B2**

♀ ⊗ **AU PETIT RHIN** (N° RR AVR 14 331) (M. Albert **Kupferchlae-
ger**) 4, rue du Port-du-Rhin ☎ 88-61-35-00 Closed Sun; public
holidays; Aug. Evening meals.

♀ ⊗ ⌂ **AU RHIN FRANÇAIS** (N° RR DEC 25 227) (M. Marcel
Wendling) 83, route du Rhin ☎ 88-61-29-00 and 61-40-93 ⊷ 10
Closed Sat afternoon, Sun. Evening meals. German, English,
Italian, Spanish, Dutch spoken. Coaches welcome (rest. seats
200). Meals served until 11pm.

♀ ⊗ **AU COIN DU PECHEUR** (N° RR MAI 24 584) (Mme Catherine
Lopez) 1, rue Migneret ☎ 88-60-33-16 **Port du Rhin** German,
Spanish spoken.

♀ ⊗ **BRASSERIE DES BATELIERS** (N° RR JUIN 27 306) (M. et Mme
Jean-Calude **Pccinelli**) rue de la Plaine des Bouchers ☎ 88-39-
19-50 Closed Sat from 3pm, Sun and 24/12 to 21/1, Easter and
three weeks in September. German spoken. Evening meals
served until 10pm.

SUEVRES 41500 L.-et-C. **RN 152 Map 12-A3**

♀ ⊗ ⌂ **LA PROVIDENCE – Chez Jacques** (N° RR
⊷ MAI 17 283) (M. Jacques **Bouchet**) 1, place de la Mairie ☎ 54-87-
80-88 ⊷ 7 Closed Sat evening, Sun evening; mid Aug to mid Sept.
Coaches welcome (rest. seats 140). Evening meals. Spanish
spoken. Specialities: *Poularde à la crème, Gras double lyon-
naise, choucroute maison*.

SUEVRES 41500 L.-et-C. **RN 152 Map 12-A3**

♀ ⊗ ⌂ **LA PROVIDENCE – Chez Jacques** (N° RR
⊷ MAI 17 283) (M. Jacques **Bouchet**) 1, place de la Mairie ☎ 54-87-
80-88 ⊷ 7 Closed Sat evening, Sun evening; mid Aug to mid Sept.
Coaches welcome (rest. seats 140). Evening meals. Spanish
spoken. Specialities: *Poularde à la crème, Gras double lyon-
naise, choucroute maison*.

SUIPPES 51600 Marne **RN 77 and 31 Maps 6-B2 and 9-A3**

♀ ⊗ **AU BON COIN** (N° RR JUL 24 623) (SDF **Tiloca**) 39, rue de la
Libération ☎ 26-67-04-85 Coaches welcome (rest. seats 100).
Evening meals. Italian spoken.

SULIGNAT 01400 Ain **RD 2 Map 18-B2**

♀ ⊗ **LA MITAINE** (N° RR MAI 26 549) (M. Philippe **Duvillard**)
Chatillon/Chalaronne ☎ 74-50-00-08 Closed Tue; Jan to Feb.
Some English spoken.

S

SULLY-SUR-LOIRE 45600 Loiret **RN 152 Map 13-A1**
 �† ⊗ ⌂ **LE ST GERMAIN** (N° RR FEV 21 807) (M. and Mme **Schwartz**) 2, place Saint-Germain ☎ 38-36-27-02 ⊷ 6 Closed Fri evening, Sun evening; Christmas to New Year. Full-board 130–140F per night. Coaches welcome (rest. seats 150). Evening meals.
 �† ⊗ ⌂ **CHEZ LIONEL – CAFÉ DE LA GARE** (N° RR OCT 26 077) (M. Lionel **Funten**) 47, rue de la Gare ☎ 38-36-26-11 ⊷ 8 Closed Sat, Sun; 10 to 27 Aug. Full-board 145–160F per night. Coaches welcome (rest. seats 35). after 1.30pm. Evening meals until 8.30pm.

SURESNES 92150 Hauts-de-Seine **Porte de St-Cloud Map 1-A/B2**
 �† ⊗ **LE RELAIS DES ÉCLUSES** (N° RR JUN 19 083) (M. Henri **Bodin**) 30, quai Gallieni ☎ 45-06-11-48 Closed Sun, public holidays; Aug. Evening meals served.

SURVILLIERS 95470 Val-d'Oise **RN 17 Map 3-B3**
 �† ⊗ **REST.DES QUATRE ROUTES** (N° RR FEV 25 811) (M. Serge **Lucas**) Carrefour de Survilliers ☎ 34-68-36-10 Closed Sun; 15 days Aug and Feb. Evening meals until 11.30pm.
 �† ⊗ **LE COQ CHANTANT** (N° RR NOV 26 370) (SARL **Le Baronnat**) Rte Nationale 17 Rte des Flandres ☎ 34-68-52-85 Coaches welcome (rest. seats 100). Evening meals.

SURY-AUX-BOIS see PONT-DES-BEIGNIERS 45530 Loiret **RN 60**

SURY-LE-COMTAL 42450 Loire **RD 8 Map 18-A2**
 �† ⊗ **LE PARILLY P.M.U.** (N° RR OCT 25 131) (M. Simon **Volle**) 13, rue du 11-Novembre ☎ 77-53-50-14.

SUZAY 27420 Eure **RN 14 Map 3-B1**
 �† ⊗ **LE RELAIS MODERNE** (N° RR AOU 26 977) (M. Jean-Claude **Laurent**) ☎ 32-55-65-01 Filling station near.

SAINT-AFRIQUE 12400 Aveyron
 �† ⊗ ⌂ **LE MAJESTIC** (N° RR JUIL 27 315) (M. Alain **Espinos**) 720, avenue du Docteur Galtier ☎ 65-99-00-0-7 ⊷ 12 English and Spanish spoken. Evening meals served until 10pm.

SAINT-AGATHON 22200 C.-du-N. **RN 12 Map 7-A2**
 �† ⊗ ⌂ **1 Star NN HÔTEL BELLE VUE** (N° RR OCT 20 294) (M. **Février**) Bel-Orme ☎ 96-43-80-53 ⊷ 20 from 120–195F, breakfast 15F, telephone. Closed Sun; 20 Dec to 3 Jan. Car park; bar; dogs allowed; fishing.

SAINT-AGNANT-LES-MARAIS 17620 Chte-Mme **Map 11-B3**
 �† ⊗ **RENDEZ-VOUS DES AMIS** (N° RR JUN 26 266) (M. Alain **Neveur**) Le Pont ☎ 46-83-30-36 Closed Sat off season; 20 Aug–5 Sept. Coaches welcome (rest. seats 100). Evening meals except Jul, Aug. German spoken.

SAINT-AIGNANT-LE-JAILLARD 45600 Loiret **RD 951 Map 13-A1**
 �† ⊗ **LE SAINT-AIGNAN** (N° RR FEV 26 464) (Mme Claudine

S

Saint-Aignant-Le-Jaillard continued
Gasnier) 78, rue Nationale ☎ 38-36-38-21 Closed Wed; Feb. Coaches welcome. Evening meals until 9pm.

SAINT-ALBAIN par MACON 71260 S.-et-L. **Autoroute A6 Map 18-B1**
♀ ⊗ **ACCOR - RELAIS BOURGOGNE** (M. Blaise **Surlet**) Aire de Service de Saint-Albain ☎ 85-33-19-00 Self-service restaurant open 24 hours. TV, shop. English, Italian, Spanish spoken.

SAINT-AMAND-LE-PETIT 81720 Haute-Vienne **Map 16-B1**
♀ ⊗ **LA PROMENADE** (N° RR AVR 25 236) (M. Fernand **Rouby**) Eymoutier ☎ 55-69-15-38 ⏤ 4 Evening meals.

SAINT-AMANS-SOULT 81240 Tarn **RN 112 Map 22-B3**
♀ ⊗ 🏠 **LE RELAIS DE LA CROIX BLANCHE** (N° RR JAN 22 637) (M. Antoine **Cuadrado**) 46, route Nationale ☎ 63-98-30-33 ⏤ 15 Full-board 120–130F per night. Coaches welcome (rest. seats 50). Evening meals. Spanish, English spoken.

SAINT-AME 88120 Vosges **RD 417 Map 10-A2/3**
♀ ⊗ **COUP' FAIM** (N° RR JUN 25 006) (Mme Réfine **Frugier**) Grande-Rue ☎ 29-61-23-26 **Minitel** Closed Feb.

SAINT-ANDRÉ-DE-LÉPINE 50680 Manche
RD 85 à 2 km D 972 St-Lò/Caen Map 4-B1
♀⊗ **SAINT-ANDRÉ BAR** N° RR DEC 25 751) (Mme Marie-Claire **Harel**) Bourg Cerisy-la-Forêt ☎ 33-57-24-00 Ferm le mercredi après midi et en août Repas servi le soir jusqu'à 22 h.

SAINT-ANDRÉ DE L'EURE 27220 Eure **RD 76 Map 8-A3**
♀ ⊗ **L'OLYMPIC** (N° RR OCT 22 982) (M. Jean-Jacques **Luyer**) Grande-Rue **Coudres** ☎ 32-37-35-20 Closed Wed.

SAINT-ANTOINE DE BREUILH 24230 Dordogne **Map 17-A/B3 21-A1**
♀ ⊗ **RELAIS DE FRANCE CHEZ KIKI** (N° RR NOV 27 077) (M. Christian **Noble**) Sarl ☎ 53-24-78-97 Closed Sun.

SAINT-ANTOINE-DE-FICALBA 47340 L.-et-G. **RN 21 Map 21-B1**
♀ ⊗ 🏠 **LE RELAIS DES ROUTIERS** (N° RR DEC 17 153) (Mme Rosette **Crozes**) ☎ 58-70-36-08 ⏤ 5 Closed Sat, Sun; public holidays.

SAINT-AUBIN-DE-BAUBIGNÉ 79700 Deux-Sèvres Mauléon **RN 159 Map 11-B3**
♀ ⊗ **LE RELAIS DES ROUTIERS** (N° RR AVR 20 438) (M. Raymond **Charrier**) ☎ 49-81-45-06 Closed Aug.

SAINT-AUBIN-DE-BLAYE 33820 Gironde **RN 137 Map 15-A3**
♀ ⊗ **SARL LES GLYCINES** (N° RR MAI 26 889) (M. Joël **Loizeau**) ☎ 57-32-62-11 ⏤ 4 English spoken. Filling station near.

SAINT-AUBIN-DES-BOIS 28300 E.-et-L. **RN 23 Map 8-B3**
♀ ⊗ **LA MORICERIE** (N° RR FEV 26 184) (M. Dominique **Libéra-**

tore) RN 23 ☎ 37-26-80-52 Coaches welcome (rest. seats 163). Evening meals. Open 24 hrs.

SAINT-AUBIN-DU-CORMIER 35140 I.-et-V. **RN 794 and 12 Map 8-B1**
Y ⊗ 🏠 **HÔTEL DE BRETAGNE** (N° RR JUL 19 424) (M. Henri **Dumont**) 68, rue de l'Écu ☎ 99-55-10-22 ⊶ 13 Closed Jan. Coaches welcome (rest. seats 125). Evening meals until 9pm.

SAINT-AUBIN-LES-ELBEUF 76410 Seine-Mme **Map 3-B1**
Y ⊗ 🏠 **LES ROUTIERS** (N° RR OCT 25 689) (M. Daniel **Delorme**) 24/26, rue du Maréchal Leclerc ☎ 35-81-09-22 ⊶ 5 Closed Sat, Sun.

SAINT-AUBIN-SUR-SCIE 76550 Seine-Mme **Map 4-A3**
Y ⊗ **CHEZ FRANÇOISE** (N° RR FEV 24 513) (Mme Françoise **Soichet**) Rue du Gouffre ☎ 35-85-44-60 Closed Sun; 15 Aug to 1 Sept.

SAINT-AUBIN-SUR-LOIRE 71140 S.-et-L. **RD 979 Map 16-A3**
Y ⊗ **LA CRÉMAILLÉRE** (N° RR JUN 25 434) (Mme Jeanine **Bellier**) Rue Nationale ☎ 85-53-92-83 Closed Sat after lunch.
Y ⊗ **BAR DE L'AMITE** (N° RR OCT 27 063) (M. Didier **Gaumard-Maison**) SNC **Le Bourg** ☎ 85-53-91-09 Closed Mon pm. English, German and Spanish spoken.

SAINT-AVOLD 57740 Moselle **Autoroute A 32 Map 10-A1**
Y ⊗ **RESTOP St-Avold** Aire de Service de Saint-Avold ☎ 87-92-23-89 Self-service restuarant open 11.00am to 10.00pm. Bar open 24 hours. TV, Shop, Showers. English, German spoken.

SAINT-BENOIT-DU-SAULT see RHODES 36170 Indre **RN 20 Map 16-A1**

SAINT-BERTHEVIN-LES-LAVAL 53000 Mayenne **RN 157 Map 8-B1**
Y ⊗ 🏠 **2 Star NN LE RESTAURANT DE L'AULNE – L'International** (N° RR JUN 20 761) (M. Henri **Garnier**) L'Aulne ☎ 43-69-31-74 ⊶ 22 from 100–130F, breakfast 16–18F, telephone, access for disabled. Closed Sun. Full-board 155–175F per night. Coaches welcome (rest. seats 200 + 105). Evening meals. Car park; bar; dogs allowed.

SAINT-BOMER-LES-FORGES 61700 Orne **RD 962 Map 8-A1**
Y ⊗ **LE SAINT BOMER** (N° RR MARS 26 845) (M. Pierre **Janniard**) Le Bourg ☎ 33-37-61-66 Closed Mon evening. Filling station near.

SAINT-BONNET-DE-FOUR 03390 Allier **RN 145 Map 16-A2**
Y ⊗ **RELAIS CENTRE OUEST** (N° RR OCT 27 061) (M. Michel **Trédoulat**) Bezènet ☎ 70-07-72-62.

SAINT-BONNET près RIOM 63200 P.-de-D. **RN 143 Map 16-B3**
Y ⊗ 🏠 **AU BON COIN** (N° RR OCT 16 729) (M. **Levadoux**) 2, rue de la République ☎ 73-63-31-14 ⊶ 10 Closed 15 Sept to 10 Oct. Full-board 110–120F per night. Coaches welcome (rest. seats 90). Evening meals.

S

SAINT-BRÉVIN-LES-PINS 44250 L.-Atl. **RD 77 Map 11-A2**
♀ ⊗ 🏠 **1 Star NN LE RELAIS DU MARCHÉ** (N° RR AVR 16 002) (M.
and Mme **Taraud**) Place Henri-Basle ☎ 40-27-22-21 ⇥ 16 Closed
Mon from Oct–Mar. Evening meals. German spoken.

SAINT-BRICE-EN-COGLES 35460 I.-et-V. **RN 155 Map 8-B1**
♀ ⊗ 🏠 **CHEZ VOUS LES ROUTIERS** (N° RR DEC 8 111) (M. Francis
Tizon) 18, rue Chateaubriand ☎ 99-98-61-45 ⇥ 6 Full-board 150F
per night. Coaches welcome (rest. seats 30). Evening meals.

SAINT-BRIEUC 22000 C.-du-N. **RN 12 Map 7-A2**
♀ ⊗ 🏠 **1 Star NN AU BEAUFEUILLAGE** (N° RR JUL 6 292) (M.
Claude **Andrieux**) 2, rue de Paris ☎ 96-33-09-16 ⇥ 29 Closed
Sun afternoon; 8 Aug to 1 Sept. Coaches welcome (rest. seats 60).
Evening meals.

SAINT-CAPRAISE-DE-LALINDE 24150 Dordogne **CD 660 Map 21-B1**
♀ ⊗ **LES GABARIERS** (N° RR DEC 27 128) (Mme Jacqueline **Stève**)
☎ 53-23-26-74 Closed Sun.

SAINT-CERE 46400 Lot **RD 677 Map 17-B1**
♀ ⊗ 🏠 **HOTEL DU QUERCY** (N° RR AVR 25 909) (Mme Claudie **Fau**)
av. Anatole-de-Monzie ☎ 65-38-04-83 ⇥ 10 Closed Fri evening.
Full-board 150–200F. Coaches welcome (rest. seats 100). English,
Spanish spoken.

SAINT-CHAMANT 1938 Corrèze **RN 120 Map 17-A1**
♀ ⊗ 🏠 **L'ESCALE** (N° RR SEP 25 106) (M. Patrick **Jumelle**) Route de
Tulle ☎ 56-28-08-95 **Minitel** ⇥ 8 Closed Sat evening, Sun
evening; 15 days during year. Full-board 130–150F per night.
Coaches welcome (rest. seats 70). Evening meals.

SAINT-CHRISTOPHE-DU-LIGNERON 85670 Vendée **Map 11-B2**
♀ ⊗ 🏠 **L'ETAPE** (N° RR NOV 24 423) (M. Claude **Hervé**) Bourg ☎ 51-68-12-11 ⇥ 5 Restaurant closed Wed evening, Sat.

SAINT-CHRISTOPHE-SUR-LE-NAIS 37370 I.-et-L. **RN 138 Map 12-A2**
♀ ⊗ **LA MALLE POSTE** (N° RR NOV 25 742) (M. Daniel **Raquy**) Rte
Nle 138 Tour-Le-Mans ☎ 47-29-24-22 Closed Sun evening May to
Sept; Sat evening, Sun Oct to April. Coaches welcome (rest. seats
50). Evening meals. Some English, Spanish spoken.

SAINT-CLAIR-DE-LA-TOUR see LA TOUR DU PIN 38110 Isère **RN
516 Map 2-B3**

SAINT-CLAIR-DU-RHONE 38370 Isère **CD 4 Map 2-B1**
♀ ⊗ **LE RELAIS FLEURI** (N° RR DEC 22 602) (M. **Tognoloni**) 3, rue
du Commandant L'Herminier ☎ 74-56-43-12 ⇥ 3 Open 24 hours.
Closed July. Italian spoken.

SAINT-CLEMENTIN 79150 Deux Sèvres **CD 28 Map12-B1/2**
♀ ⊗ **L'ÉCU DE FRANCE** (N° RR SEPT 26 991) (M. Valentin **Soulard**)
Le Bourg ☎ 49-80-26-32 Closed Wed.

S

SAINT-COSME-EN-VAIRAIS 72580 Sarthe **Map 8-B2**
♀ ⊗ **LE RELAIS DE LA POSTE** (N° RR AVR 25 381) (Mme Colette **Gueranger**) 66, rue Nationale ☎ 43-97-55-56 Closed Sun.

SAINT-CHÉLY-D'APCHER 48200 Lozère **Rn 9**
♀ ⊗ ⌂ **LE BARCELONNE** (N° RR MARS 27 228) (Mme Monique **Vitré**) 33 av. de la Gare ☎ 66-31-01-22 ⇔ 5

SAINT-CYR-EN-PAIL 53140 Mayenne **RN 12**
♀ ⊗ **LES ROUTIERS** (N° RR FEV 27 182) (Mme Antoinette **Dupont**) Le Bourg Pré-en-Pail ☎ 43-03-03-21 Closed Sun pm. English spoken.

SAINT-CYR-SUR-MENTHON 01380 Ain **RN 79 Map 18-B1**
♀ ⊗ **LE RELAIS DES ROUTIERS – Chez Raymond** (N° RR MAR 18 033) (M. Raymond **Ducote**) Le Logis ☎ 85-36-30-69 Closed Sun 4.00pm to Mon; 15 to 31 May; 3 weeks in Aug. Coaches welcome (rest. seats 50). Evening meals until 10pm.

SAINT-CYR-SUR-MER 83270 Var **Map 24-B3**
⊗ **MICKEY RESTO** (N° RR MARS 25 852) (M. Christian **Reverberi**) 20, rue d'Arquier ☎ 94-26-49-98 Closed Sun low season; 1 week at Christmas and New Year. Coaches welcome (rest. seats 42). Evening meals.

SAINT-DENIS 93200 Seine-St-Denis **Portes de la Chapelle et de Clignancourt Map 1-A2**
♀ ⊗ **LE RELAIS DU FRET Chez Daniel** (N° RR JUN 26 272) (M. **Dahan**) 53, avenue du Président Wilson ☎ 48-09-41-22 Closed Sun. Coaches welcome (rest. seats 60). Evening meals. Spanish, English spoken.
♀ ⊗ **A L'ARRET DES TRANSPORTS** (N° RR FEV 7 482) (Mme **Sahut**) 47, bd de la Libération Génovési ☎ 48-20-13-81 Closed Sat, Sun; Aug. Evening meals.
♀ ⊗ **LA CHEMINÉE** (N° RR SEPT 26 665) (Mme Edwige **Brizot**) 56, rue Ambroise Croizat ☎ 48-09-92-92 Closed Sat, Sun; Aug. Evening meals until midnight.
♀ ⊗ **LAS VEGAS** (N° RR SEPT 26 666) (Mme Éliane **Duquesnoy**) 4, rue Beau ☎ 20-61-83-10 Closed Sun. Evening meals served until 10pm.
♀ ⊗ **LE MORETTI** (N° RR FEV 27 176) (Mme Jeanne **Cervantes**) 72, av. Paul-Vaillant-Couturier ☎ 48-27-35-02 Spanish spoken.

SAINT-DENIS-DE-L'HOTEL 45550 Loiret **RN 721 Map 13-A1**
♀ ⊗ **LE ROUTIER DE LA GARE** (N° RR MAR 24 166) (M. Yves **Hedde**) ☎ 38-59-02-09 Closed Sun.

SAINT-DENIS-DE-MAILLOC 14100 Calvados **RD 579 Map 4-B2**
♀ ⊗ **LA FORGE** (N° RR AVR 26 871) (M. Yvan **Leroy**) Lisieux ☎ 31-63-73-19 Closed Sun. Filling station near.

SAINT-DENIS-DE-MÈRE 14110 Calvados RD 562 Map 8-A2
♀ ⊗ **LE RELAIS DES LANDES** (N° RR JAN 25 271) (M. Jean-Hugues

S

Saint-Denis-de-Mère continued
Neveu) Condé-sur-Noireau ☎ 31-69-01-07 ⊷ 7 Coaches welcome (rest. seats 70). Evening meals.

SAINT-DENIS-DES-MONTS 27520 Eure **RN 138 Map 4-B3**
♀ ⊗ **Tabac LE LAMA** (N° RR OCT 27 068) (M. Christian **Chuette**) ☎ 32-42-60-10 Closed on Saturday.

SAINT-DENIS-LES-SENS 89100 Yonne **RN 5 Map 9-B2**
♀ ⊗ **LES CERISIERS** (N° RR SEP 24 670) (M. Michel **Ferrière**) 1, rue de Paris ☎ 86-65-28-52 Closed Sat, Sun; Aug. Coaches welcome (rest. seats 44). Evening meals until 9pm. English spoken.

SAINT-DENIS-SUR-SARTHON 61420 Orne **RN 12 Map 8-A/B2**
♀ ⊗ 🏠 **LE RELAIS DE LA GARE - LES AMIS DES ROUTIERS** (N° RR NOV 20 585) (M. and Mle Marcel **Tessier**) Mélivier ☎ 33-27-30-03 ⊷ 11 Closed Sat, Sun; Aug. Evening meals.

SAINT-DIDIER-DE-BEAUJEU 69430 Rhône **C 37 Map 18-A2**
♀ ⊗ **LE RELAIS BEAUJOLAIS** (N° RR JUN 24 249) (M. Georges **Bass**) Les Dépôts ☎ 74-04-87-53 ⊷ 4 Closed Mon. Full-board 160–180F per night. Coaches welcome (rest. seats 100). Evening meals.

SAINT-DIÉ see SAINTE-MARGUERITE

SAINT DIÉ 88100 Vosges **RN 59 Map 10-A/B2**
♀ ⊗ 🏠 **LA CROISETTE** (N° RR AVR 25 884) (M. Bernard **Roumier**) 41, av. de Verdun ☎ 29-56-14-37 ⊷ 14 Closed Sat, Sun; end of year. Full-board 135-150F per night. Coaches welcome by reservation at weekends (rest. seats 180). Evening meals.

SAINT-DIZIER 52100 Haute-Marne **RN 401 and 4 Map 14-A1**
♀ ⊗ **LE MOLIERE** (N° RR JUL 25 978) (M. René **Castello**) 10, rue Le Moliere ☎ 25-56-02-90 Closed Sat, Sun; Aug. Coaches welcome (rest. seats 43). Evening meals until 12.30am. English, German spoken.

SAINT-ÉLIX-LE-CHATEAU 31430 Hte-Gar. **RN 117 Map 22-A2**
♀ ⊗ 🏠 **1 Star NN RELAIS DU CHATEAU** (N° RR FEV 26 435) (M. Gérard **Serrano**) Le Fousseret ☎ 61-87-60-23 ⊷ 12.

SAINT-ÉLOY-LES-MINES 63700 P.-de-D. **RN 144**
♀ ⊗ **LE RELAIS DU COMMERCE** (N° RR SEPT 26 316) (M. Daniel **Stecher**) 174, rue Jean-Jaurès ☎ 73-85-05-66. Evening meals.

SAINT-EPAIN 37800 Indre-et-Loire **Autoroute A 10 Map 12-B2**
⚑ **LE RELAIS SAINT-MAURE** (N° RR JUN 22 826) (M. Dominique **Clément**) ☎ 47-65-65-59 Open 24 hours. English, Spanish spoken.

SAINT-ERBLON 35230 Ille-et-Vilaine **RD 82 Map 7-B3**
♀ ⊗ 🏠 **CHEZ MICHEL ET SYLVIE** (N° RR FEV 26 819) (M. Michel **Martin**) Place de l'Eglise ☎ 98-52-28-40 English spoken.

SAINT-ETIENNE 42000 Loire **RN 82 Maps 2-B1 and 18-A2/3**

Y ⊗ **LE MISTRAL** (N° RR AVR 26 873) (Mme Martine **Gant**) 4, rue Jean-Neyret ☎ 77-32-95-39 Closed Sat; Sun; Aug. English, Spanish, Arabic spoken. Filling station near.

Y ⊗ **LE RELAIS DE L'OCTROI** (N° RR FEV 25 816) (Mme Viviane **Merieux**) 5, rue du Cros ☎ 77-21-11-98 Near ring road and market. Car park, HGV also. Closed Sun. German, English spoken. Evening meals.

Y ⊗ **CHEZ HÉLÈNE** (N° RR OCT 27 064) (Mme Hélène **Cherbut**) 37, rue Thimonier ☎ 77-57-61-29 Closed Sun.

SAINT-ETIENNE-DU-ROUVRAY 768000 Seine-Maritime **RN 13 Bis and RD 18 Map 3-A1**

Y ⊗ ⌂ **AU RENDEZ-VOUS DES ROUTIERS** (N° RR AOU 9 847) (Mme **Defosse**) 13, avenue des Canadiens ☎ 35-65-35-23 ⚬ 8 Closed Sat evening, Sun; Aug. Restaurant closed Sat evening, Sun. Coaches welcome (rest. seats 48). Evening meals until 9.30pm.

SAINT-ETIENNE-EN-BRESSE 71130 S.-et-L. **Map 18-B1**

Y ⊗ **LE RELAIS DE L'OASIS** (N° RR MARS 25 859) (M. Alain **Sarim**) ☎ 85-96-40-26 Evening meals.

SAINT-EUGÈNE 17520 Chte-Mme **Map 15-A2**

Y ⊗ **LES DEUX CHARENTES** (N° RR JUN 26 556) (Mme Marcelle **Blanchard**) Fontenelle Archiac ☎ 46-49-13-28 Closed Wed (off season); 15 days Feb. Coaches welcome (rest. seats 210). Some German spoken.

SAINT-EUSÈBE 71210 S.-et-L. **RN 74 Map 18-A1**

Y ⊗ ⌂ **RELAIS DU PONT DES MORANDS** (N° RR JANV 27 153) (S.A.R.L.) ☎ 85-78-10-54 ⚬ 9 Closed Sun. Evening meals. German and English spoken.

SAINT-EVARZEC 29170 Fouesnant - Finistère **RD 783 Map 7-B1**

Y ⊗ ⌂ **1 Star NN AU BON REPOS** (N° RR JUN 25 005) (M. Roger **Guillou**) **Poullogoden** ☎ 98-56-20-09 ⚬ 30 Closed Sat in winter. 15 Dec to 10 Jan. Full-board 140-180F per night. Coaches welcome (rest. seats 150). Evening meals. English spoken.

SAINT-EVROULT-DE-MONTFORT 61230 Orne **RN 138**

Y ⊗ ⌂ **HOTEL DU RELAIS** (N° RR SEP 26 050) (M. Daniel **Conan**) Le Bourg ☎ 33-35-60-58 ⚬ 5 Closed Sun. Full-board 120F per night. Coaches welcome (rest. seats 120). Evening meals until 10pm.

SAINT-FÉLIX-DE-LAURAGAIS 31540 Haute-Garonne **RN 622 Map 22-A/B2**

Y ⊗ **LE GRILLON** (N° RR DEC 23 582) (Mme Aliette **Bonnes**) Route de Castelnaudary ☎ 61-27-65-27 Closed Sun; 15–31 Aug. Evening meals.

SAINT-FIRMIN 05800 Hautes-Alpes **RN 85 Map 19-A3**

Y ⊗ ⌂ **1 Star NN RELAIS DE LA TRINITÉ** (N° RR NOV 19 998) (M. Pascal **Poncet**) Route Nationale ☎ 92-55-21-64 ⚬ 12 Closed Jan.

S

Saint-Firmin continued
Full-board 140–200F per night. Coaches welcome (rest. seats 50). Evening meals.

SAINT-FLORENT 18400 Cher **RN 151 Map 13-B1**
♀ ⊗ ⌂ **BAR RESTAURANT DE LA GARE ET DE L'EUROPE** (N° RR MARS 26 848) (Mme Colette **Lacombe**) 38, rue Pierre-Sémard ☎ 48-55-00-66 Closed Sat afternoon, Sun. Filling station near.
L'IMPRÉVU (N° RR AVR 27 252) (M. Bernard **Ruellan**) 60, rue Jean-Jaurès ☎ 48-55-12-00 Closed Sun pm and 15 days in August. Evening meals.

SAINT-FLOUR 15100 Cantal **RN 17 Map 17-A1/B3**
♀ ⊗ ⌂ **LE RELAIS DU VIEUX PONT** (N° RR AOU 22 015) (Mme Liliane **Teissèdre**) 49, place de la Liberté ☎ 71-60-23-00 **Minitel** ◄ 7 Closed Sun; Jan, Feb. Full-board 125–170F per night. Coaches welcome (rest. seats 45). Evening meals. English, Spanish spoken.
♀ ⊗ ⌂ **HÔTEL LE PROGRÈS** (N° RR AVR 23 757) (M. Alain **Mourgues**) 61, rue des Lacs ☎ 71-60-03-06 ◄ 16 Full-board 110-150F per night. Coaches welcome (rest. seats 50). Evening meals.

SAINT-GAULTIER 36800 Indre **RN 151 Map 16-A1**
♀ ⊗ **CHEZ PAQUERETTE** (N° RR OCT 22 979) (Mme Marie-Louise **Malpiece**) Lespez Commune de Chasseneuil ☎ 54-47-07-20 Closed Sat, Sun; Aug. Coaches welcome.
♀ ⊗ **LE COMMERCE** (N° RR JAN 25 266) (Mme Marie **Pilorget**) ☎ 54-47-14-81 ◄ 4 Closed Thur.

SAINT-GAUX 33340 Gironde **RN 215 Map 20-A1**
♀ ⊗ **LE RELAIS Chez Monique** (N° RR AOU 26 974) (Mme Monique **Buscail**) Saint Germain-d'Esteuil, Lesparre Medoc ☎ 56-41-25-15 Closed Sun; 1st fortnight Oct. Filling station 4km distant.

SAINT-GENCE 87510 Hte Vienne **RD 20 Map 16-B1**
♀ ⊗ **LE CAMPANELLE** (N° RR FEV 26 445) (M. Albert **Denardou**) rte de St-Gence ☎ 55-48-02-83 Closed Sat (except for banquets or wedding receptions); Aug. Coaches welcome (rest. seats 100). Evening meals.

SAINT-GEORGES-D'OLÉRON 17190 Chte-Mme **Map 11-B1**
♀ ⊗ ⌂ **1 star NN RELAIS DE LA PETITE PLAGE** (N° RR OCT 26 688) (M. Jacky **Pasdelou**) Rte de l'Océan-Domino ☎ 46-76-52-28 ◄ 9 Closed 15 Dec–15 Jan. Italian spoken.
⊗ **AUBERGE D'ALIENOR** (N° RR DEC 26 751) (M. Patrick **Audovin**) 5, Place de Verdun ☎ 46-76-76-33. Closed Wed; 15 Nov–15 Dec.

SAINT-GEORGES-DE-MONTCLARD 24140 Dordogne) **RD 21 Map 15-B3**
♀ ⊗ ⌂ **LE BON COIN** (N° RR AVR 25 901) (M. Jean **Dauthuille**) ☎ 53-82-98-47 ◄ 7 Closed Sun. Evening meals. Full-board 110–140F per night.

S

SAINT-GEORGES-DES-GARDES 49120 M.-et-L. **RN 161 Map 11-B3 and 12-B1**

♀ ⊗ **LE RELAIS DES ROUTIERS** (N° RR DEC 19 223) (M. Louis **Jolivet**) ☎ 41-63-64-35 ⇥ 5.

SAINT-GEORGES-SUR-EURE 8190 E.-et-L. **RD 610 Map 8-B3**

♀ ⊗ ⌂ **AU RENDEZ-VOUS DES PECHEURS** (N° RR NOV 26 718) (M. Amokrane **Mezair**) 9, Raymonde Bataille ☎ 37-26-75-30 ⇥ 9 Closed Mon afternoon; Aug.

SAINT-GÉRAND-LE-PUY 03150 Allier

♀ ⊗ ⌂ **HÔTEL DE LA PAIX** (N° RR MAI 22 798) (Mme **Knoche**) Ne 7 ☎ 70-99-80-15.

SAINT-GERMAIN-DES-PRÉS 45230 Loiret **RN 443 Map 13-A1/2**

♀ ⊗ ⌂ **AU BON ACCUEIL** (N° RR NOV 22 087) (Mme Catherine **Lapeyrade**) M,oulin Plateau ☎ 38-85-78-87 ⇥ 10 Closed Sat, Sun; Aug.

SAINT-GERMAIN-DU-BEL-AIR 46310 Lot **RD 23**

♀ ⊗ **CAFÉ DE FRANCE** (N° RR JANV 27 168) (Mme Mélina **Francoual**) Moulin Plateau ☎ 65-31-06-99 Closed Sun.

SAINT-GERMAIN-DU-PLAIN 71370 S-et-L. **RD 978 Map 18-B1**

♀ ⊗ **RELAIS DES SPORTS** (N° RR AVR 26 508) (M. Gilles **Tenedor**) rte de Louhans ☎ 85-47-37-27.

SAINT-GERMAIN-LA-GATINE 28300 E.-et-L. **RN 154 Map 8-A3**

♀ ⊗ **LE RELAIS DE SAINT-GERMAIN** (N° RR AVR 26 869) (Mme Madeleine **Tarrou**) 1, ave de Chartres ☎ 37-22-80-31.

SAINT-GERMAIN-LES-ARPAJON 91290 Essonne **RN 20 Map 1-B2**

♀ ⊗ **L'AS DE TRÈFLE** (N° RR NOV 26 084) (Mme Gisèle **Belin**) 7 RN 20 La Petite-Folie ☎ 64-90-02-24 ⇥ 5 Closed Sun. Coaches welcome (rest. seats 70). English spoken.

SAINT-GERMAIN-LES-BELLES 87380 Hte-Vienne **RN 20 Map 16-B1**

♀ ⊗ ⌂ **RELAIS BORNE 40** (N° RR JAN 26 139) (M. Jacques **Larue**) Beausoleil-la-Porcherie ☎ 55-71-87-12 ⇥.

SAINT-GERMAIN-DE-TALLEVENDE 14500 Calvados **RD 577 Map 8-A1**

♀ ⊗ **SARL LA MASURE** (N° RR OCT 24 718) (Mme Maria **Baclet**) La Lande Vaumont ☎ 31-68-24-02 Closed Sun. Spanish, English spoken.

SAINT-GERMAIN-SUR-MORIN 77740 S.-et-M. **RN 34 Map 9-A2**

♀ ⊗ **LE RELAIS DE LA MAIRIE** (N° RR AVR 5 9880) (M. **de Letter**) 29, rue de Paris ☎ 60-04-00-63 Closed Sun. Aug.

SAINT-GERVAIS 85230 Vendée

♀ ⊗ ⌂ **LE BOIRAT** (N° RR MARS 27 231) (M. Rémi **Verdeau**) 13, rue du Haras ☎ 51-49-23-40 ou 51-49-23-93 ⇥ 4 English and Spanish spoken.

S

SAINT-GERVAIS-DE-VIC 72120 Sarthe **RD 303 Map 12-A3**
♈ ⊗ **CHEZ ODETTE-LE SAINT ELOI** (N° RR AVR 26 872) (Mme Odette **Hervé**) ☎ 43-35-09-00 Closed Sun; public holidays. Italian spoken. Filling station 3km distant.

SAINT-GILDAS-DES-BOIS 44530 L. Atl. **RN 773 Map 11-A2**
♈ ⊗ ⌂ **LE RELAIS DES ROUTIERS** (N° RR NOV 19 193) (M. Michel **Gaidano**) 1, rue du Pont ☎ 40-01-42-15 and 01-44-70 ⊨ 10 Full-board. Coaches welcome (rest. seats 380). Evening meals.

SAINT-GILLES 30800 Gard **RN 572 Map 24-A3**
♈ ⊗ **LE MIRADOR** (N° RR JUL 25 502) (M. Michel **Bosq**) Route de Montpellier ☎ 66-87-31-20 Closed Mon low season. Coaches welcome (rest. seats 60). English, Spanish, Italian spoken.

SAINT-GILLES 35590 Ille-et-Vilaine **RN 12 Map 7-B3**
♈ ⊗ **LES RELAIS** (N° RR MAI 26 895) (Mme Jeanine **Abiven**) 23, rue de Rennes ☎ 99-64-63-04 English, German spoken. Filling station near.

SAINT-GILLES 50180 Manche **RD 972 RD 77 Map 4-B1**
♈ ⊗ **CARREFOUR SAINT-GILLES** (N° RR MAI 26 884) (M. Jean-Jacques **Billy**) Le Bourg-Agneaux ☎ 33-05-24-50. Closed Thur afternoon. English, German spoken. Filling station 3km.

SAINT-GRÉGOIRE 35760 Ille-et-Vilaine)
♈ ⊗ **RESTAURANT DE L'ÉTANG** (N° RR JUIN 27 303) (M. Michel **Hubert**) rue de l'Étang au Diable ☎ 99-38-49-43 Closed Sat and Sun. Evening meals served until 9pm.

SAINT-HELEN
♈ ⊗ **RELAIS DE LA CROIX DU FRESNE** (N° RR AVR 27 260) (M. Guy **Gabillard**) La Croix du Fresne ☎ 96-83-25-02 Evening meals.

SAINT-HILAIRE-DE-LA-CÔTE 38260 Isère **RD 73**
♈ ⊗ **AUBERGE DE LA FONTAINE** (N° RR MARS 27 218) (Mme Raymonde **Glandut**) La Côte St-André ☎ 74-54-60-17 Closed Mon. English and Italian spoken.

SAINT-HILAIRE-DE-LOULAY 85600 Vendée **RN 137 Map 12-B1**
♈ ⊗ **LE RELAX** (N° RR JUL 23 361) (M. Luc **Van Wanghe**) **Les Landes de Roussais** ☎ 51-94-02-44 or 51-06-39-41 **Minitel** Closed Sat; 1 to 21 Aug. Coaches welcome (rest. seats 78). Evening meals. German, some English spoken.

SAINT-HILAIRE-DU-HARCOUET 50600 Manche **RN 977 Map 8-A1**
♈ ⊗ ⌂ **1 Star NN LES ROUTIERS – Chez Jacques** (N° RR MAI 20 183) (M. Jacques **Guillochon**) Route de Caen-Rennes - La Gare ☎ 33-49-10-55 ⊨ 5 Closed Sun; 24 Dec to 1 Jan. Full-board 150F per night. Coaches welcome (rest. seats 90). Evening meals.

S

SAINT-HILAIRE-DU-ROSIER VILLAGE 38840 Isère **RN 92 Map 18-B3**
♀ ⊗ 🏠 **LE RELAIS CHEZ JEANINE** (N° RR OCT 17 652) (Mme **Domenech**) Route Nationale 92 ☎ 76-36-53-84 **Minitel** ⊶ 5 Closed Mon; April/May. Full-board 140–175F per night. Coaches welcome (rest. seats 60). Evening meals until 10pm. Spanish spoken.

SAINT-HILAIRE-LA-GRAVELLE 41160 Loir-et-Cher **RN 19 Map 12-A3 and 8-B3**
♀ ⊗ 🏠 **AUBERGE DU LOIR** (N° RR OCT 22 066) (M. **Pierdos**) 10, rue Léon Cibié ☎ 54-82-65-00 ⊶ 5 Closed Wed evening. Evening meals. English spoken.

SAINT-IGNEUC 22270 C.-du-N. **RN 796 Map 7-A3**
♀ ⊗ **LE RELAIS DES 4 ROUTES** (N° RR MARS 26 849) (Mme Annie **Bal**) Les 4 Routes, Jugon-les-Lacq ☎ 96-31-61-77 Open 24 hrs. English spoken.

SAINT-INGLEVERT 62250 Pas-de-Calais **RN 1 Map 5-A2**
♀ ⊗ **LA MURAILLE** (N° RR JAN 26 422) (Mme Jocelyne **Salmon**) RN 1 ☎ 21-33-75-44 Closed Sun. English spoken.

SAINT-JEAN-DE-BEUGNE 85210 Vendée **RN 137 Map 11-B2**
♀ ⊗ **L'OASIS** (N° RR JUN 25 953) (M. Guy **Teillet**) Ste-Hermine ☎ 51-

SAINT-JEAN-DE-BOURNAY 38440 Isère **RN 518**
♀ ⊗ **RELAIS DE LA GARE** (N° RR AVR 26 496) (Mme Viviane **Laurent** et Josianne **Hingant**) 10 av, de la Libération ☎ 74-58-70-33 ⊶ 5.

SAINT-JEAN-DE-CHEVELU 73170 Savoie **RN 521 A Map 19-A2**
♀ ⊗ 🏠 **LE RELAIS DES QUATRE CHEMINS** (N° RR NOV 26 388) (M. Jean **Rubad**) ☎ 79-36-80-06 ⊶ 10 Closed Sat evening, Sun from Oct to Jan. English spoken.

SAINT-JEAN-DE-LA-RUELLE 45140 Loiret **RN 155 Map 13-A1**
♀ ⊗ **LE RELAIS DU PETIT PONT** (N° RR MAR 14 290) (M. Gilbert **Germain**) 15, rue Charles-Beauhaire ☎ 38-88-38-47 Closed Sun; Aug.
♀ ⊗ **LE RELAIS DE LA MAIRIE** (N° RR OCT 24 389) (M. André **Finet**) 142, rue Nationale ☎ 38-88-44-98 Closed Sat, Sun; 24 Dec 2.00pm to 3 Jan; 3 weeks in Jul or Sept.

SAINT-JEAN-DE-MAURIENNE 73300 Savoie **RN 6 Map 19-B3**
♀ ⊗ **CAFÉ-RESTAURANT DU CHAMP DE FOIRE** (N° RR JUN 21 971) (Mme Angèle **Dompnier**) Place du Champ de Foire, 66, rue Louis-Sibué ☎ 79-64-12-03 Closed Sun. Coaches welcome (rest. seats 80). Evening meals until 11pm. Italian spoken.

SAINT-JEAN-DE-MOIRANS 38430 Isère **RN 92 Map 19-A3**
♀ ⊗ **LE RIO BRAVO** (N° RR OCT 24 371) (Mme Michele **Courty-Jacolin**) Nationale 92 Lieu-dit La Patinière Rue Gaston-Bouardel ☎ 76-05-28-65 Closed Sun; Evening meals.

S

SAINT-JEAN-LA-POTERIE 56350 Morbihan **RD 775 Map 11-A2**
𝖄 ⊗ **RESTAURANT DES CARRIÈRES** (N° RR MAR 26 830) (Mme
Andrée **Delhaye**) 1, rue de la Butte, Aucfer ☎ 99-72-13-64
Closed Mon afternoon and from 24 Dec–1 Jan. Filling station
near.

SAINT-JEAN-SUR-COUESNON 35140 Ille-et-Vilaine **RN 12 and D 23
Map 8-B1**
𝖄 ⊗ **LA JUELLERIE** (N° RR DEC 23 050) (M. **Besquel**) ☎ 99-55-11-85
Closed Sat, Sun. Coaches welcome (rest. seats 24). Evening
meals.

SAINT-JEAN-SUR-VILAINE 35220 I.-et-V. **RN 157 Map 8-B1**
𝖄 ⊗ ⌂ **RELAIS DU CHEVAL BLANC** (N° RR DEC 26 118) (M. Alain
Bellevin) 4, rue de Rennes ☎ 99-00-32-67 ⇥ 10.

SAINT-JOSEPH-DE-RIVIÈRE 38134 Isère **Map 19-A2**
𝖄 ⊗ ⌂ **LE RELAIS CHAMPÊTRE** (N° RR OCT 27 051) (Mme
Adeline **Mandrillon**) **Le Pont Demay** ☎ 76-55-49-08 ⇥ 7 Closed
Sat low season and 15/10 to 15/11. Italian spoken.

SAINT-JULIEN-EN-BEAUCHENE 05140 Hautes-Alpes **RN 75 Map 19-
A3 and 24-B1**
𝖄 ⊗ ⌂ **AU REFUGE DES AMIS** (N° RR JUN 23 839) (M. **Pizzichelli
Certano**) ☎ 92-58-03-59 ⇥ 7 Closed Sat, Sun; 15 days in Jan; May;
Oct. Coaches welcome (rest. seats 40). Evening meals. Italian
spoken.

SAINT-JULIEN-DE-CHAPTEUIL see BOUSSOULET 43260 Haute-
Loire

SAINT-JULIEN-DE-CIVRY 71610 Saône-et-Loire **RD 985 Map 18-A1**
𝖄 ⊗ **RESTAURANT DES VOYAGEURS** (N° RR MAR 26 855) (M.
Hubert **Dumoulin**) The Station ☎ 85-70-62-10 Closed Tue after-
noon. English, German spoken. Filling station 3km distant.

SAINT-JULIEN-DE-LA-NEF 30440 Gard **Map 23-B1**
𝖄 ⊗ ⌂ **2 stars NN AUBERGE DE LA CASCADE D'AIGUES FOL-
LES** (N° RR JUN 26 915) (M. Alain **Danis**) Sarl 6 ☎ 67-82-42-78 ⇥
17 from 180–200F, breakfast 15–25F. Closed Mon (off season).
Filling station near. Car park; bar; dogs allowed; recreation
(bathing, walking, riding, canoeing). Places to visit. Grotte des
Demoiselles, Tarn gorges, Bambouseraie d'Anduze.

SAINT-JULIEN-DE-PIGANIOL 12300 Aveyron **RD 963 Map 17-B2**
𝖄 ⊗ **A L'AUBERGE DE ST.-JULIEN** (N° RR SEPT 26 657) (Mme
Évelyne **Carrière**) Rte Dle 963 ☎ 65-64-05-92 Closed Mon
afternoon.

SAINT-JULIEN-LE-FAUCON 14140 Calv. **RN 511 Map 4-B2**
𝖄 ⊗ **CHEZ JEAN-PIERRE** (N° RR JUN 26 261) (Mme Gisèle **Goupil**)
Livarot ☎ 31-63-80-96 Closed Sun. English spoken. Evening
meals until 8pm.

S

SAINT-JULIEN-LA-VÊTRE 42440 Loire **RN 89 Map 18-A2 16-B3**

⧠ ⊗ **L'ESCALE 89** (N° RR OCT 27 065) (M. René **Pasinetti**) ☎ 77-97-85-30 German, Italian and English spoken.

SAINT-JUNIEN 87200 Haute-Vienne **RN 141 Map 16-B1**

⧠ ⊗ **L'ETOILE** (N° RR AVR 25 872) (M. Alain **Noble**) 8, av. Barbusse ☎ 55-02-15-19 ⊷ 7 Closed Fri evening; 20 Dec to 6 Jan. Full-board 130F per night. Coaches welcome (rest. seats 120). Evening meals. English spoken.

⧠ ⊗ **L'ESCALE** (N° RR JUN 26 565) (M. Jean-Louis **Gaudiez**) 5, Ave Henri-Barbusse ☎ 55-02-03-11 Closed Sun. English, Spanish spoken.

SAINT-JUST-LE-MARTEL 87590 Haute-Vienne **RN 141 Map 16-B1**

⧠ ⊗ **LE PETIT SALÉ** (N° RR FEV 25 310) (M. Jean-Pierre **Teyti**) Les Chabanes ☎ 55-09-21-14 Coaches welcome (rest. seats 50). Evening meals until 11pm.

SAINT-LANGIS-LES-MORTAGNES 61400 Orne **RD 938 after 138 bis, 1km from Nle Map 8-A2**

⧠ ⊗ ⌂ **LE RELAIS DE LA GARE** (N° RR JUL 24 278) (M. and Mme Michel **Gaudin**) Rue de la Gare ☎ 33-25-16-10 ⊷ 9 Closed Sun; Aug. German spoken.

SAINT-LAURENT-DU-VAR 06700 Alpes-Mmes **Map 25-B2**

⊗ **LE RELAIS** (N° RR JAN 26 730) (Mme Sylviane **Bliehast**) allée des Cableurs Secteur B21 ☎ 93-31-26-47 Closed Sat, Sun. Italian, German spoken.

⧠ ⊗ **AU COUP DE FUSIL** SARL Floreje (N° RR JANV 27 159) (M. Eugène **Bagi**) bd Pierre-Marie Curie Zl Secteur B ☎ 93-31-60-55 Closed Sun. Italian spoken.

SAINT-LÉGER-CARCAGNY 14740 Calvados **RN 13 Map 4-B2**

⧠ ⊗ **AUX JOYEUX ROUTIERS** (N° RR SEP 24 683) (M. Charles **Candavoine**) **Hameau de St-Léger** ☎ 31-80-22-01 Closed Sun in winter.

SAINT-LÉGER-SUR-DHEUNE 71510 S.-et-L. **RD 978 Map 18-A1**

⧠ ⊗ ⌂ **AU BON ACCUEIL** PMU (N° RR JAN 22 147) (Mme Nelly **Roland**) ☎ 85-45-30-65 ⊷ 5 Evening meals.

SAINT-LON-LES-MINES 40300 Landes **CD6 Map 20-A2**

⧠ ⊗ ⌂ **l star NN HOTEL DU FRONTON** (N° RR MAI 26 880) (M. Daniel **Laffitte**) ☎ 58-57-80-45 ⊷ 20 Closed Nov. Spanish spoken. Filling station 2km distant.

SAINT-LOUIS 68300 Ht-Rhin

⧠ ⊗ **LE PARADIS** (N° RR JAN 26 146) (M. Robert **Metzger**) 57, rue Gl-de-Gaulle ☎ 89-67-73-59 Closed Tue; Aug. Evening meals.

SAINT-LOUP-DE-VARENNES 71240 S.-et-L. **RN 6 Map 18-B1**

⧠ ⊗ **LA PETITE AUBERGE** (N° RR AOU 26 980) (M. Jacques **Demeuzoy**) ☎ 85-44-21-87 Closed Sun; Aug. Filling station near.

S

SAINT-LOUP-SUR-SEMOUSE 70800 Haute-Saône **RN 64 Map 10-A3 and 14-B2**

⚹ ⊗ **LE RELAIS DE LA TERRASSE** (N° RR MAI 6 059) (Mme Jean **Ballot**) Rue de la Gare ☎ 84-49-02-20 **Minitel** ⊷ 4 Closed Sun; 1 to 15 Aug.

SAINT-MALO 35400 I.-et-V. **RN 155 and 137 Map 7-A3**

⚹ ⊗ ⌂ **L'ARRIVÉE** (N° RR AVR 18 681) (M. Robert **Hervé**) 83, rue Ville-Pépin, Saint-Servan-sur-Mer ☎ 99-81-99-57 ⊷ 16 Closed Sun; Oct. Full-board 160–180F per night. Evening meals.

SAINT-MARC-SUR-SEINE 21450 Côte-d'Or **RN 71 Map 13-A3**

⚹ ⊗ ⌂ **LE SOLEIL D'OR** (N° RR DEC 22 133) (Mme Geneviève **Girard**) ☎ 80-93-21-42 ⊷ 6 Closed Sat. Christmas. English spoken.

SAINT-MARCEL 27950 Eure **Map 3-B1**

⚹ ⊗ ⌂ **LE TERMINUS** (N° RR DEC 26 123) (Mme Louise **Ragazzini**) 3N RN 15 **Le Goulet** ☎ 32-52-50-07 ⊷ 18 Closed Sat afternoon, Sun. Evening meals.

SAINT-MARCEL see ARGENTON 36200 Indre **RN 20 Map 16-A1**

SAINT-MARCEL-LÈS-VALENCE 26320 Drôme **RN 532 à 100m Map 18-B3**

⚹ ⊗ **LA PRAIRIE** (N° RR SEPT 27 021) (M. Michel **Montusciat**) 8, rue de la Liberté ☎ 75-58-70-38 Closed Tues pm, Wed pm, and 15 days in August. Italian and English spoken.

SAINT-MARCELLIN 38160 Isère **RN 92 Map 24-B1**

⚹ ⊗ **LE RELAIS LE SIROCCO** (N° RR OCT 24 394) (Mme Martine **Glé**) Gare de la Sône, Chatte ☎ 76-38-03-73 Closed Sat 3.00pm, Sun.

SAINT-MARD 17700 Chte-Mme RN 139 Map 11-B1 **RN 139 Map 11-B1**

⚹ **AUBERGE DE SAINT MARD** (N° RR OCT 26 694) (M. J. **Madeux**) Surgères ☎ 46-07-04-26 Closed Mon. English, some Spanish spoken.

SAINT-MARS-LA-BRIÈRE 72680 Sarthe **RN 157 Map 8-B2**

⚹ ⊗ **AUBERGE DU NARAIS** (N° RR OCT 27 067) (M. Rémy **Tressy**) ☎ 43-89-87-30 Closed Sun.

SAINT-MARTIAL-D'ARTENSET 24700 Dordogne **RN 89 Map 15-B3**

⚹ ⊗ **AUBERGE DE SAINT-MARTIAL** (N° RR OCT 20 840) (Mme **Rolland**) ☎ 53-80-35-74 ⊷ 4 Closed Sat; Sept. English, German spoken.

SAINT-MARTIN-D'AUBIGNY 50190 Manche **RD 900 Map 4-B1**

⚹ ⊗ **LES RUETTES** (N° RR SEPT 26 627) (M. Michel **Lepage**) Les Ruettes ☎ 33-46-71-45. Closed Wed from 2pm. English spoken.

SAINT-MARTIN-DES-BESACES see CAEN 14350 Calvados **RN 175 Map 4-B2 and 8-A1**

SAINT-MARTIN-DE-CRAU 13310 B.-du-R. **RN 113 Map 24-B3**
🍷 ⊗ 🏠 **LA CABANE BAMBOU** (N° RR AVR 13 594) (M. Jacques and Georgette **Giraud**) Route Nationale 113 between Salon and Aries ☎ 90-58-17-25 and 90-58-02-52 ⊷ 10 Closed Sun (except summer time). Open 24 hrs. Coaches welcome (rest. seats 100). Evening meals. English, Italian, Spanish spoken.
🍷 ⊗ 🏠 **HÔTEL DE LA GARE** (N° RR AVR 26 511) (Mme Andrée **Sicard**) rte de la Dynamite ☎ 90-47-05-18 ⊷ 8 Closed Sat afternoon. Full-board 140F per night. Coaches welcome (rest. seats 50). Evening meals.

SAINT-MARTIN-EN-BRESSE 71620 Saône-et-Loire **RN 73 Map 18-B1**
🍷 ⊗ **LA MARANDE** (N° RR SEPT 26 634) (M. Gilles **Piponnier**) Le Bourg-St. Maurice en Rivière ☎ 85-47-50-25 Closed Tue.

SAINT-MARTIN OSMONVILLE 76680 S.-Mme **RN 28 Map 4-A3**
🍷 ⊗ **LA GRANGE** (N° RR JAN 25 784) (Mme Denise **De La Boissière**) ☎ 35-34-14-34.

SAINT-MAUR 36250 Indre **RN 20 Map 12-B3**
🍷 ⊗ **LES TERRES NOIRES** (N° RR NOV 26 096) (Mme Nathalie **Bourdin-Favereau**) Les Terres Noires ☎ 54-92-03-29 Closed Sun. English spoken.

SAINT-MAUR-DES-FOSSÉS 94100 Val de Marne **Map 1-B3**
🍷 ⊗ **LA PASSERELLE** (N° RR OCT 26 699) (M. Jean **Dias**) 45, Bld Gl Fernier ☎ 42-83-21-71 Portuguese, Spanish spoken.

SAINT-MAURICE 94410 Val-de-Marne **RN 303 Map 1-B3**
🍷 ⊗ 🏠 **LE TERMINUS-CHEZ JEAN** (N° RR NOV 7 284) (M. Jean **Giacomelli**) 111, avenue du Général-Leclerc ☎ 48-86-50-69 ⊷ 8 Closed Sun; Aug.

SAINT-MAURICE-SUR-ADOUR 40270 Landes **Map 20-B2**
🍷 ⊗ **RELAIS DE LA MARIANNE** (N° RR AVR 26 876) (Mme Maria **Toribio**) ☎ 58-45-97-36. Closed Sat. Spanish spoken. Filling station near.

SAINT-MAURICE-LA-SOUTERRAINE 23300 Creuse **RN 142 RN 20 Map 16-B1 SEE LA CROISIÈRE**
SAINT-MAURICE-SUR-DARGOIRE 69440 Rhône **RD42 Map 2-B1**
🍷 ⊗ **CHEZ ROSE** (N° RR JUL 26 604) (Mme Rosiane **Blé**) ☎ 78-81-20-10 Coaches welcome (rest. seats 40). Evening meals.

SAINT-MAURICE-SUR-DARGOIRE 69440 Rhône **Map RD 42 Map 2-B1**
🍷 ⊗ **CHEZ ROSE** (N° RR JUL 26 9604) (Mme Rosiane **Blé**) Le Grand Bulsson ☎ 78-81-20-10 Cars touristiques (2 sailes de 40 places) Repas servi le soir.

SAINT-MAURICE-SUR-FESSARD 45700 Loiret **Map 9-B1**
🍷 ⊗ **RESTAURANT DE LA GARE** (N° RR JANV 26 800) (Mme Colette **Jehl**) Villemandeur ☎ 38-97-81-00 English, Spanish spoken.

S

Saint-Maurice-sur-Fessard continued
♟ ⊗ **LE RELAIS DE SAINT-MAURICE** (N° RR MARS 26 840) (M. Pascal **Crouvisier**) Villemandeur ☎ 38-97-80-59 'Total' filling station near.

SAINT-MAXIMIN-LA-SAINTE-BAUME 83470 Var **Maps 24-B3 and 25-A2**
♟ ⊗ 🏠 **LE RELAIS DU CARILLON** (N° RR OCT 23 989) (M. Robert **Berton**) 5, rue de la République ☎ 94-78-00-38 ◄ 9 Closed Thur. Coaches welcome (rest. seats 115). Evening meals.

SAINT-MEEN-LE-GRAND 35290 I.-et-V. **RN 164 Bis and 166 Map 7-B3**
♟ ⊗ **LE RELAIS DU MIDI** (N° RR OCT 26 732) (M. Christian **Posnic-SARL**) 25, place Patton ☎ 99-09-60-02 ◄ 6 Closed Sat after lunch; 8–31 Aug.

SAINT-MIHIEL 55300 Meuse **RD 964 Map 14-A1**
♟ ⊗ 🏠 **LES ROUTIERS** (N° RR AOU 22 460) (M. Claude **Rousselot**) 19, rue de Verdun ☎ 28-89-00-44 ◄ 8 Closed Sat, Sun. Evening meals served until 9pm. English spoken.

SAINT-NAUPHARY 82370 T.-et-G. **RD 999 Map 22-A1**
♟ ⊗ 🏠 **LES AYÈRES** (N° RR FEV 22 645) (M. **Monruffet**) ☎ 63-67-85-09 ◄ 6 Closed Sat; 8–31 Aug; 1 week Christmas/New Year. Full-board 140–160F per night. Coaches welcome (rest. seats 100).

SAINT-NAZAIRE 44600 Loire-Atl. **RN 771 Map 11-A2**
♟ **LE LAFAYETTE** (N° RR SEP 24 671) (M. Gilbert **Renou**) avenue de Penhoët ☎ 40-22-53-82 **Minitel** Closed Sat afternoon, Sun; Jul. Coaches welcome (terrace of 40 seats).
♟ ⊗ 🏠 **LA MARINE** (N° RR AVR 26 866) (M. Patrick **Feidel**) 15, avenue de Penhoët. ☎ 40-66-42-40 ◄ 8 Closed Sun. Filling station near.

SAINT-NICOLAS-DE-BOURGUEIL 37140 Indre-et-Loire **CD 035 Map 12-B2**
♟ ⊗ **LE RELAIS** (N° RR OCT 25 717) (M. Joël **Joulin**) Le Bourg - Place de Église ☎ 47-97-75-39 ◄ 3 Closed Sat, Sun from Dec to Mar; 15 to 31 Aug.

SAINT-NICOLAS-DE-LA-GRAVE 82210 T.-et-G. **Aut. A 61 Map 22-A1**
⛽ **Service Station ELF GARONNE** (N° RR JAN 24 812) (M. Christian **Roux**) Le Montet ☎ 63-94-80-30 Open 24 hours. Spanish, French, English spoken.

SAINT-NICOLAS-DE-REDON 44460 Loire-Atl. **Map 11-A2**
♟ ⊗ **LE RELAIS DES ROUTIERS** (N° RR JAN 23 081) (Mme Marie-Annick **Hemery**) 84, avenue Jean-Burel ☎ 99-71-01-96 **Minitel** Closed Sat, Sun; Aug. Coaches welcome (rest. seats 52). Evening meals until 11pm.

SAINT-NOLF 56250 Morbihan **RN 166 Map 11-A2**
♈ ⊗ **LE RELAIS BELLEVUE** (N° RR JUN 22 374) (M. Joël **Guegan**)
Bellevue ☎ 97-45-44-04 Closed 1 to 30 Aug. Evening meals.

SAINT-OMER 62500 P.-de-C. **RN 43 Map 5-A2**
♈ ⊗ ⌂ **LE RELAIS DE LA RENAISSANCE** (N° RR AVR 10 573)
(SARL **Vanyper Fils**) 10, place du 11-Novembre ☎ 21-38-26-55
↤ 18 Closed Sun. Coaches welcome (rest. seats 100). Evening
meals until 9.15pm. English spoken.

SAINT-OUEN 93400 Seine-St-Denis **Pont de St-Ouen Map 1-A2**
♈ ⊗ **AU ROUTIER SYMPA** (N° RR SEP 22 466) (M. Bernard **Delouv-
rier**) 93, boulevard Victor-Hugo and 1, place du Capitaine Glaner
☎ 40-11-00-31 ↤ 10 Closed Sun; Aug. Evening meals.
♈ ⊗ **LE RELAIS DU PAVILLON BLEU** (N° RR JUN 23 830) (M.
Ramdane **Kerdous**) 7, quai de Seine ☎ 40-11-03-67 Closed Sun;
half-July. Coaches welcome (rest. seats 60). Evening meals.

SAINT-PANDELON 40180 Landes **Map 20-A2**
♈ ⊗ **HÔSTELLERIE DU PONT** (N° RR MAI 27 286) (M. Jean-Yves
Lasserre) ☎ 58-98-71-17 Closed Mon and Tues pm. Spanish and
English spoken.

SAINT-PAUL 60650 Oise **RN 31 Map 3-A2**
♈ ⊗ **AU RELAIS SAINT-PAUL** (N° RR SEPT 27 035) (Mme Marie-
France **Mouligneaux**) ☎44-82-20-19 Closed Sun and August.
English spoken.

SAINT-PAUL-DU-BOIS LA REVEILLERE 49310 M.-et-L. **RN 748
Map 12-B1**
♈ ⊗ **CHEZ MAITE** (N° RR FEV 20 394) (Mme **Bonnin**) ☎ 41-64-81-44
Closed Sun. Evening meals.

SAINT-PAUL-CAP-DE-JOUX 81220 Tarn **RD 112 Map 22-B2**
♈ ⊗ **LES GLYCINES** (N° RR SEPT 23 452) (M. Claude **Peyrard**) rue
Philippe Pinel ☎ 63-70-61-37.

SAINT-PAUL-LES-DAX 40990 Landes **RN 124 Map 20-A/B2**
♈ ⊗ **RELAIS PLAISANCE** (N° RR MAI 23 784) (M. Alain **Escos**) route
de Bayonne ☎ 58-74-04-70 English, Spanish spoken.

SAINT-PAUL-DE-LOUBRESSAC 46170 Lot **RN 20 Map 22-A1**
♈ ⊗ ⌂ **1 Star NN LE RELAIS DE LA MADELEINE** SARL (N° RR
⇱ JUL 9 786) (M. Bernard **Devianne**) 100 m from Route National, 20
km from Cahors, 35 km from Mautauban ☎ 65-21-98-08 ↤ 16 from
85–165F, breakfast 17F, access for disabled. Closed Sat; 1 Nov for
8 days; 1 Dec to 10 Jan. Full-board 150–170F per night. Coaches
welcome (rest. seats 85 plus terrace). Evening meals. English
spoken (Spanish in Summer). Car park; bar; dogs allowed;
recreations (*pétanque*, childrens games). Menus 48–54F. Specialities: *Médaillon de ris de veau maison, foie gras, cèpes.*

SAINT-PAUL-LE-JEUNE 07460 Ardèche **RD 104 Map 23-B1**
♈ ⊗ **LE RELAIS ROUTIERS DE CHEYRÈS** (N° RR JUN 23 309) (Mme

S

Saint-Paul-le-Jeune continued

Marie-Thérèse **Vernède**) Cheyres-Banne ☎ 75-39-30-09 **Minitel**
Closed Sun. Coaches welcome (rest. seats 70). Evening meals.
Car park (5,000m²).

SAINT-PAUL-TROIS CHATEAUX 26130 Drôme **RN 59 near Autoroute A7 Map 24-A2**
♀ ⊗ ⌂ **LE RELAIS DE PROVENCE** (N° RR MAI 21 109) (Mme
Hélène **Entringer**) 11, avenue du Général-de-Gaulle ☎ 75-04-72-
48 ⊷ 7 Closed 15 Jan to 15 Feb.

SAINT-PELLERIN 50500 Manche **RN 13 Map 4-B1**
♀ ⊗ **AUBERGE DE LA FOURCHETTE** (N° RR DEC 25 752) (Mme
Henriette **Letourneur**) Carantan ☎ 33-42-16-56 English spoken.
Filling station 2km distant.

SAINT-PHAL 10130 Aube **Map 9-B3**
♀ ⊗ **RESTAURANT DU COMMERCE** (N° RR FEV 26 821) (M. Daniel
Godefroy) Evry-le-Châtel ☎ 25-42-16-39 Closed Mon; Aug.

SAINT-PHILBERT-DE-BOUAINE 85660 Vendée **CD 937 Map 11-B3**
♀ ⊗ ⌂ **2 Stars NN LE RELAIS DES ETANGS** (N° RR AUG 26 975) (M.
Khemaïs **Chargui**) Route de Rocheservière ☎ 51-41-92-44 ⊷ 15
120F, breakfast 21F, telephone, TV in room. Closed Sun evening
(off season); Tue; Christmas week; 1–15 Feb. English, German
spoken. Filling station (5km). Public car park; lift; bar; dogs
allowed; recreational facilities. Places to visit: Puy du Fou festival
(in season), countryside of the Vendée.

SAINT-PHILBERT-DE-GRAND'LIEU 44310 Loire-Atl. **RD 18 Bis Map
11-B2**
♀ ⊗ ⌂ **LA BOULOGNE** (N° RR MAR 24 162) (M. Bernard **André**) 11,
place de l'Abbatiale ☎ 40-78-70-55 ⊷ 6 Closed Sat, Sun. Full-
board 125F per night. Coaches welcome (rest. seats 80). Evening
meals.

SAINT-PIERRE DE CHANDIEU 69780 Rhône **RD 149 Map 2-B2**
♀ ⊗ **LE BLE D'OR** (N° RR OCT 24 712) (Mme Jeannine **Girogio**)
avenue Amédée-Ronin ☎ 78-40-32-41 Closed Sept. Italian spoken.

SAINT-PIERRE-DU-CHEMIN 85120 Vendée **Map 11-B3**
♀ ⊗ ⌂ **LE SAINT-PIERRE** (N° RR FEV 25 307) (M. Patrick **Lamarre**)
☎ 51-69-60-35 – 51-51-71-35 ⊷ 10 English spoken.

SAINT-PIERRE-DES-CORPS 37700 I.-et-L. **RN 751 Map 12-A3**
♀ ⊗ **LE GRILLON** (N° RR DEC 21 721) (Mme and M. **Latour**) 9, quai
de la Loire ☎ 47-44-74-90 Closed Sat, Sun; Jul or Aug.

SAINTE-PIERRE-DU-FRESNE 14260 Calv **RN 175 Map 4-B1/2**
♀ ⊗ **AU VERT BOCAGE** (N° RR OCT 26 704) (M. Robert **Servain**)
SARL Les Haïes Tigards ☎ 31-77-80-89 Closed Sat, Sun; Aug.

SAINT-PIERRE-LANGERS 50530 Manche **RN 173 Map 8-A1**
♀ ⊗ ⌂ **A LA GRILLADE** (N° RR AVR 24 197) (M. Philippe **Ledoux**)
🍽 La Havaudière (5 km from Sartilly) ☎ 33-48-83-71 ⌿ 8 Closed Sat,
Sun. Full-board 145–155F per night.

SAINT-PIERRE-LE-MOUTIER 58240 Nièvre **RN 7 Map 16-A3**
♀ ⊗ ⌂ **HÔTEL DU CHEVAL BLANC** (N° RR JAN 6 961) (M. Jacques
Beaudoin) 1, rue du Commandant-Leiffeit ☎ 86-37-42-45 ⌿ 5
Closed Tues. Full board 180F. Coaches welcome (rest. seats 60).
Menus from 50 to 110F. Specialities: Coq au Vin, Picardie Tripe
and Escalope.

SAINT-PIERRE-LES-ELBEUF 76320 S.-Mme **Map 3-B1**
♀ ⊗ **SARL LA SAUVAGINE** (N° RR AOU 26 020) (M. Lionel **Hublet**)
611, chemin du Halage ☎ 35-78-37-70 Closed Sat, Sun. Evening
meals.

SAINT-PIERRE-DE-QUIBERON 56510 Morbihan **RD 768 Map 11-A1**
♀ ⊗ **LA CHALOUPE DE KERHOSTIN** (N° RR MAI 21 916) (Mme **Le
Bellour**) place du Marché **Kerhostin** ☎ 97-30-91-54 Closed Sun
in winter; 15 Oct–15 Nov. Coaches welcome (rest. seats 80).

SAINT-PIERREMONT 88700 Vosges **RD 414 Map 14-B1**
♀ ⊗ ⌂ **2 Stars LE RELAIS VOSGIEN** (N° RR NOV 14 581) (Mme
Prevost) Rambervilliers ☎ 29-65-02-46 **Minitel** ⌿ 9 Closed Mon
afternoon; 15 to 31 Sept. Full-board 170–220F per night. Coaches
welcome (rest. seats 100). Evening meals. Car park; bar; dogs
allowed; amusement park. Places to visit: Petit Versailles, Lune-
ville.

SAINT-PIERRE-SUR-DIVES 14170 Calvados **D 511 Map 8-A2**
♀ ⊗ **AU RENDEZ-VOUS DES NORMANDS Chez Liliane** (N° RR
DEC 26 764) (Mme Liliane **Desoleau**) 134, rue Falaise ☎ 21-20-
53-66 Closed Tue afternoon.

SAINT-POL-DE-LÉON 29250 Finistère
♀ ⊗ **LES ROUTIERS** (N° RR JUN 26 267) (M. Jean-Louis and Marie-
Pierre **Floc'h**) 28, rue Pen-Ar-Pont ☎ 98-69-00-52 Closed Sun;
Aug. Coaches welcome (rest. seats 50). English, German spoken.

SAINT-PONS 34220 Hérault **RN 112 Map 23-A2**
♀ ⊗ ⌂ **1 Star NN LE SOMAIL** (N° RR FEV 22 681) (M. André **Cros**) 2,
avenue de Castres ☎ 67-97-00-12 ⌿ 18 Restaurant closed in Feb.
Full-board 150–210F per night. Coaches welcome (rest. seats 70).
Evening meals.

SAINT-POURCAIN-SUR-SIOULE 03500 Allier **Map 16-A3**
♀ ⊗ **HÔTEL-DU-CENTRE** (N° RR DEC 26 757) (M. Michel **Delage**) ☎
70-45-97-57.

SAINT-PRIEST-DE-GIMEL 19800 Corrèze **RN 89 Map 17-A1**
♀ ⊗ **LE RELAIS CHEZ MOUSTACHE** (N° RR JUL 20 791 bis) (M.
Jean-Claude **Laval**) Gare de Corrèze ☎ 55-27-32-58 ⌿ 3 Closed
Sun; Aug.

S

SAINT-PRIVAT-DES-VIEUX 30340 Gard **RD 216 Map 23-B1**
♀ ⊗ ⌂ **Tobacconist L'ESCALE** (N° RR JAN 18 303) (Mme Ginette **Calcat**) ☎ 66-30-09-40 ↤ 8 English spoken. Evening meals.

SAINT-PROUANT 85110 Vendée **RD 760 Map 11-B3**
♀ ⊗ ⌂ **LE ZODIAC** (N° RR MAR 24 159) (M. Daniel **Arru**) 2, rue G. Clemenceau Le Bourg ☎ 51-67-40-55 ↤ 5 Closed Mon; 23 Jul to 7 Aug. Full-board 110–130F per night. Coaches welcome (rest. seats 80). Evening meals. English, Spanish spoken.

SAINT-QUAY-PORTRIEUX 22410 C.-du-N. **RN 786 Map 7-A2**
♀ ⊗ ⌂ **LE RELAIS DU MOULIN LES ROUTIERS** (N° RR DEC 23 049) (M. **Guitton**) 42, rue des 3 Frères Salün ☎ 96-70-40-19 ↤ 8 Closed Sun in winter.

SAINT-QUENTIN 02100 Aisne **RN 44 Maps 5-B3 and 6-A1**
♀ ⊗ **LES ROUTIERS** (N° RR SEPT 26 322) (M. **Balique**) 134, route de la Fère, Pont de Guise ☎ 23-68-26-79 ↤ 13 Closed Sat afternoon, Sun afternoon; Evening meals.
♀ ⊗ **BRASSERIE DE LA VALLÉE** (N° RR MAI 27 291) (M. Jean **Boyard**) 28 bis, Chaussée Romaine ☎ 23-62-43-67 Closed Sun and August. German, English and a little Dutch spoken.

SAINT-QUENTIN-LES-ANGES 53400 Mayenne **RD 26 Map 12-A1**
♀ ⊗ **LE RELAIS** (N° RR NOV 24 419) (Mme Marie-Annick **Trottier**) Craon ☎ 43-06-10-62 ↤ 8 Closed Aug. Full-board 125F per person. Coaches welcome (2 dining rooms 45/100). Evening meals.

SAINT-QUENTIN-LA-MOTTE 80880 Somme
♀ ⊗ **LES ROUTIERS** (N° RR NOV 26 375) (M. Bruno **Vassard**), Route Départementale 925 ☎ 22-60-50-11 Closed Sun. Opening hours (restaurant) 5am-midnight. Coaches welcome (rest seats 30).

SAINT-QUENTIN-SUR-ISÈRE 38210 Isère **RN 532 Map 19-A3**
♀ ⊗ **LA CABANE BAMBOU** (N° RR JUL 24 631) (M. **Ruggiero**) **Le Replat** ☎ 76-93-80-05.
♀ ⊗ **LE GIBRALTAR** (N° RR JUN 26 907) (Mme Isabelle **Brisquet**) ☎ 76-93-65-28 Closed Sun. Filling station near.

SAINT-RAPHAEL 83700 Var **RN 98 Map 25-B2**
♀ ⊗ ⌂ **1 Star NN LE RELAIS BEL AZUR** (N° RR FEV 19 663) (Mme Marguerite **Magnani**) 247, boulevard de Provence ☎ 94-95-14-08 ↤ 20 Closed Sat, Sun; 24 Dec to 5 Jan. Full-board 195–215F per night. Coaches welcome (rest. seats 115). Evening meals until 9.00pm. Italian spoken.
♀ ⊗ ⌂ **2 stars NN HÔTEL MODERNE** (N° RR JUIN 26 568) (M. Michel **Hortal**) 331, avenue de Général-Leclerc ☎ 94-51-22-16 ↤ 25 Closed Sun evening in winter; 24–27 Dec. Full-board 160–220F per night. Coaches welcome (2 dining rooms: 25/130 seats). Evening meals.

SAINT-REMY-SUR-AVRE 28380 E-et-L. **RN 12 Map 8-A3**
♀ ⊗ **LE RELAIS DU PLESSIS – Chez Liliane et Pierrot** (N° RR MAI

24 962) (M. Pierre **Cottereau**) 71 RN 12 ☎ 37-48-92-16 Closed Sun; Feb. English spoken.

SAINT-RIQUIER 80135 Somme **Map 5-A3**
♀ ⊗ **LE CENTULOIS** (N° RR JUIL 26 970) (Mme Lili **Colinet**) 70, rue du Général de Gaulle ☎ 22-28-88-15 Closed Wed afternoon. Filling station near.

SAINT-ROMAIN-DE-COLBOSC 76430 Seine-Mme **Map 4-A3**
♀ ⊗ **LE RELAIS DU FRESCOT** (N° RR JAN 25 257) (M. Jacques **Chapelet**) 18, Nationale ☎ 35-20-15-09 ⇀ 6 Closed Sun; Aug. Coaches welcome (high-speed breakfast only, for 40–60). Evening meals.

SAINT-ROMAIN-LA-MOTTE near ROANNE 42640 Loire **RN 7 Map 16-B3**
♀ ⊗ **AU BON ACCUEIL** (N° RR JUN 25 463) (Mme Lucienne **Galichon**) Les Baraques ☎ 77-72-00-07 ⇀ 3 Coaches welcome (rest. seats 45). Evening meals.

SAINT-ROMAIN-LE-PUY 42610 Loire **Map 18-A2**
♀ ⊗ **LE PETIT VINCENNES** (N° RR JANV 26 774) (M. Alain **Bouchet**), 16, rue Léon Portier ☎ 77-76-63-54 English spoken.

SAINT-ROME-DE-CERNON 12490 Aveyron **Map 23-A1**
♀ ⊗ ⌂ **RELAIS CHEZ JEANNOT** (N° RR FEV 18 334) (M. Jean **Fabry**) avenue de Millau ☎ 65-62-33-56 ⇀ 7 Closed Sat, 15 Sept to 15 Oct. Coaches welcome (rest. seats 70). Evening meals.

SAINT-SAMSON-DE-BONFOSSE 50750 Manche **RD 999 Map 4-B1**
♀ ⊗ **CHEZ PIERRE ET MICHELE** (N° RR AVR 25 379) (M. Pierre **Petit**) Canisy ☎ 33-55-73-71 Closed Wed.

SAINT-SAMSON-DE-LA-ROQUE 27680 Eure **RN 815 A Map 4-B3**
♀ ⊗ **LE RELAIS NORD BRETAGNE** (N° RR OCT 23 974) (M. Gérard **Guerrier**) route du Pont-de-Tancarville ☎ 32-57-67-30 Closed Fri evening 3.00pm to Sat 9.00am; Sept. Coaches welcome (2 dining rooms: 40/50 seats). Evening meals until 10.30pm.

SAINT-SAUVEUR 70370 Haute-Saône **RN 57 Map 10-A3 and 14-B2**
♀ ⊗ ⌂ **LE RELAIS CHEZ MAXIM** (N° RR AVR 21 055) (Mme Colette **Lack**) 10, avenue Georges- Clémenceau ☎ 84-40-02-91 ⇀ 8 Closed Sun evening; Feb. Full-board 120–160F per night. Coaches welcome (rest. seats 150). Evening meals. German, English spoken.

SAINT-SAUVEUR-D'AUNIS 17540 Chte-Mme **Map 11-B1**
♀ ⊗ ⌂ **HÔTEL DU CENTRE** (N° RR JUIL 26 972) (M. Alain **Quellard**) rue de Ligoure ☎ 46-01-80-31 ⇀ 6 English spoken. Garage, filling station nearby.

SAINT-SAUVIER D'ÉMALLEVILLE 76110 Seine-Maritime **CD 925 Map 4-A2/3**
♀ ⊗ **RELAIS DE SAINT SAUVEUR** (N° RR SEPT 27 017) (M. Phillippe **Guèrin**) Route Nationale ☎ 35-27-21-56.

S

SAINT-SÉBASTIEN-DE-MORSENT 27180 Eure **RN 830 Map 8-A3**
♀ ⊗ **LE C'Y DOUBLE** (N° RR JUL 26 615) (M. Éric **Leboudec**) 15, rte de Conches ☎ 32-33-11-52.

SAINT-SORNIN 16220 Charente TD 6 Map 15-B2
♀ ⊗ **LES ROUTIERS Tobacconist** (N° RR AVR 25 914) (M. Jean-Michel **Dubois**) Le Bourg Montbron ☎ 45-23-12-83 Closed Mon 2pm. Evening meals served.

SAINT-SULPICE-DE-GRAINBOUVILLE 27210 Eure **RD 312 Map 4-B3**
♀ ⊗ **LE RELAIS DE ST. SULPICE** (N° RR JUL 26 285) (M. Patrice **Pottier**) **Beuzeville** ☎ 32-41-50-99 Closed Sun.

SAINT-SULPICE-LES-FEUILLES 87160 Haute-Vienne **Map 16-A1**
♀ ⊗ ⌂ **HOTEL DU COMMERCE** (N° RR JAN 23 626) (M. Robert **Dionnet**) 1, rue du Commerce ☎ 55-76-70-72 ⊷ 6 Evening meals.

SAINT-SYMPHORIEN-DES-MONTS par LAPENTY-DU-HARCOUET
50600 Manche **RN 176 Map 8-A1**
♀ ⊗ ⌂ **1 Star NN LE RELAIS DU BOIS LEGER** (N° RR JUL 10 872)
⊷ (M. and Mme Raymond **Pinet**) Lapenty ☎ 33-49-01-43 point phone 33-49-36-08 ⊷ 10 Closed Sun evening; 3 weeks in Sept; 1 week Feb. Full-board 160–190F per night. Coaches welcome (rest. seats 50). Evening meals until 9pm. English spoken.

SAINT-THEGONNEC 29223 Finistère **RN 12 Map 7-A1**
♀ ⊗ **REST DU COMMERCE** (N° RR NOV 25 198) (M. Alain **Mevel**) 1, rue de Paris ☎ 98-79-61-07 ⊷ 3 Closed Sat. Coaches welcome (rest. seats 92). Evening meals.

SAINT-VALLIER see **MONTCEAU-LES-MINES** 71230 Saône-et-Loire

SAINT-VICTURNIEN 87420 Haute-Vienne **RN 141**
♀ ⊗ **LE RELAIS DE LA MALAISE** (N° RR JUL 26 293) (M. Jean-Marie **Faure**) **La Malaise** ☎ 55-03-87-03 ⊷ 4 Coaches welcome (rest. seats 60). Evening meals. English spoken.

SAINT-VIGOR-LE-GRAND see BAYEUX 14400 Calvados **RN 13 Map 4-B2**

SAINT-VINCENT-DE-CONNEZAC 24190 Dordogne **CD 709 Map 15-B3**
♀ ⊗ **AU BON ACCUEIL** (N° RR JANV 27 142) (M. Jacques **Magne**) Route de Mussidan ☎ 53-91-82-17 Closed Mon and 15 days in Oct. English and Italian spoken.

SAINT-VINCENT-LES-FORTS 04570 Alpes-de-Haute-Provence
♀ ⊗ **LE RELAIS DU LAUTHARET** (N° RR AVR 26 222) (Mme Anne-Marie **Dejonghe**) ☎ 92-85-50-01 ⊷ 7 Coaches welcome (2 rooms: 30/20 seats). Evening meals. English, German spoken. Evening meals.

SAINT-VINCENT-DE-PAUL 33440 Gironde **RN 10 Map 20-A1**
Ⓨ ⓧ ⊷ **1 Star NN CHEZ ANATOLE** (N° RR MAR 23 718) (M. Michel **Denechaud**) Ambarès ☎ 56-38-95-11 ⊷ 8 from 72–110F, breakfast 14F Closed Sat. Car park; dogs allowed; sports and recreations (pool table, *pétanque*, swings, shaded garden). Places to visit: Citadelle de Blaye Grot 'Pair non Pair', Bec d'Ambes.

SAINT-VINCENT-DE-PAUL 40990 Landes **RN 124 Map 20-B2**
Ⓨ ⓧ **AUX PLATANES** (N° RR OCT 20 315) (M. **Vicente**) ☎ 58-73-90-13 Closed Sun. Spanish spoken.

SAINT-YAN 71600 S.-et-L. **RN 982 (via Flèche Bison Fûté) Map 18-A2**
Ⓨ ⓧ **LA CHAUMIÈRE** (N° RR FEV 26 463) (M. Pascal **Germain**) 12, rue de la Gare ☎ 85-84-97-20 ⊷ 6 Closed Tue; Sept. Full-board 130F per night. Coaches welcome (rest. seats 45). Evening meals until 11pm.

SAINT-YORRE 03270 Allier **RN 106 Map 16-B3**
Ⓨ ⓧ ⌂ **NOUVEL HOTEL** (N° RR JUN 26 559) (Mme Pascale **Rougelin**) 17, rte de Vichy ☎ 70-59-41-97 ⊷ 16 Closed Sat midday; Feb. Full-board 155–165F per night. Coaches welcome (2 rooms: 120/30 seats). English, some German spoken.

SAINTE-CATHERINE-LEZ-ARRAS 62000 P.-de-C. **RN 25 Map 5-B3**
Ⓨ ⓧ ⌂ **L'AUBERGE DU MOULIN** (N° RR MAR 16 914) (M. Charles **Minguy**) 135, Route Nationale ☎ 21-23-41-56 ⊷ 8 Closed Sun; Aug. Evening meals.

SAINTE-CECILE 50800 Manche **RN 24 Bis Map 8-A1**
Ⓨ ⓧ ⌂ **LE CÉCILIA** (N° RR MAI 26 883) (M. Daniel **Le Huby**) Le Bourg ☎ 33-61-07-81 ⊷ 5 Closed Sat. Filling station 2km. English, German spoken.

SAINTE-CROIX-HAGUE 50440 Manche **RD 901**
Ⓨ ⓧ ⌂ **LE PETIT BACCHUS** (N° RR MARS 27 233) (M. Michel **Oury**) ☎ 33-52-77-53 ⊷ 11 Closed Sat, Sun.

SAINTE-FORTUNADE 19490 Correze **Map 17-A1**
Ⓨ ⓧ **CHEZ JEAN-PIERRE ET BRIGITTE** (N° RR MARS 25 333) (Mme Brigitte **Cariou**) Taxi ☎ 55-27-14-84 Closed Sun during winter. English spoken.

SAINTE-FOY-L'ARGENTIERE 69610 Rhône **Map 2-A1**
Ⓨ ⓧ **AUBERGE DE LA PLACE** (N° RR AVR 24 915) (Mme Yvonne **Goubier**) ☎ 74-70-00-51 Closed Sat; Aug.
Ⓨ ⓧ ⌂ **HOTEL DE LA POSTE** (N° RR NOV 25 736) (M. Michel **Jenestier**) ☎ 74-70-02-75 ⊷ 6 Closed Mon; 8 days end of Aug; 8 days end of Feb.

SAINTE-FOY-LES-LYON see **ACQUEDUCS-DE-BEAUNANT** 69110 Rhône

S

SAINTE-FOY-LA-GRANDE 33220 Gironde **Maps 15-B3 and 21-A1**
⚲ ⊗ ⌂ **CAFE DE L'ORIENT** (N° RR JUIL 26 941) (M. Michel **Thomas**) 2, avenue Paul Bert ☎ 57-46-13-94 ⊷ 9 Closed Sun. English, German spoken a little. Filling station near.

SAINTE-FOY-DE-MONTGOMERY 14140 Calv. **RN 179 Map 8-A2**
⚲ ⊗ **LE RELAIS DE MONTGOMERY** (N° RR AOU 14 917) (Mme **Planckeel**) ☎ 31-63-53-02 ⊷ 4 Closed Sun.

SAINTE-GENEVIEVE 60730 Oise
⚲ ⊗ **CHEZ L'AUVERGNAT** (N° RR OCT 26 362) (M. Joël **Deroq**), 150, Route Nationale 1 ☎ 44-08-64-38 Closed Sat, Sun. Coaches welcome (rest. seats 60). Evening meals.

SAINTE-LIVRADE 47110 L.-et-G. **RN 111 Map 21-B1**
⚲ ⊗ ⌂ **1 Star NN AU BON ACCUEIL** (N° RR JUL 19 426) (M. **Cougouille**) route de Villeneuve ☎ 58-01-02-34 ⊷ 10 Closed Sun evening; 24 Dec to 2 Jan. Full-board 120–140F per night. Coaches welcome (rest. seats 60). Evening meals.

SAINTE-LIZAIGNE 36260 Indre **RN 718 Map 13-B1**
⚲ ⊗ **RELAIS DE CHAMPAGNE** (N° RR JAN 25 775) (Mme Jeannine **Samour**) 10, Grande-Rue ☎ 54-04-06-07 Closed Sun; Aug. Coaches welcome (rest. seats 50). Evening meals until 8pm.

SAINTE-LUCE see NANTES 44470 L.-Atl.

SAINTE-MARGUERITE 88100 Vosges **RN 59 Map 10-B2**
⚲ ⊗ ⌂ **1 Star NN LE RELAIS DES AMIS** (N° RR JUN 16 108) (M. François **Bernat**) rue d'Alsace ☎ 29-56-17-23 ⊷ 16 from 75–120F, breakfast 15–20F. Closed Sun in winter. Full-board 165–175F per night. Coaches welcome (rest. seats 40). Evening meals. Car park; bar; dogs allowed. Opportunities to walk in woods, on hills.
⚲ ⊗ **LE RELAIS DU CENTRE** (N° RR JUN 22 839) (M. Emile **Mathieu**) 183, rue d'Alsace ☎ 29-56-28-74 Closed Sat, Aug. Coaches welcome (rest. seats 40).

SAINTE-MARIE-DE-GOSSE 40390 Landes **RN 117 Map 20-A2**
⚲ ⊗ ⌂ **1 Star NN LE RELAIS ROUTIER, ON MANGE ON BOIT,**
⊷ **ON DORT** (N° RR AVR 12 815) (M. Marc **Deloube**) RN 117 ☎ 59-56-32-02 ⊷ 15 Closed Fri evening, Sat low season; Oct. Full-board 120–140F per night. Coaches welcome (rest. seats 120). Spanish spoken.

SAINTE-MAURE-DE-TOURAINE 37800 I.-et-L. **RN 10 Map 12-B3**
⚲ ⊗ **LA PIERRE PERCEE** (N° RR MAI 25 937) (MM. **Malin Bouquet**) Route Nationale 10 ☎ 47-65-08-64 **Minitel** Closed Sat, Sun; Aug. Evening meals until 11.30pm. English, some Portuguese, Italian spoken.
⚲ ⊗ ⌂ **LE BELLEVUE** (N° RR MARS 26 489) (M. Christophe **Bardeau**) RN 10 ☎ 47-65-40-61. Closed Mon midday. English, German, Spanish spoken.

S

SAINTE SCOLASSES/SARTHE 61170 Orne **CD 8 and CD 6 Map 8-A2**
♀ ⊗ ⌂ **HOTEL DU CHEVAL BLANC** (N° RR SEPT 26 995) (M. Daniel
Millière) Place de L'Église ☎ 33-27-66-30 ⊷ 3 Filling station
near.

SAINTE-SIGOLENE 43600 Haute-Loire **RD 43 Map 18-A3**
♀ ⊗ ⌂ **LE RELAIS DE LA POSTE** (N° RR NOV 18 246) (M. **Mounier**)
2, place Leclerc ☎ 71-61-61-33 ⊷ 20 Closed Aug. Coaches
welcome (rest. seats 60). Evening meals.

SAINTE-SEVERE-SUR-INDRE 36160 Indre **RN 117 Map 16-A2**
♀ ⊗ ⌂ **LE RELAIS DU COMMERCE** (N° RR FEV 21 783) (Mme
Denise **Duplaix**) rue de Verdun ☎ 54-30-50-46 ⊷ 11.

SAINTE-TERRE 33350 Gironde **Map 15-A3**
♀ ⊗ ⌂ **CHEZ RÉGIS** (N° RR JANV 25 783) (M. Jacques **Astarie**)
Avenue du Gal-de-Gaulle ☎ 57-47-16-21 Closed Mon and Jan.

T

TALANGE 57300 Moselle
♀ ⊗ **RELAIS DE LA LIBERTÉ** (N° RR JANV 26 785) (M. René **Zeuli**)
131, rue de Metz ☎ 87-72-27-29.

TALMONT-ST-HILAIRE 85440 Vendée **Map 11-A1**
♀ ⊗ ⌂ **HOTEL DU CENTRE** (N° RR OCT 26 698) (M. Michel
Leblond) 1, rue du Centre ☎ 51-90-60-35 ⊷ 12.

TARARE 69170 Rhône **RN 7 Map 2-A1**
♀ ⊗ **BAR PROVENÇAL** (N° RR MAI 23 294) (M. Georges **Bidot**) 8,
av. Edouard-Herriot ☎ 74-63-33-64 Closed Sun; public holidays; 1
week in Aug. Evening meals until 8.30pm.

TARBES 65000 Hautes-Pyr **RN 21 Map 21-A3**
♀ ⊗ ⌂ **1 Star NN LE VICTOR HUGO** (N° RR FEV 26 438) (Mme
Patricia **Guy**) 52, rue Victor-Hugo ☎ 62-93-36-71 ⊷ 8 (with WC)
from 45–60F, breakfast 12F. Closed Sun. Full-board 140 per night.
Evening meals. English, Spanish spoken. Car park; bar; dogs
allowed, TV. Places to visit: Donjon des Aigles, Pyrenees National Park (ski-runs), grottes de Bétharron.
♀ ⊗ **LE CLAUZIER** (N° RR OCT 25 665) (M. Didier **Chaussalet**) 2,
place Germain Claverie ☎ 62-93-18-57 Closed Sun.

TARTAS 40400 Landes **RN 124 Map 20-B2**
♀ ⊗ ⌂ **LA CAHUTE** (N° RR AVR 26 517) (Mme Martine **Thomas**), RN
124 Moulin ☎ 58-73-43-17 ⊷ 7 Closed Sat; Sun afternoon. Full-
board 160F per night. Coaches welcome (rest. seats 50). Evening
meals. English, German spoken.

T

TASSIN-ECULLY see ECULLY 69130 Rhône **RN 7 Map 2-A1**

TATRE (LE) par BAIGNES 16360 Charente **RN 10 Map 15-A2/3**
♀ ⊗ ⌂ **LA CAMBROUSSE** (N° RR FEV 26 436) (M. Jean-Claude **Pichon**) Le Pont du Noble Reignac ☎ 45-78-52-83 ⊷ 10 Closed Sat afternoon, Sun.

TAUVES 63690 P.-de-D. **RN 122 Map 17-A2**
♀ ⊗ **HOSTELLERIE DE LA POSTE** (N° RR JUN 15 262) (M. Robert **Agay**) ☎ 73-21-11-09.

TAVAUX 39500 Jura **RN 73 Map 14-A3**
♀ ⊗ **Les Routiers BP Service Station STATION DES CHARMES** (N° RR NOV 23 534) (M. Marc **Joffroy**) ☎ 82-71-41-57 German spoken.
⛽ **Elf Service Station DECOSNE AUTOMOBILE** (N° RR JUL 550000089) (Mme Nicole **Greco**) RN 73 6, rte de Dôle ☎ 84-81-12-79 Open 6.00am to 10.00pm German, Spanish, Yugoslavian spoken.

TAVEL 30126 Gard **Autoroute A 9 Map 24-A2**
♀ ⊗ **RESTOP de TAVEL** (M. Sylvain **Guariento**) ☎ 66-50-04-19 Self-service restaurant open 11.00am to 10.00pm. TV, Shop. German, English spoken.

TAVERS 45190 Loiret
♀ ⊗ **LA PIERRE TOURNANTE** (N° RR JUL 26 283) (M. Antoine **Pereira**) 36 RN 152 ☎ 38-44-92-25 Closed Sun; Spanish, Portuguese spoken.

TEIL (LE) 07400 Ardèche **RN 86 Map 24-A2**
♀ ⊗ **AU BON COIN** (N° RR DEC 20 616) (Mme Marie **Gineste**) 11, rue Henri-Barbusse ☎ 75-49-02-61 Closed Aug.

TELLANCOURT 54260 Meurthe-et-Moselle **Map 6-B3**
♀ ⊗ **MUTIZG** (N° RR AVR 25 900) (Mme Sigride **Boucher**) Tobacconist 15, rte Nationale ☎ 82-26-77-00 Closed Mon; Oct. Evening meals.

LE TEMPLE-SUR-LOT 47110 L.-et-G. **RN 911 Map 21-B1**
♀ ⊗ ⌂ **LE VAL DU LOT "GOUNOT"** (N° RR MAR 21 817) (MM. Lionel and Christian **Hutrel**) ☎ 58-84-90-26 ⊷ 5 Closed Sat; 20 Aug to 15 Sept. Full-board (winter) 150F per night. Coaches welcome (rest. seats 60). Evening meals. English spoken.

TENCE 43190 Haute-Loire **Map 18-A3**
♀ ⊗ **RESTAURANT DES CARS** (N° RR AOU 25 623) (Mme Marie-Françoise **Souvignet**) 13, Grande-Rue ☎ 71-59-84-01 Closed Wed afternoon. Evening meals until 9pm.

TENDU 36200 Indre **RN 20 Map 16-A1**
♀ ⊗ ⌂ **LE RELAIS DES ROUTIERS** (N° RR DEC 11 179) (M. André **Luneau**) ☎ 54-24-14-10 ⊷ 10 Closed Wed low season; 1 week

Oct, 1 week Feb. Full-board 130–150F per night. Coaches welcome (rest. seats 70). Evening meals.

TERCIS-LES-BAINS
Y ⊗ ⌂ **L'ÉTOILE** (N° RR MAI 27 284) (M. Thierry **Mortelette**) Route de Payrehorade ☎ 58-57-68-49 ⊷ 5 English and Spanish spoken. Evening meals served until 11pm.

TERNUAY 70510 Haute-Saône **RN 486 Map 10-A3**
Y ⊗ **CHEZ MARTINE** (N° RR JUL 13 854) (Mlle Martine **Géhant**) ☎ 84-20-42-98 ⊷ 2 Closed Sat; 24 Aug to 7 Sept. Full-board 130F per night. Coaches welcome (rest. seats 48). Evening meals.

TERRASSON-LA-VILLEDIEU 24120 Dordogne **RN 89 Map 17-A1**
Y ⊗ **AU RELAIS DES ROUTIERS** (N° RR JUN 21 142) (M. Jacques **Lasfargeas**) 42, avenue Victor-Hugo ☎ 53-50-00-89 Closed Sat; 20 Jun to 14 Jul. Coaches (rest. seats 100). Evening meals.
Y ⊗ ⌂ **LE RELAIS DES ROUTIERS** (N° RR MAR 9 404) (M. Charles **Leyrie**) 62, avenue Émile-Zola ☎ 53-50-00-75 ⊷ 12 Full-board 170–220F per night. Coaches welcome (rest. seats 70).

TERRENOIRE 42100 Loire **Map 2-B1 and 18-A2**
Y ⊗ **RELAIS DE L'AUTOROUTE** (N° RR DEC 26 771) (Mme Régine **Roux**) 57 Les Marandes ☎ 77-95-70-92 Closed Sat, Sun.

TESSY-SUR-VIRE 50420 Manche **Map 4-B1**
Y ⊗ **LES ROUTIERS** (N° RR MAR 26 854) (M. Maurice **Robert**) place du Marché ☎ 33-56-35-25 Closed Thur afternoon; Sun afternoon. Filling station 150m.

THAON-LES-VOSGES 88150 Vosges **RN 57**
Y ⊗ ⌂ **RELAIS ROUTIER 6010** (N° RR JAN 26 148) (M. Robert **Gehin**) 200, rue de Lorraine ☎ 29-39-21-67 ⊷ 4 Closed Fri afternoon. Coaches welcome (rest. seats 60). Evening meals.

THAURON see COMBEAUVERT 23250 Creuse **RN 940 Map 16-B1**

THEIL (LE) 61260 Orne **Map 8-B3**
Y ⊗ **LE RELAIS DE L'ARCHE** (N° RR AOU 24 665) (M. Gérard **Leroux**) La Rouge ☎ 37-49-62-92.

THENEZAY see LA FERRIERE 79390 Deux-Sevres **RN 148 Bis Map 15-A1**

THENON 24210 Dordogne **RN 89 Maps 15-B3 and 17-A1**
Y ⊗ ⌂ **LES TOURNISSOUS - CHEZ SERGE** (N° RR MAR 23 159) (M. Serge **Leymarie**) ☎ 53-05-20-31 ⊷ 10 Closed Christmas, New Year. Full-board 120–140F per night. Coaches welcome (rest. seats 200). English, Spanish spoken.

THIEL-SUR-ACOLIN 03230 Allier **RD 12 Map 16-A3**
Y ⊗ **LE RELAIS DE LA TERRASSE** (N° RR OCT 19 511) (M. **Tregouboff**) Route de Dompière ☎ 70-92-50-89 ⊷ 4 Coaches welcome (rest. seats 60).

T

THIMERT 28170 E.-et-L. **RN 839 Map 8-A3**
♟ ⊗ **LA CRÉMAILLÈRE** (N° RR MAR 21 829) (Mme Madeleine **Breton**) 1, rue de Chartres ☎ 37-51-60-90 Closed Sat afternoon. Coaches welcome (rest. seats 60). Evening meals.

THIVARS 28630 E.-et-L. **RN 10 Map 8-B3**
♟ ⊗ ⌂ **CHEZ BARBICHE** (N° RR NOV 26 717 (M. Serge **Noel**) 15, rue Nationale ☎ 37-26-40-05 ⊷ 9.

THODURE 38260 Isère **RD 157 Map 24-A1**
♟ ⊗ **AUBERGE DE LA FONTAINE** (N° RR MAI 24 965) (M. Elio **Bernabini**) **La Côte St-André** ☎ 74-54-04-49 ⊷ 4 Closed Wed; 2nd fortnight Sept. Full-board 135F. Coaches welcome (2 rooms: 80/25 seats). Italian spoken.

THOISSEY 01140 Ain **RD 933/17 Map 18-A2**
♟ ⊗ **LA CROISÉE** (N° RR MAI 23 798) (M. Jean **Servigne**) Guereins ☎ 74-66-14-93 Closed Sun; Aug.

THONES 74230 Hte-Savoie **RN 509 Map 19-A2**
♟ ⊗ ⌂ **1 Star NN L'HERMITAGE** (N° RR AVR 26 523) (M. Pierre **Bonnet**) avenue du Vieux-Pont ☎ 50-02-00-31 **Minitel** ⊷ 40 Closed Fri afternoon; 25 Oct to 15 Nov. Full-board 150–175F. Coaches welcome (rest. seats 160).

THORÉE-LES-PINS (72800 Sarthe **CD 306 Map 12-A2**
♟ ⊗ **CAFÉ RESTAURANT DES PÊCHEURS** (N° RR DEC 27135) (M. Marcel **Guillaume**) Le Bourg ☎ 43-45-03-79 Closed Wed pm. English and German spoken.

THORENS-LES-GLIÈRES 74570 Hte-Savoie **RN 203 Map 19-A2**
♟ ⊗ ⌂ **LA HAUTE BISE** (N° RR FEV 26 460) (M. René **Pelletan**) RN 203 ☎ 50-22-47-61 ⊷ 6 Closed Sun. Spanish spoken.

THOU 45420 Loiret **RN 65 Map 13-A2**
♟ ⊗ **AU LIT ON DORT** (N° RR MAI 18 413) (M. Bernard **Bertrand**) ☎ 38-31-62-07 4 Closed Mon pm and August. Evening meals.
♟ ⊗ **LE CHEVAL BLANC** (N° RR JUL 26 952) (Mme Luigina **Zen**) Le Bourg ☎ 38-31-62-39 Italian spoken. Filling station near.

THOUARS 79100 Deux-Sèvres **RN 1 Map 12-B2**
♟ ⊗ **LE MILLE PATTE** (N° RR MAI 24 957) (Mme Martine **Valleau**) 17, rue de Launay ☎ **Minitel** English and German spoken. Evening meals.

THOURIE 34134 Ille-et-Vilaine **CD 163 et 53 Map 7-B3 8-B1**
⊗ **LES ROUTIERS** (N° RR OCT 27 046) (M. Patrick **Gilouppe**) **Le Bourg** ☎ 99-44-33-67 Closed Sat and Sun. English spoken.

THUET-PONTCHY 74130 Haute-Savoie **RN 506 Map 19-B2**
♟ ⊗ **LE RELAIS DES CYCLAMENS** (N° RR AVR 13 654) (Mme **Delavenay**) ☎ 50-97-02-39.

THUILES (LES) 04400 Alpes de Haute-Provence **Map 25-A1**
♇ ⊗ 🏠 **LES SEOLANES** (N° RR JUL 24 620) (M. Hubert **Maure**) Barcelonnette ☎ 92-81-07-37 ⊷ 6 Closed one day a week; Jan. English, Italian spoken.

TIGNIEU 38230 Isère **RD 18 Map 2-A2**
♇ ⊗ **AUBERGE DES CHARMILLES** (N° RR DEC 24 444) (Mme Josiane **Renon**) 71, route de Bourgoin ☎ 78-32-23-57 Closed Aug. Evening meals.

TILLOY-LES-MOFLAINES 62000 Pas-de-Calais **Map 5-B3**
♇ **Bar Brasserie LE TILLOY** (N° RR MAI 24 973) (M. Denis **Hiolet**) Rte Nle 39 Arras ☎ 21-73-44-15 Closed Sun.

TINCHEBRAY 61800 Orne **RN 24 Bis Map 8-A1**
♇ ⊗ **LE RELAIS** (N° RR SEP 21 242) (M. Yves **Tessier**) 1, place du Général-Leclerc ☎ 33-66-60-54 Closed Sat; Aug. English, Spanish spoken.

TOLLEVAST 50820 Manche **RN 13 Map 4-A1**
♇ ⊗ **LES ROUTIERS** (N° RR OCT 26 705) (M. André **Maleuvre**) Brix ☎ 33-43-77-92 Closed Sat, Sun; 3 weeks Aug. English spoken.

TONNAY-CHARENTE 17430 Charente-Maritime **RN 137 Map 11-B1**
♇ ⊗ **L'OASIS CHEZ VACHON** (N° RR JAN 23 093) (M. **Vachon**) 27, rue de Lattre-de-Tassigny ☎ 46-88-70-84 Closed Mon; 1–15 Aug. Coaches welcome (rest. seats 60).
♇ ⊗ **LES FONTAINES** (N° RR SEPT 26 652) (Mme Christiane **Trouve**) 110, av. d'Aunis ☎ 46-83-79-11 Closed Sun.

TONNEINS 47400 lot-et-Garonne **RN 113 Map 21-A/B1**
♇ ⊗ **LE ROBINSON** (N° RR DEC 27 021) (Mme Marie-France **Trehiou**) Route d'Agen ☎ 53-84-45-37 Closed Sat pm and Sun.

TORCY 71210 S.-et-L. **RN 80**
♇ ⊗ **LA SPIAGGIA** (N° RR DEC 26 114) (M. Salvatore **Lotito**) Rte Express Montchanin ☎ 85-55-35-45 Italian, English, German, French spoken.

TORTERON 18320 Cher **Gc 26 Map 13-B2**
♇ ⊗ 🏠 **LE RELAIS DU LABOUREUR** (N° RR JAN 10 216) (M. Céleste **Gosselin**) Grande-Rue ☎ 36-74-48-77 ⊷ 6.

TOTES 76890 Seine-Marit **RN 27 Map 3-A1**
♇ ⊗ **LES AMIS RÉUNIS** (N° RR FEV 19 282) (M. Michel **Guilbert**) Route de Dieppe ☎ 35-79-91-27.
♇ ⊗ **LE NORMANDY** (N° RR MARS 26 187) (Sté de Fait M. **Perrero-Morel**) Rte d'Yvetôt ☎ 35-32-91-35 Closed Sat evening, Sun.

TOTES see VAL-DE-SAANE 76960 Seine-Maritime

TOULON 83100 Var **RN 8 Map 25-A3**
♇ ⊗ **LE RELAIS DE L'ESCAILLON** (N° RR MAI 24 967) (M. Bernard

T

Toulon continued

Lemaire) 1, rue Chateaubriand ☎ 94-24-21-02 Closed 15 to 31 Aug. Evening meals.

♀ ⊗ **LE SPORTING BAR** (N° RR JUN 24 606) (**SNC Calmus & C°** M. René **Calmus**) 676, Bld du Maréchal Joffre ☎ 94-41-38-56 Coaches welcome (rest. seats 55). Evening meals.

♀ ⊗ **LA FRINGALE – Chez Jo** (N° RR JUL 25 059) (SARL **Prim and Gonzalez**) 522, avenue de la République ☎ 94-36-00-47 Closed Wed in winter; 1 week Oct, 1 week Feb. Coaches welcome (rest. seats 25). Meals throughout the night. English, Italian spoken.

TOULON-SUR-ALLIER 03400 Allier **RN 7 Map 16-A3**
♀ ⊗ **LE RELAIS FLEURI** (N° RR NOV 22 088) (M. **Belain**) Route Nationale 7 ☎ 70-44-47-16 Closed Sun; Aug.

TOULOUSE 31000 Haute-Garonne **RN 20 Map 22-A2**
♀ ⊗ **LE NOUVEAU CORTIJO** (N° RR OCT 25 659) (M. René **Andrieu**) 181, avenue des États-Unis ☎ 61-47-68-64 **Minitel** Closed Sat, Sun; 1 to 15 Aug. Evening meals. Spanish spoken.

TOULOUSE-SAINT-MARTIN-DU-TOUCH 31300 Haute-Garonne **RN 124 Map 22-A2**
♀ ⊗ ⌂ **LE RELAIS DU PROGRÈS** (N° RR DEC 20 037) (M. Félix **Ober**) 185, route de Bayonne ☎ 61-49-22-75 ⊷ 6 Closed Sun; Aug. Coaches welcome (rest. seats 80). Evening meals until 11 pm.

TOUQUES-DEAUVILLE 14800 Calvados **Dles 74 and 52 Map 4-B2**
♀ ⊗ **AUBERGE LA CROIX SONNET** (N° RR OCT 26 344) (Mme **Pedrazzi**) La Croix-Sonnet ☎ 31-88-19-62 ⊷ 4 Full-board 200–230F per night. Coaches welcome (rest. seats 40). Evening meals. English, Spanish, Italian spoken.

TOUQUIN 77131 Seine-et-Marne **RD 231 Map 9-A2**
♀ ⊗ **LE TOUQUINOIS** (N° RR JAN 26 160) (M. Marcel **Breuil**) 8, rue du Commerce ☎ 64-04-18-37 Closed Sun. Evening meals.

TOURCOING 59200 Nord **RN 17 Map 5-B1**
♀ ⊗ ⌂ **AU SIGNAL D'ARRET** (N° RR DEC 24 452) (M. Michel **Guilbert**) 28, rue des Francs ☎ 20-26-56-74 **Minitel** ⊷ 5 Closed Sat, Sun; 16 to 31 Aug; 24 Dec–1 Jan. Evening meals.
♀ ⊗ **LE SAPHIR** (N° RR NOV 26 723) (M. Jacques **Mareel**) 11 bis, Chaussée Berthelot ☎ 20-01-88-03 Closed Sun.

TOUR-DU-MEIX (LA) 39270 Jura **RN 470 Map 19-B1**
♀ ⊗ **AUBERGE DU PONT DE LA PYLE** (N° RR MAR 23 698) (M. Jacques **Berger**) ☎ 84-25-41-92 Closed Wed; Oct. Coaches welcome (2 rooms: 90/60 seats). Meals served until midnight.

TOUR-DU-PIN (LA) 38110 Isère **RN 516 Map 2-B3**
♀ ⊗ ⌂ **LE RELAIS DES ROUTIERS** (N° RR SEP 24 332) (M. Roger **Cantel**) Le Passeron-St-Clair de la Tour ☎ 74-97-14-88 ⊷ 11 Closed Sun afternoon.

T

TOUR-DU-PIN (LA) 38110 Isère **RN 6**
Υ ⊗ **CHEZ BABETH** (N° RR NOV 25 744) (Mme Elisabeth **Rostaing**)
St-Didier-de-la-Tour ☎ 74-97-15-87 Coaches welcome (rest.
seats 60). Evening meals.

TOURETTES (LES) 26740 Drôme **RN 7 Map 24-B1**
Υ ⊗ 🏠 **MA CAMPAGNE** (N° RR MAI 26 897) (M. Achour **Ait
Aoudia**) ☎ 75-90-06-46 → 6 English, Spanish, Arabic spoken.
Filling station near.

TOURNES 08540 Ardennes **RN 51 Map 6-A2**
Υ ⊗ **LE GASTRO DES MILLE PATTES** (N° RR SEPT 26 643) (M.
René **Filiatre**) 17, route Nationale ☎ 24-35-94-35 Coaches welco-
me (rest. seats 70). Evening meals until 11pm.

TOURNON-D'AGENAIS 47370 L.-et-G. **RN 656 Map 21-B1**
Υ ⊗ 🏠 **1 Star NN LE RELAIS DES VOYAGEURS** (N° RR AOU 14 918)
(M. **Gary**) rue de Cahors ☎ 58-71-70-28 → 8 Closed Fri evening;
Sat midday; 15 days in Oct. Swimming pool open 30 Jun to 15
Sept.

TOURNUS 71700 S.-et-L. **RN 6 Map 18-B1**
🍴 **Les Routiers Antar Service Station PARIS-SAVOIE** (N° RR JAN
23 117) (M. Paul **Lucet**) ☎ 85-51-17-76 Open 24 hours, except Sat–
8.00pm to 7.00am. Italian spoken.

TOURS 37000 I.-et-L. **RN 10 Map 12-A2/3**
Υ ⊗ 🏠 **L'AVIATION** (N° RR JUN 26 554) (Mme Michelle **Mary**) 295,
avenue Maginot ☎ 47-51-19-50 → 8 (17 beds) Closed Sat, Sun;
Full-board 140F, half-board 103F per night. Coaches welcome (3
rooms: 45/26/26 seats). Evening meals.
Υ ⊗ 🏠 **1 STAR NN LE RELAIS DE SAINTE-RADEGONDE** (N° RR
NOV 27 095) (Mme Annie **Fuster**) 178, quai Paul-Bert ☎ 47-51-28-
45 → 14 Closed Sun pm low season.
Υ ⊗ **LE STRASBOURG** (N° RR NOV 26 368) (M. **Bottin**) 76, bd Thiers
☎ 47-38-66-06.

TOURS-MONNAIE 37380 I.-et-L. **Autoroute A 10**
Υ ⊗ **Accor L'ARCHE** Autoroute A 10 - 2 sens Passerelle ☎ 47-56-15-
49 Self-Service restaurant open 24 hours. Shop. English, Spanish
spoken.

TOURY 28390 E.-et-L. **RN 20 Map 9-B1**
Υ ⊗ **LE RELAIS DE LA CHAPELLE** (N° RR FEV 25 797) (Mme
Claudine **Comarlot**) 60, av. de la Chapelle ☎ 37-90-64-96 Closed
Sat; Aug. Coaches welcome (rest. seats 150). Evening meals until
11pm.

TOUT-Y-FAUT see LOULAY 17330 Charente-Maritime

TRAIT (LE) 76580 Seine-Maritime **RD 982 Map 3-A1**
Υ ⊗ **LE JEAN BART** (N° RR AOU 23 902) (M. **Mahier**) 488, rue Jean-
Bart ☎ 35-37-22-47 → 3 furnished. Closed Sun; 10 to 30 Aug.
Coaches welcome (rest. seats 60). Evening meals.

T

TRAMAIN 22640 Côtes-du-Nord **RN 12 Map 7-A3**
♀ ⊗ **AU RELAIS DE TRAMAIN** (N° RR MAI 26 894) (M. Jack **Hutteau**) rue du Bourg ☎ 96-31-82-28. Closed Sat, Sun; Jul–Aug. Filling station 4km.

TRANSLAY (LE) 80140 Somme
♀ ⊗ **AU RELAIS FLEURI** (N° RR MARS 27 220) (Mme Gladys **Duboille**), 5, rue de Oisemont ☎ 22-28-48-98 Closed Wed pm.

TREBES 11800 Aude **RN 113 Map 22-B2**
♀ ⊗ ⌂ **LE RELAIS DES CAPUCINS** (N° RR JUL 25 041) (M. Gilbert **Laffont**) 34, route de Narbonne ☎ 68-78-70-07 ⊶ 14 Closed Sat, Sun; 1 week in Jul; 3 weeks at Christmas. Coaches welcome (rest. seats 56). Evening meals.

TREFFENDEL 35380 Ille-et-Vilaine **RN 24 Map 7-B3**
♀ ⊗ **RELAIS RN 24** (N° RR FEV 26 809) (M. Gilles **Guimard**) La Gare ☎ 99-07-93-75 Closed Sun; 3 days Christmas. English spoken.

TREGUIDEL 22290 Côtes-du-Nord **RD 51/CD 6 Map 7-A2**
♀ ⊗ **LE BOUTOU** (N° RR JUN 25 003) (M. Bernard **Glaudel**) Bourg de Tréguidel ☎ 96-70-02-42 Coaches welcome (rest. seats 60). Evening meals until 9pm. English spoken.

TREILLIÈRES 44119 L.-Atl. **RN 137 Map 11-A2**
♀ ⊗ **LE PIGEON BLANC** (N° RR AVR 26 527) (Mme Règine **Plat**) Le Pigeon Blanc ☎ 40-94-67-72 or 40-94-51-26 **Minitel** Closed Sun low season. Evening meals.

TRELISSAC 24000 Dordogne **Map 15-B3**
♀ ⊗ **BAR DE LA STATION** (N° RR AVR 24 912) (M. Jean-Philippe **Burgarella**) Rte Nle 21 ☎ 53-54-40-24 Closed Feb. English spoken.

TREMOREL 22230 Côtes-du-Nord **N 164 bis Map 7-B3**
♀ ⊗ **LE RELAIS DE LA FORÊT** (N° RR FEV 26 820) (M. Yvon **Sohier**) Bourg ☎ 96-25-21-70.

TREON 28100 E.-et-L. **RN 828 Map 8-A3**
♀ ⊗ **LE RELAIS DE TREON** (N° RR JUL 26 583) (Mme **Cuvellier**) 20, rue de Chateauneuf ☎ 37-82-62-35 ⊶ 5 Closed Sun evening. Evening meals until 9.30pm.

TRESNAY 58240 Nièvre **RN 7**
♀ ⊗ **LA SCIERIE** (N° RR FEV 27 180) (M. Martial **Pettinger**) Rte Nle 7 St-Pierre-le-Moutier ☎ 86-38-62-14 Closed Sat evening and Sun. English spoken.

TRESSÈRE 66300 Pyrénées-Orientales **RN 9 Map 23-A3 Voir LE BOULOU**

TRETS 13530 Bouches-du-Rhône **RN 7 Map 24-B3**
♀ ⊗ **BAR DE L'AÉRODROME** (N° RR MAR 26 853) (M. Christian **Daumas**) ☎ 42-61-49-45 English spoken. Filling station near.

TRIMOUILLE (LA) 86290 Vienne **RN 675 Map 16-A1**
� ⊗ ⌂ **L'AUBERGE FLEURIE** (N° RR FEV 15 533) (M. Monique **Dufour**) rue Octave-Bernard ☎ 49-91-60-64 ⊸ 5 Closed Sun, public holidays after lunch. Evening meals (May to Sept). Menus 43–60F. Specialities: *Moules au vert, Medaillon de ris de veau à la Trimouillaise, Langouste Thermidor.*

TRINITÉ SURZUR (LA) 56190 Morbihan **RN 165 Map 11-A2**
☐ ⊗ **AUBERGE LA VIEILLE FONTAINE SARL** (N° RR SEPT 26 994) (M. Daniel **Malherbe**) Le Bourg Muzillac ☎ 97-42-16-45 ⊸ 12 Closed Sun. English spoken.

TRONQUAY (LE) 14490 **RD 572 Map 4-B1**
☐ ⊗ **AU ROUTIER SYMPA** (N° RR MAI 26 531) (M. Jacques **Lerosier**) ☎ 31-92-38-68.

TRONSANGES par BARBELOUP 58400 Nièvre **RN 7 Map 13-B2**
☐ ⊗ **L'AUBERGE DU SOLEIL LEVANT** (N° RR AVR 18 065) (M. Jean **Reichhard**) ☎ 86-70-01-08 Closed Sun; Sept. Coaches welcome.

☐ ⊗ **LE RELAIS DE LA CROIX DU PAPE** (N° RR DEC 24 770) (Mme Marinette **Beunardeau**) Nationale ☎ 86-70-01-04 Closed Sat, Sun; 10–25 Aug. English spoken.

TRONVILLE-EN-BARROIS 55310 Meuse **Map 14-A1**
☐ ⊗ **L'ESPÉRANCE** (N° RR OCT 27 036) (M. Michel **Walbin**) 64, route nationale ☎ 29-78-88-15/78-11-03 ⊸ 4 Closed Sun.

TROSLY-BREUIL 60350 Oise **RN 31 Map 6-B1**
☐ ⊗ **LE RELAIS DE LA TERRASSE** (N° RR OCT 14 019) (MM. **Wiamont** and **Salvi**) Route Nationale ☎ 44-41-70-39 ⊸ 3 (5 beds) Open 24 hours. Closed Sun.

TROUVILLE ALLIQUERVILLE 76210 S-Mme **RN 15 Map 4-A3**
☐ ⊗ **L'AUBERGE NORMANDE** (N° RR JUN 25 562) (M. Philippe **Malhouitre**) ☎ 35-31-15-21 ⊸ 5 Closed Fri evening; Sun.

TROYES 10000 Aube **RN 19 and 60 Map 9-B3**
☐ ⊗ **CAFÉ DU MIDI – Chez Maurice and Ariette** (N° RR FEV 24 848) (M. Maurice **Khristian**) 2, avenue Chaumedey Maisonneuve ☎ 25-80-03-10 Closed Sun midday; 15 days in Sept. Car park.

TULLINS 38140 Isère **RN 92 Maps 18-B3, 19-A3 and 24-B1**
☐ ⊗ ⌂ **LE RELAIS DES NÉGOCIANTS** (N° RR MAI 16 078) (M. René **Bracco**) 1, rue du Général-de-Gaulle ☎ 76-07-00-67 ⊸ 6 Closed Mon pm and August. Coaches welcome (rest. seats 70).

U

UCKANGE 57270 Moselle **RD 952 Maps 6-B3 and 10-A1**
♀ ⊗ **LE PRESSOIR** (N° RR JAN 21 339) (M. Silvio **Piccin**) 22, rue
Jeanne-d'Arc ☎ 82-58-20-38 Closed Sat 1.00pm to Sun; Aug.

ULMES (LES) 49700 M.-et-L. **RD 960 Map 12-B2**
♀ ⊗ **LA GRAPPE D'OR** (N° RR AVR 26 498) (Mme Monique **Fore-
stier**) Restau Gril Le Moulin Cassé ☎ 41-67-00-06 Closed Sun
evening. English, German spoken. Evening meals.

UNIENVILLE 10140 Aube **RD 46**
♀ ⊗ **CHEZ MARCEL ET CHRISTIANE** (N° RR JANV 21 760) (M.
Marcel **Saget**) ☎ 25-26-30-80.

UPAIX 05300 Hautes-Alpes **Voir ROUREBEAU**

UROU 61200 Orne **RN 56 Bis**
♀ ⊗ **LE CLOS FLEURI** (N° RR FEV 26 181) (M. Gilbert **Estelle**)
Argentan ☎ 33-67-08-25 English, German spoken.

V

VAILLY-SUR-SAULDRE 18260 Cher **RD 926 Map 13-A1**
♀ ⊗ **REST DU MARCHÉ** (N° RR FEV 25 313) (M. Gérard **Coste**) ☎
48-73-72-25 ⊷ 5 Closed Wed afternoon; Jan. Full-board 140–160F
per night. Coaches welcome (rest. seats 50). Evening meals until
10pm.

VALS-LES-BAINS 07600 Ardèche **Map 24-A1**
♀ ⊗ **LE TONNEAU** (N° RR MAI 23 255) (M. Patrick **Gueriot**) 89, rue
Jean-Jaurès ☎ 75-37-45-36 Closed Mon evening 15 days in
October. Evening meals.

VAL-DE-SAANE 76960 Seine-Maritime **Map 3-A1**
♀ ⊗ **LE CLOS DE VARVANNES** (N° RR SEP 26 637) (Mme Nadine
Ballerais) RN 29 **Totes** ☎ 35-32-16-52 Closed Sun.

VALENÇAY 36600 Indre **RN 156 Map 12-B3**
♀ ⊗ **LE RELAIS DES ROUTIERS** (N° RR FEV 15 128) (M. Pierre
Bougault) ☎ 54-00-02-94 ⊷ 4 Closed Sun low season; Sept.
Evening meals.

VALENCE NORD 26300 Drôme **RN 7 Map 18-B3**
⚑ **Les Routiers Total Service Station RELAIS DU 45ᵉ PARALLE-
`LE** (N° RR OCT 23 519 (M. Daniel **Bianco**) Châteauneuf-sur-Isère
☎ 75-58-60-22 English, German, Italian spoken.

VALENCE-SUR-BAÏSE 32310 Gers **Map 21-B2**
♀ ⊗ **LADOUCH** (N° RR AOU 25 615) (Mme Ginette **Ladouch**) Place

de l'Hôtel-de-Ville ☎ 62-28-50-45 Closed Sun. Spanish, Italian spoken.

VALENCIENNES 59300 Nord **RN 29 Maps 6-A3 and 5-B1**
♈ ⊗ ⌂ **AUBERGE DU RELAIS DE LA POTERNE** – Les Routiers (N° RR DEC 17 689) (M. **Demolle**) 9, boulevard Eisen (Place Poterne) bd extérieur Itinéraire P.L. Exit from autoroute. A2 - Valenciennes Sud ☎ 27-46-44-98 **Minitel** ⊷ 13 Closed Sun; Christmas; May to mid Oct open daily. Coaches welcome (weekends only – rest. seats 50 bookable). Evening meals until 9.30pm.

VALENTON-VAL-POMPADOUR 94460 Val-de-Marne **RN 5 Map 1-B3**
♈ ⊗ **AU BON ACCUEIL** (N° RR OCT 25 165) (M. Marco **Roméro**) 46, rue Henri-Barbusse ☎ 43-89-06-70 Closed Sat, Sun; Aug. Spanish spoken.

VALENTY-VENTAVON 05300 Htes-Alpes **RN 85 Map 25-A1**
♈ ⊗ **LA GALÈRE Tobacconist** (N° RR OCT 24 327) (M. Michel **Da Silva**) Laragne ☎ 92-66-40-31.

VALERGUES 34130 Hérault **RN 113**
♈ ⊗ ⌂ **RELAIS DE VALERGUES** (N° RR JUL 25 495) (M. Claude **Bernabé**) RN 113 ☎ 67-86-75-27 ⊷ 8 Closed Sun. Spanish spoken.

VALLET 44330 Loire-Atl. **RD 756 and 763 Maps 11-A1/B3 and 12-B1**
♈ ⊗ ⌂ **LE RELAIS DE LA GARE** (N° RR AVR 20 151) (Mme **Jouy**) ☎ 40-33-92-55 **Minitel** ⊷ 25 Closed Sun. Full-board 130–150F per night. Coaches welcome (rest. seats 160). Evening meals. English spoken.

VALLON-EN-SULLY 03190 Allier
♈ ⊗ **LES ROUTIERS** (N° RR FEV 26 822) (M. Jean Claude **Schneider**) Allée des Soupirs (beside camp site) ☎ 70-06-50-66. Closed Thurs 2pm. English, Dutch, German spoken.

VALLON-PONT-D'ARC 07150 Ardèche **RN 579 Map 24-A2**
♈ ⊗ **BAR DE LA POSTE** (N° RR OCT 22 952) (M. Bernard **Garrido**) rue Jean-Jaurès ☎ 75-88-02-11 Closed Sun low season; Dec. Open 7am–9pm; Spanish spoken.

VALOGNES 50700 Manche **RN 13 Map 4-B1**
♈ ⊗ **AU PETIT MONTROUGE** (N° RR DEC 12 588) (M. and Mme François **Leblond**) 104, rue des Religieuses.

VALS-LE-BAINS 07600 Ardèche **Map 24-A1**
♈ ⊗ **LE TONNEAU** (N° RR MAI 23 255) (M. Patrick **Guériot**) 89, rue Jean-Jaurès ☎ 75-37-45-36. Closed Sun evening; 15 days Oct.

VANNES 56000 Morbihan **RN 165 Map 11-A1/2**
♈ ⊗ ⌂ **1 star NN LE RELAIS DE LUSCANEN** (N° RR NOV 27 104) (M. Jean-Marc **Giteau**) Route d'Auvay ☎ 97-63-45-92 ⊷ 22 Closed Sun. English spoken.

V

VANVES 92170 Hauts-de-Seine **Porte de Vanves Map 1-B2**
♈ ⊗ **LE RELAIS DES ROUTIERS** (N° RR DEC 26 395) (M. Émile **Bourget**) 38, avenue Pasteur ☎ 46-42-36-08 Closed Sun; 20 Jul to Aug.

VARANGES 21110 Côte d'Or **RN 5 Map à 1 km**
♈ ⊗ **L'AUBERGE** (N° RR MARS 27 223) (M. Jean-Pierre **Hul**) Rue Nouvelle ☎ 80-31-30-17

VARENNES-CHANGY 45290 Loiret **RD 41 Map 13-A1**
♈ ⊗ **HOTEL DU CENTRE** (N° RR MARS 26 211) (Mme Claudine **Michot**) 1, Grande-Place ☎ 38-94-50-14 ⊨ 8 Closed Sun evening. English, Spanish spoken.

VARENNES-LE-GRAND 71240 S.-et-L. **RN 6 Map 18-B1**
♈ ⊗ ⌂ **RELAIS DE LA GARE** (N° RR NOV 26 384) (Mme **Meyer**) ☎ 85-44-22-76 ⊨ 9 Closed Sun in winter. Coaches welcome (rest. seats 100). Evening meals. English spoken.
♈ ⊗ ⌂ **LE MISTRAL** (N° RR OCT 27 042) (M. Mohand **Aitaoudia**) ☎ 85-44-12-70 ⊨ 10 English spoken.

VARENNES-LAS-MACON 71000 S.-et-L. **RN 6 Map 18-A/B1**
♈ ⊗ ⌂ **LE RELAIS DES ROUTIERS – CHEZ MARCEL** (N° RR JUN 1 893) (M. and Mme **Revillon**) ☎ 85-34-70-44 ⊨ 24 Closed Sat, Sun; Aug.

VARENNES-SUR-ALLIER 03150 Allier **RN 7 Map 16-A3**
♈ ⊗ ⌂ **LE RELAIS DES TOURISTES – REST. DE FRANCE** (N° RR MAI 14 802) (M. André **Juniet**) 1, rue des Halles ☎ 70-45-00-51 ⊨ 9 Closed Sat from Oct to May.
♈ ⊗ **LA RENAISSANCE** (N° RR MAR 24 887) (Mme **Gardel**) Route Nle 7 ☎ 70-45-62-86 Closed Sat, Sun. Evening meals. Portuguese spoken.

VARENNES-SUR-SEINE see LE PETIT-FOSSARD

VARIZE 28140 E.-et-L. **Voir ORGÈRES-EN-BEAUCE**

VATAN 36150 Indre **RN 20 Map 13-B1**
♈ ⊗ ⌂ **LE RELAIS DU CHENE VERT** (N° RR JAN 3 823) (Mme **Lahaye**) 13, avenue de Paris, sur la Nle 20 ☎ 54-49-76-56 ⊨ 7 Closed Sat evening, Sun; 5 Sep–26 Sep. Evening meals until 9.30pm.

VATRY 51320 Marne **RN 77 Map 9-A3**
♈ ⊗ ⌂ **L'ÉTAPE** (N° RR JANV 27 149) (Mme Éliane **Fouquet**) RN 77 ☎ 26-67-41-06 ⊨ 7 Closed Sat pm and Sun in winter.

VAUCHAMPS 51210 Marne RD 33 Map 9-A2
♈ ⊗ **AU SOLEIL D'OR** (N° RR OCT 26 708) (Mme Francine **L'hopital**) RD 33 Montmirail ☎ 26-81-11-19 Closed Sun.

VAUCIENNES Voir Chaussée-de-Damery

V

VAUDIOUX (LE) 38300 Jura **RN 5 Map 19-A1**
♀ ⊗ **LES ROUTIERS LA BILLAUDE** (N° RR AVR 25 873) (M. Georges **Chagre**) La Billaude Champagne ☎ 84-52-07-95 Closed Sun. HGV parking.

VAUNANEYS-LA-ROCHETTE 26400 Drôme **RD 538**
♀ ⊗ **AUBERGE CHEZ MIJO** (N° RR JANV 27 172) (M. Joël **Piaud SARL**) La Gare ☎ 75-25-01-57 Closed Wed pm.

VAUVERT 30600 Gard **RD 56 Map 23-A2**
♀ ⊗ 🏠 **LE CRISTAL** (N° RR JUL 24 647) (Mme Roselyne **Guyon**) 13, rue de la République ☎ 66-88-21-77 ⌐ 11 Closed Sat afternoon, Sun; 23 Dec to 2 Jan. Full-board 105–150F per night. Coaches welcome (rest. seats 70). Evening meals.

VAUX-EN-BUGEY 01860 Ain **RN 75 Map 2-A2**
♀ ⊗ **LE RAMEQUIN** (N° RR NOV 27 094) (Mme Michelle **Gallon**) ☎ 74-35-95-09 Closed Sat pm and Sun.

VAUX-SUR-SEINE 21510 Côte d'Or **RD 32 Map 1-A1**
♀ ⊗ **LA TAVERNE DES ROUTIERS** (N° RR JUN 26 567) (M. Paul **Thomassin**) Aignay-le-Duc ☎ 80-93-88-04.

VEMARS 95470 Val-d'Oise **Autoroute A 1 Map 3-B3**
♀ ⊗ **RELAIS ILE-DE-FRANCE** (SERA Vemars) (M. **Fossey**) Autoroute A1-A5 de Vemars - Fosses - Survilliers ☎ 34-68-39-20 Telex 699538 Self-service restaurant open 6.00am to 11.00pm. Showers, TV, Shop. English, German spoken.

VENANSAULT 85190 Vendée **RN 160 Map 11-B3**
♀ ⊗ 🏠 **1 Star NN LE MOULIN DE LA BERGERIE** (N° RR JUN 22 375) (**EURL Le Moulin de la Bergerie**) la Grolle crossroad, on road to Landeronde (9 km from La Roche-sur-Yon, going towards Les Sables-d'Olonne) ☎ 51-40-36-94 ⌐ 10 Closed Fri evenings from 1 Oct–Easter; 1 Jan–15 Jan; 15 Sep–1 Oct. Full-board 1 pers 200F, 2 pers 310F per night. Coaches welcome (4 rooms: 120 seats).

VENDEGIES-S/ECAILLON 59213 Nord **Map 6-A3**
♀ ⊗ 🍽 **RELAIS LES BELLES FILLES** (N° RR NOV 26 724) (M. Bernard **Beauquel**) 1111, route de Solesmes ☎ 27-27-12-47 Closed Mon. German spoken. Evening meals until 11pm. Menus 58,50F–125F.

VENDENHEIM 67500 Bas-Rhin **RN 63 Map 10-B2**
♀ ⊗ **LE RELAIS DE LA MAISON ROUGE Tobacconists** (N° RR AOU 16 194) (Mme Germaine **Michielin**) 2, route de Brumath ☎ 88-69-51-79 Closed Wed. Evening meals. German spoken.

VENDEUVRE 14170 Calvados **RD 511 Map 8-A2**
♀ ⊗ 🏠 🍽 **LE RELAIS DE LA GARE** (N° RR JUN 23 836) (M. André **Denis**) Saint-Pierre-sur-Dives ☎ 31-40-92-77 or 32-77 ⌐ 11 Closed 21 Dec to 15 Jan. Full-board 155–185F per night. Coaches welcome (rest. seats 120). Evening meals until 9.30pm.

V

VENDINE 31460 Hte-Gar **RN 126 Map 22-A2**
♈ ⊗ **AUBERGE DE VENDINE** (N° RR FEV 26 466) (Mme Yvette **Bertocchi**) Nle 126 ☎ 61-83-12-05 Closed Mon.

VENDŒUVRES 36500 Indre **RD 925 Map 12-B3**
♈ ⊗ **RELAIS DE LA BRENNE** (N° RR AUG 26 981) (Mme Marie-Thérèse **Boué**) place St-Jean ☎ 54-38-31-16 Evening meals until 9.30pm.

VENDOME 41100 L.-et-C. **RN 10 and 817 Map 12-A3**
♈ ⊗ ⌂ **LE RELAIS D'ARMOR – CHEZ MÉMÈRE** (N° RR AOU 19 132) (Mlle Andrée **Touchard**) 127, faubourg Chartrain ☎ 54-77-00-32 ⊷ 14 Closed Mon except public holidays; 15 Feb to 10 Mar. Full-board 120F per night. Coaches welcome (3 rooms: 130 seats). Meals served until 9.30pm.

VENISSIEUX 69200 Rhône **Map 2-A2**
♈ ⊗ **LES ROUTIERS** (N° RR FEV 26 458) (M. Hervé **Ligier**), 66, bd Irène-Joliot-Curie ☎ 78-76-49-94 Closed Sat, Sun. 14 Jul to 15 Aug. Spanish spoken.

VENOY par AUXERRE 89290 Yonne **Autoroute A6 Map 13-A2**
♈ ⊗ **ACCOR – Relais de Venoy** (N° RR RA-21) ☎ 86-52-35-52 Champs-sur-Yonne Sens Province-Paris Self-service restaurant open 10.30am to 3.00pm, 6.30pm to 11.00pm. Telex: 800921.
♈ ⊗ **ACCOR L'ARCHE** (M. Gérard **Gain**) Autoroute A6 Paris-Province direction ☎ 86-52-31-71 Télex: 800921 Self-service restaurant open 24 hours. Shop.
⛽ **Total Service Station DE VENOY** Autoroute A6 ☎ 86-52-33-72 Open 24 hours. Accepts Carte Bleue, Diners club, Eurocard, DKV.

VENSAC 33590 Gironde **Map 20-A1**
♈ ⊗ ⌂ **CHEZ NICOLE** (N° RR JUN 25 466) (Mme Nicole **Figerou**) St-Vivien ☎ 56-09-44-05 ⊷ 6 Full-board 150F per night. Coaches welcome (rest. seats 120). Evening meals.

VERBERIE 60410 Oise **RD 932 Map 3-B3**
♈ ⊗ **BAR-RESTAURANT DE LA GARE** (N° RR SEP 22 928) (Mme Irène **Colladant**) 3, place de la Gare ☎ 44-40-90-68 Closed Sat; Sun. Meals until 9pm.

VERCHENY 26340 Drôme **RD 93 Map 24-B1**
♈ ⊗ **LA GRAPPE D'OR** (N° RR SEPT 26 653) (M. **Manas**) ☎ 75-21-70-44.

VERDUN 55100 Meuse **RN 3 Map 6-B3**
♈ ⊗ ⌂ **LE RELAIS CHEZ MARIA** (N° RR FEV 12 050) (Mme **Maffioletti**) 68, avenue Miribel ☎ 29-86-07-28 ⊷ 7 Closed Sun; Christmas to New year. Full-board 150F per night. Coaches welcome (rest. seats 50). Evening meals.
♈ ⊗ **A LA BONNE AUBERGE** (N° RR SEP 3 102) (Mme **Gaiotti-Morano**) 11, rue Garibaldi.
♈ ⊗ **ROAD BAR** (N° RR NOV 23 547) (M. Christian **Antoine**) 5, rue

St-Victor ☎ 29-86-05-08 Coaches welcome (rest. seats 55). Evening meals until midnight. English, German spoken.

VERDUN see BELLEVILLE 55100 Meuse

VERDUN 55100 Meuse **Autoroute A4 Map 6-B3**
𝖸 ⊗ **ACCOR L'ARCHE** (N° RR RA-22) (M. Serge **Monceau**) Aire de Service de Saint-Nicolas ☎ 29-86-41-18 Self-service restaurant open 6.30am to 11.00pm winter, 5.00am to midnight summer. Showers, TV, Shop. German, English spoken.

VERGEZE 30310 Gard **RN 113 Map 24-A3**
𝖸 ⊗ 🏠 **RELAIS DE LA SOURCE** (N° RR JUL 26 279) (M. Richard **Erquera**) RN 113 ☎ 66-35-05-51 ⊷ 9 English, Spanish spoken.

VERGT 24380 Dordogne **RD 21 Map 15-B3**
𝖸 ⊗ **LE PHENIX** (N° RR JUN 26 929) (Mme Raymonde **Legeard**) place Jean-Jaurès ☎ 53-54-91-89 Closed Mon; 15–28 Feb; 15–30 Nov. German, Italian spoken. Filling station nearby.

VERMENTON 89270 Yonne **RN 6 Map 13-A2**
𝖸 ⊗ 🏠 **AU NOUVEAU RELAIS** (N° RR MAI 6 826) (M. Pierre **Jean**) 74, Route Nationale 6 ☎ 86-53-51-51 ⊷ 12 Closed Sun; Dec. Open 5am to midnight. Coaches welcome (2 rests. seats 80). Evening meals.

VERN-D'ANJOU 49220 M.-et-L. **RD 770 Maps 11-A3 and 12-A1**
𝖸 ⊗ **LE RELAIS DES SPORTS** (N° RR DEC 24 067) (Mme Marie-Thérèse **Chevallier**) 21, rue du Commerce ☎ 41-61-41-32. Closed Fri afternoon; 15–31 Aug. Evening meals until 9pm.

VERN-SUR-SEICHE
𝖸 ⊗ **WELCOME-BAR** (N° RR MAI 27 280) (M. Philippe **Brossault**) Le Clos Berquet ☎ 99-62-83-18 Closed Sun and winter. Evening meals.

VERNEGUES see CAZAN 13116 B.-du-R. **RN 7 Map 24-B3**

VERNEUIL-SUR-AVRE 27130 Eure
𝖸 ⊗ **RELAIS DE L'ESPÉRANCE** (N° RR MARS 26 192) (M. **Agullo**), 65, Porte de Breteuil.

VERNON 27200 Eure **RN 181 and 13 Map 3-B1**
𝖸 ⊗ **LA CHOPE** (N° RR SEPT 26 638) (Mme Josiane **Plantain**) 9, route de Rouen ☎ 32-51-57-94 Closed Sun.
𝖸 ⊗ 🏠 **HOTEL DE FRANCE** (N° RR MARS 26 193) (M. Thierry **Bonté**) 70, route de Rouen ☎ 32-51-53-55 **Minitel** ⊷ 8 Closed Sat afternoon, Sun. Coaches welcome (rest. seats 150). Evening meals.
𝖸 ⊗ **CAFÉ NORMAND Chez Marinette et Michel** (N° RR JUL 24 282) (M. Michel **Schibiness**) 29–31, avenue de l'Ile-de-France Le Petit Val ☎ 32-51-08-41 Closed Sun pm. German and English spoken. Evening meals.

V

VERRERIE-DE-ROYE par LURE see ROYE 70200 Haute-Saône

VERRUE 86420 Vienne **RN 147 Map 12-B2**
♀ ⊗ ⌂**CHEZ RÉMY ET PAULETTE** (N° RR SEPT 27 011) (Mme Paulette **Nativelle**) Monts-sur-Guesnes ☎ 49-22-84-01 ⊶ 8.

VESLY 27870 Eure **RD 181 Map 3-B2**
♀ ⊗ **LE RELAIS DE L'AGRICULTURE** (N° RR MAI 24 225) (M. Claude **Benteyn**) ☎ 32-55-62-37 Closed Sat. Coaches welcome (rest. seats 44).

VEUREY-VOROIZE 38113 Isère **RN 532 Map 19-A3**
♀ ⊗ ⌂ **AUBERGE DU VAL ROSE** (N° RR JUIN 26 904) (M. Jean-Louis **Quercia**) chemin de la Rive ☎ 76-53-95-04 ⊶ 8 Closed Sun. English, Italian spoken. Filling station nearby.

VEYRINS THUELLIN 38115 Isère **RN 75 Map 2-B3**
♀ ⊗ ⌂ **1 Star NN LA BONNE AUBERGE** (N° RR AVR 25 874) (M. Raymond **Belingherl**) ☎ 74-33-94-27 Closed Tue. Italian, English spoken.

VEZENOBRES 30360 Gard **RD 106 Map 23-B1**
⊗ **LE GRES** (N° RR SEP 25 108) (Mme Hélène **Pillot**) Route Nationale 106 de Nimes ☎ 66-83-52-89 Closed Sat. Coaches welcome (2 rest. seats 80 and 35). Evening meals until 9pm.

VIAS 34450 Hérault **RN 112 Map 23-A2**
♀ ⊗ ⌂ **LE PETIT VATEL** (N° RR MARS 26 476) (M. Albert **Matagotte**) avenue de la Gare ☎ 67-21-22-02 Closed Mon (except Jul/Aug). English, Spanish spoken.

VIC-EN-BIGORRE 65500 Htes-Pyr. **Map 21-A3**
♀ ⊗ **LE RANCH** (N° RR JAN 25 788) (M. Bernard **Griffon**) Rte de Rabastens ☎ 62-96-72-32 Closed Sat; Sep. Evening meals until 11pm.

VICHY 03200 Allier **RN 9A Map 16-B3**
♀ ⊗ **LE RELAIS DE LA PASSERELLE** (N° RR MAI 14 797) (M. **Pesce**) 1, rue de Bordeaux ☎ 70-98-57-70 ⊶ 4 Closed Sun; 2 weeks in Aug. Evening meals.

VIEILLE-BRIOUDE 43100 Hte-Loire **RN 102 Map 17-A3**
♀ ⊗ ⌂ **2 Stars NN LES GLYCINES** (N° RR NOV 25 748) (Mme Viviane **Chardonnal**) ☎ 71-50-91-80 Coaches welcome (rest. seats 100). Evening meals. English spoken.

VIERZON 18100 Cher **RN 20 and 76 Map 13-B1**
♀ ⊗ ⌂ **MODER'N SPORT** (N° RR MAI 26 247) (M. Anik **Augy**) 141, av. E.-Vaillant ☎ 48-75-13-63 ⊶ 4 Closed Sat; Aug. Coaches welcome (rest. seats 60). Evening meals.
♀ ⊗ **AUX MILLE PATTES** (N° RR JUL 26 600) (M. Ludwig **Jakubik**) 85, route de Tours ☎ 48-75-46-38 Closed Sun afternoon. Coaches welcome (rest. seats 40). Evening meals until 12.30pm.

VIEUX-CONDE 59690 Nord **Maps 5-B1 and 6-A3**
ϒ ⊗ **TORRE DEL SALTO** (N° RR FEV 23 677) (M. **Manti**) 49, place
de la République ☎ 27-40-31-74 ⊷ 3 Closed Aug. Italian, English,
Portuguese, Polish spoken.

VIGNOLLES 16300 Charente **RN 10 Map 15-A2**
ϒ ⊗ **L'IMPRÉVU** (N° RR JUL 26 936) (Mme Monique **Blanchard**)
Barbezieux ☎ 45-78-38-54 Closed Sat afternoon; Sun. Filling
station 6 km away.

VIJON 36160 Indre **RD 917 Map 16-A2**
ϒ ⊗ **L'ESTAMINET** (N° RR OCT 26 684) (M. Dominique **Hayo**) Le
Marembert ☎ 54-30-60-95 German spoken.

VILDE-GUINGALAN 22270 C.-du-N. **RN 176 Map 7-A3**
ϒ ⊗ ⌂ **SNACK LES ROUTIERS** (N° RR MAR 22 725) (M. Jean-Claude
Certenais) La Borgnette ☎ 96-27-61-00 **Minitel** ⊷ 10 English
spoken.

VILLABE see also LISSES 91100 Essonne **Autoroute A6 Map 1-B3**
⛽ **Service Station – LES ROUTIERS – LE RELAIS DE VILLABE**
(N° RR JUN 22 825) (M. Georges **Buono**) ☎ 60-86-22-17 Open 24
hours. English, Portuguese spoken.

VILLARD SALLET 73110 Savoie **RD 925 Map 19-A2**
ϒ ⊗ ⌂ **AUBERGE DE LA ROUTE** (N° RR JUL 26 947) (Mme Francine
Loy) ☎ 79-25-52-20 ⊷ 9 Filling station nearby.

VILLE-AUX-BOIS (LA) par les PONTAVERT 02160 Aisne **RN 44
Map 6-B1**
ϒ ⊗ **LE RELAIS SAINT-MARIE** (N° RR SEP 23 921) (SARL **Le Relais
Sainte-Marie**) Les Pontavert ☎ 23-20-74-34 Open 24 hours
(except Sat night to Sun). English, German, Polish, Spanish
spoken.

VILLEBAUDON 50410 Manche **RD 999 and 13 Map 8-A1**
ϒ ⊗ **LE SPORTIF** (N° RR JUN 26 918) (Mme Agnès **Osouf**) Le Bourg
☎ 33-61-20-52 ⊷ 3 Filling station nearby.

VILLEDIEU-LES-POELES 50800 Manche **RN 175 and Dle 799 Map 8-
A1**
ϒ ⊗ **HOTEL DES VOYAGEURS** (N° RR SEPT 26 626) (SNC.
Louaintier-Lecannellier) 37, avenue du Mal-Leclerc ☎ 33-61-
00-76 ⊷ 4.

VILLEDIEU-SUR-INDRE 36320 Indre **RN 143 Map 12-B3**
ϒ ⊗ **CAFE DES SPORTS** (N° RR MARS 26 828) (Mme Joëlle **Gatefin**)
69. rue de Général de Gaulle ☎ 54-26-56-18 Closed Mon. Filling
station nearby.

VILLEDOMER 37110 I.-et-L. **RN 10 Map 12-A3**
ϒ ⊗ **LE RELAIS DES GRANDS VINS DE TOURAINE** (N° RR JUN 12
910) (M. Claude **Romain**) La Grand'Vallée ☎ 47-55-01-05 ⊷ 4
Closed Wed; 15 to 25 Jul. Coaches welcome (rest. seats 100).

V

Villedomer continued

Evening meals; menus 44–68F. Specialities: rabbit leg sausage with Vouvray and kidney sauce; frogs legs.

VILLEFRANCHE-DE-ROUERGUE 12200 Aveyron **RD 926 Map 22-B1**
 ♀ ⊗ **RELAIS DES CABRIÈRES** (N° RR JUL 26 592) (M. Alain **Toulouse**) route de Montauban ☎ 65-81-16-99 Closed Sun. Coaches welcome (2 rest. seats 120). Evening meals.

VILLEFRANCHE-SUR-SAONE 69400 Rhône **Déviation Nle 6 Map 2-A1 Motorway exit Macon Paris.**
 ♀ ⊗ **RELAIS CALADOIS** (N° RR AVR 26 513) (M. Denis **Gimaret**) 511, avenue de l'Europe ☎ 74-60-69-88 **Minitel** Closed Sat; Sun. Coaches welcome. English, Spanish spoken.

VILLE FRANCŒUR 41330 Loir-et-Cher **RD 957 Map 12-A3**
 ♀ ⊗ **LE CONCORDE** (N° RR AOU 26 976) (Mme Andrée **Gehanno**) Le Breuil ☎ 54-20-12-04 Closed Mon. Italian spoken. Filling station nearby.

VILLEGENON 18260 Cher **D 926 Map 13-A1**
 ♀ ⊗ **LA CROIX BLANCHE** (N° RR DEC 26 752) (Mme Joëlle **Beauvois**) Le Bourg ☎ 48-73-86-63 English spoken.

VILLENEUVE 04130 Alpes-de-haute-Provence **RN 96 Map 24-B2**
 ♀ ⊗ 🏠 **LE RELAIS CHEZ ROGER** (N° RR OCT 15 814) (SARL Pierre **Curri**) route de Marseille-Gap ☎ 92-78-42-47 ➜ 7 Closed Sun; 15 to 31 Aug; 21 Dec to 5 Jan. Coaches welcome (rest. seats 60). Evening meals until 11pm.

VILLENEUVE-AU-CHEMIN 10130 Aube **RN 77 Map 9-B3**
 ♀ ⊗ **LE PETIT SAINT-JEAN** (N° RR MARS 26 859) (M. Mohammed **Nait-Mohand**) 19, route Nationale ☎ 25-42-10-51 Closed Sun.

VILLENEUVE-D'ASCQ 59650 Nord **Map 5-B1**
 ♀ ⊗ **CHEZ GUY** (N° RR MARS 25 853) (M. Guy **Way**) 221, rue Jean-Jaurès ☎ 20-89-25-23 **Minitel** Closed Sat; Sun; Aug.

VILLENEUVE-D'AVEYRON 12260 Aveyron **RD 922 Map 22-B1**
 ♀ ⊗ **L'ORÉE DU BOIS** (N° RR NOV 26 727) (M. Michel **Boulesque**) Dle 922 ☎ 65-81-65-77 Closed Sat. Spanish spoken.

VILLENEUVE-L'ARCHEVEQUE 89190 Yonne **RN 60 Map 9-B2**
 ♀ ⊗ 🏠 **L'ESCALE 60** (N° RR MARS 26 188) (M. Dominique **Boire**) 10, route de Sens ☎ 86-86-74-42 ➜ 5 Closed Sat eve; Sun; Aug. Coaches welcome (rest. seats 70). Evening meals; full-board 130F per night. English spoken.

VILLENEUVE-SAINT-MARTIN (LA) 95450 Val-d'Oise **déviation RN 14 and D28 Map 1-A2**
 ♀ ⊗ **AU VEAU QUI TETE** (N° RR MAR 25 314) (SARL **Saint-Martin**) 12, rue François-Vaudin ☎ 30-39-24-82 Closed Sun.

V

VILLENEUVE-SUR-LOT 47300 L.-et-G. **RN 21 Map 21-B1**
♀ ⊗ ⌂ **RELAIS DE GASCOGNE** (N° RR AVR 26 519) (M. Alain **Guiraud**) 31, avenue due Gal-Laclerc ☎ 53-70-06-48 ⊷ 8 Closed Sun from 1 Nov–1 May; end of year. Coaches welcome (rest. seats 120). Full-board 140–160F per night. Evening meals. Spanish spoken.

VILLERS-BOCAGE 14310 Calvados **Map 4-B2**
♀ ⊗ ⌂ **HOTEL DE LA GARE** (N° RR JUL 26 287) (Mme Paulette **Golasse-Marie**) 6, rue du Mal-Foch ☎ 31-77-00-23 ⊷ 10 Closed Sun. Full-board 140-170F per night. Evening meals.

VILLERS-SUR-MER 14640 Calvados **RN 813 Map 4-B2**
♀ ⊗ ⌂ **1 Star NN LE NORMAND – Les Routiers** (N° RR MAI 20 735) (Mme Suzanne **Dujardin**) 44, rue du Maréchal-Foch ☎ 31-87-04-23 ⊷ 8 (158–220F) Closed Sun from 1 Oct; Dec. Coaches welcome (rest. seats 50). Full-board 199F per night, breakfast 18F. Evening meals until 9pm. Parking; bar; beach; horse-riding; tennis nearby. Sites to visit: Lisieux and Bayeux.

VILLETOUREIX see RIBERAC 24600 Dordogne

VILLEURBANNE 69100 Rhône
♀ ⊗ **CHEZ NICOLE** (N° RR AVR 27 244) (Mme Nicole **Grass**) 165, rue Jean Voillot ☎ 72-37-52-00. Closed Sat pm and Sun.

VILLEVALLIER 89127 Yonne **RN 6 Map 9-B2**
♀ ⊗ ⌂ **RELAIS 89** (N° RR JUIL 26 956) (Mme Yvette **Petit**) 9, rue de la République ☎ 86-91-11-17 ⊷ 6 Closed Sat afternoons; Sun evenings.

VILLIERS-AU-BOUIN 37330 I.-et-L. **RN 159 and CD 959 Map 12-A2**
♀ ⊗ ⌂ **2 Stars NN LE GRAND CERF** (N° RR SEP 23 450) (M. Jean **Meunier**) La Porerie ☎ 47-24-11-06 ⊷ 20 Closed Sat in winter; 20 Oct–20 Nov. Full-board 200F per night. Coaches welcome (rest. seats 140, 130 and 50). Evening meals.
♀ ⊗ **L'ETAPE** (N° RR JAN 26 778) (Mme Chantal **Hais**) 15, rue de la Libération CD 135 ☎ 47-24-03-76 Closed Sun (unless booked); 20 Dec to 3 Jan.

VILLIERS-SAINT-GEORGES 77560 Seine-et-Marne **Map 9-A2**
♀ ⊗ **L'ESCALE** (N° RR MAI 24 959) (Mme Arlette **Oreste**) 64, route de Provins ☎ 64-01-90-16 Closed Tues.

VIMOUTIERS 61120 Orne **RN 179 Map 8-A2**
♀ ⊗ ⌂ **LE RELAIS DE LISIEUX** (N° RR FEV 23 635) (Mme Yvette **Larivière**) 37, avenue Lyautey ☎ 33-39-02-62 ⊷ 5 Closed Sun; Jun. Coaches welcome.

VINEZAC 07110 Ardèche **RN 104 Maps 23-B1 and 24-A2**
♀ ⊗ **L'AUBERGE DES COTES** (N° RR MAI 15 217) (M. Serge **Zagar**) Les Côtes ☎ 75-36-80-10 Closed Sat; 1 to 15 Sept.

V

VIRAZEIL 47200 L.-et-G. **RD 933 Map 21-A1**
Ⓧ Ⓧ **LE RALLYE** (N° RR FEV 24 126) (M. Claude **Marchet**) ☎ 58-64-18-77 Closed Sat.

VIRE 14500 Calvados **RN 177 and 24 Bis Map 8-A1**
Ⓧ Ⓧ **L'AVENIR** (N° RR MAI 26 533) (M. Hervé **Gautherot**) 30, rue Émile-Chenel ☎ 31-67-76-94 Closed Sun. Coaches welcome (rest. seats 40). Evening meals until 9pm. English, Spanish, Portuguese spoken.
Ⓧ Ⓧ ⌂ **2 Stars NN HOTEL DE FRANCE** (N° RR OCT 24 705) (M. Roger **Carnet**) 4, rue d'Aignaux ☎ 31-68-00-35 **Minitel** ⌐ 20 (with bath or shower, WC, telephone). Closed 20 Dec–10 Jan. Full-board 160–230F per night. Coaches welcome (rest. seats 160). Evening meals. English spoken.

VIRONVAY 27400 Eure **Autoroute A 13 Map 3-B1**
Ⓧ Ⓧ **L'ARCHE** (N° RR RA-23) Aire de Vironvay (Dominique **Cordier**) ☎ 32-40-21-51 Self-service restaurant open 7.00am to 11.00 pm. Shop. English spoken.

VIRY-CHATILLON 91170 Essonne **RN 7 and RD 91 Map 1-B2**
Ⓧ Ⓧ **AU BON ACCUEIL** (N° RR SEP 12 440) (M. Fernand **Gadreau**) 100, route de Fleury ☎ 69-05-28-46 Closed Sun; public holidays. Evening meals.

VITARELLE (LA) 12210 Aveyron **RN 121 Map 17-B2**
Ⓧ Ⓧ ⌂ **LE RELAIS DE LA VITARELLE** (N° RR AVR 20 696) (Mme Francine **Falguier**) Montpeyroux ☎ 65-44-36-01 ⌐ 6 Closed Sat low season. Coaches welcome (rest. seats 80). Full-board 120–130F per night. Evening meals.

VITROLLES 13127 B.-du-R. **RN 113 Map 24-B3**
Ⓧ Ⓧ ⌂ **O'ROUTIERS-ANJOLY** (N° RR MAI 27 274) (M. William **Lequem** Centre Routier Z.A. d'Anjoly ☎ 42-75-19-60 **Minitel** ⌐ 47.With showers. English, Spanish and Italian spoken. Evening meals served until midnight.

VITRY-EN-CHAROLAIS 71600 S.-et-L. **RN 79**
Ⓧ Ⓧ **TOM BAR** (N° RR AVR 26 232) (M. André **Borrego**) RN 79 ☎ 85-81-02-85 Closed Sat midday; Aug. Evening meals until midnight. Spanish spoken.

VITRY-EN-ARTOIS 62490 P.-de-C.
☕ **Service Station RELAIS DU PETIT VITRY** (N° RR 550000100) (M. **Deponchaux** SARL) 5, Rte Nle ☎ 21-50-13-63 Closed Sun.

VITRY-LE-FRANÇOIS 51300 Marne **RN 4 Map 19-A3**
Ⓧ Ⓧ ⌂ **LE ROND POINT – CHEZ NICOLAS** (N° RR SEPT 26 328) (M. Nicolas **Cicchini**) 28, avenue de la République ☎ 26-74-02-84 ⌐ 10 Closed Sat evening (unless booked) Coaches welcome (rest. seats 28 and 24). English, Italian spoken.

VITTEAUX 21350 Côte-d'Or **RN 5 and 70 Map 13-A/B3**
Ⓧ Ⓧ ⌂ **LES ROUTIERS** (N° RR FEV 9 286) (M. **Le Gall**) route de

Dijon ☎ 80-49-60-13 ⟼ 5 Closed Sun ; Sept or Oct. Evening meals until 9.30pm.

VIVIERS-SUR-RHONE 07220 Ardéche **RN 86 Map 24-A2**

♀ ⊗ ⌂ **1 Star NN CHEZ ESPERANDIEU - LE RELAIS DU VIVAR-AIS** (N° RR FEV 7 485) (M. André **Esperandieu**) Route Nationale 86 Lieu-dit-Les Sautelles ☎ 75-52-60-41 ⟼ 10 (65–160F) Closed 20 Dec–20 Jan. Full-board 120–150F per night; breakfast 15F. Coaches welcome (rest. seats 60). Evening meals. English spoken. Parking; bar; dogs permitted; fishing and tennis nearby. Note: this hotel is 2 km north of the town, towards Lyons.

VIVONNE 86370 Vienne **RN 10 Map 15-B1**

♀ ⊗ **LE RELAIS ROUTIERS DE VIVONNE** (N° RR JAN 26 143) (M. Fernand **Judes** SARL) RN 10 ☎ 49-43-41-03 Open 24 hours. Coaches welcome (rest. seats 220). Evening meals.

VIVY 49680 M.-et-L. **RN 147 Map 12-A2**

♀ ⊗ ⌂ **1 Star NN LE RELAIS SAINT-PAUL** (N° RR OCT 16 736) (Mme Marie-Louise **Bidet**) 30, rue Nationale ☎ 41-52-50-13 and 52-51-65 ⟼ 25 Full-board 150–230F per night. Coaches welcome (rest. seats 150 and 250). Evening meals. Some English spoken.

VOINSLES-ROZAY-EN-BRIE 77540 S.-et-M. **Map 9-A2**

♀ ⊗ **SARL RELAIS DE VOINSLES** (N° RR OCT 26 354) RN 4 ☎ 64-07-72-38 Closed Sat 2.00pm–Mon morning. Coaches welcome (2 rest. seats 40). Evening meals.

VOISINS par MOUROUX 77120 S.-et-M. **RN 34 Map 9-A2**

♀ ⊗ **LE RELAIS DU SOMMET** (N° RR AOU 16 173) (M. Jacques **Santerre**) 968, rue du Général de Gaulle ☎ 64-03-05-47 ⟼ 7 Closed Sun; Aug.

♀ ⊗ **AUBERGE DE BISHA** (N° RR OCT 26 681) (M. Moutiha **Duvoisin**) 1072, avenue de Général de Gaulle ☎ 64-03-50-52 ⟼ 11 Closed Thurs; 15 Aug–15 July. English, Italian, Arabic spoken.

VOIVRES 72210 Sarthe **RD 23 Map 10-A3**

♀ ⊗ ⌂ **LE TAMARIS** (N° RR MAI 26 252) (M. Patrick **Le Guy**) Rte de la Suze ☎ 43-88-52-60 ⟼ 5 Closed Sun evening. Coaches welcome (rest. seats 200). Full-board 148,50F per night.

VOREY-SUR-ARZON 43800 Haute-Loire **RN 103 Maps 18-A3 and 17-A3**

♀ ⊗ **LE RELAIS DE LA BASCULE** (N° RR MAR 16 920) (Mme **Tirtaine**) place des Moulettes ☎ 71-03-41-67.

VOULTE (LA) 07800 Ardèche **Map 24-A1**

♀ ⊗ **LE PROVENÇAL** (N° RR AVR 26 507) (M. Bernard **Bonneau**) 15, rue Boissy-d'Anglas ☎ 75-85-35-66 Closed Sun.

VOULX 77940 S.-et-M. **RD 219 Map 9-B2**

⊗ **LA BRUYÈRE** (N° RR AOU 22 914) (M. Alban **Baldran**) 72, Grande-Rue ☎ 64-31-92-41 Bar. Closed Sun evening; 15–31 Feb;

V

Voulx continued

16 Aug–6 Sept. Coaches welcome (rest. seats 160). Evening meals until 9.30pm.

VOUVRAY 37210 Indre-et-Loire **Map 12-A3**

 RELAIS DE VOUVRILLON (N° RR SEPT 27 076) (M. Marcel **Le Dortz**) 14, avenue Brûlé ☎ 47-52-78-80 ⊷ 5 Closed Sun and ten days in August. English spoken.

W

WANCOURT 62128 Pas-de-Calais

 RELAIS DE L'ARTOIS Autoroute A1 Aire de Wancourt ☎ 21-55-97-83 Telex 133-924 Open 24 hours. Self-service restaurant, panoramic views, rest and games room, electronic surveillance of vehicles, showers, TV, shop.

WANEL 80490 Somme

LA CLÉ DES CHAMPS (N° RR JUIL 27 318) (M. Mohammed **Lamine**) Hallencourt ☎ 22-28-60-54 Closed Mon, English and Tunisian spoken. Evening meals.

WARGNIES-LE-PETIT 59144 Nord **RN 49**

LE PETIT QUÉBEC (N° RR OCT 25 670) (M. Bruno **Leclercq**) 10, route de Bry ☎ 27-49-97-93.

WASSELONNE 67310 Bas-Rhin **RN 4 Map 10-B2**

AU ROCHER (N° RR SEP 19 489) (Mme **Leippi**) 18, route de Strasbourg ☎ 88-87-06-72 ⊷ 5 Closed Sun.

WINGLES 62410 Pas-de-Calais **RD 165 Map 5-A1**

LE RELAIS CHEZ JULES (N° RR FEV 17 205) (M. Jules **Hennache**) 37, rue Jules Guesde ☎ 21-69-52-88 ⊷ 9 Closed Sun; Aug. Evening meals until 10pm.

WITRY-LES-REIMS 51420 Marne **RN 51 Map 6-B2**

RELAIS LE 51-08 (N° RR JAN 26 144) (Mme Gisèle **Pierront**) 62, rue de Reims ☎ 26-97-08-30 ⊷ 4 Closed Sun. Full-board 110–150F per night. Coaches welcome (rest. seats 60). Evening meals until 10.30pm.

WITTELSHEIM-GRAFFENWALD 68310 Haut-Rhin **RN 83 Map 10-B3**

HOTEL DES VOSGES (N° RR OCT 26 351) (M. **Riedle**) 137, rue de Reiningue ☎ 89-55-10-20 ⊷ 11 Closed Sun. Evening meals. Full-board 140F per night. Coaches welcome (rest. seats 60). German spoken.

WOIPPY 57140 Moselle **RN 412 Maps 6-B3 and 10-A1**
Ⓨ ⊗ **LE CHARDON LORRAIN** (N° RR JUN 23 333) (Mme Françoise **de Cecco**) 58, rue de Metz ☎ 87-30-46-61 **Minitel** → 3 Closed Sun; 20 Dec to 15 Jan. Full-board 128–170F per night. Coaches welcome (rest. seats 70). Evening meals until 8pm. German spoken.

WOLFGANTZEN 68600 Haut-Rhin **Map 10-B2**
Ⓨ ⊗ **A L'AGNEAU D'OR** (N° RR JAN 25 247) (M. Etienne **Heimburger**) 37, rue Principale ☎ 89-72-86-66 Closed Wed; Feb. German, Alsatian spoken.

WORMHOUDT 59470 Nord **RN 16 Map 5-A2**
Ⓨ ⊗ **LE RELAIS DE LA FORGE** (N° RR JUN 14 406) (M. Guy **Depriester**) 84, Grand'Place ☎ 28-65-62-33 Closed 15–31 Aug. Evening meals.

YEBLES 77390 S.et-M. **RN 19 Map 1-B3**
Ⓨ ⊗ ⌂ **RELAIS DE L'EST** (N° RR OCT 26 680) (Mme Maria **Nunes**) ☎ 64-06-00-40 → 11 Closed Sun. Portuguese, Spanish spoken.

YERVILLE 76760 S.-Mme **RN 29 Maps 4-A3**
Ⓨ ⊗ **L'ESCALE ROUTIERE** (N° RR DEC 25 771) (M. Christian **Delahaye**) Rte d'Yvetot ☎ 35-96-80-45 Closed 6pm Fri–12am Sat; Aug. Coaches welcome (rest. seats 140). Evening meals.

YMONVILLE 28150 E.-et-L. **RN 154 Map 9-B1**
Ⓨ ⊗ ⌂ **LE RELAIS DE L'ÉTOILE** (N° RR OCT 21 259) (Mme Thérèse **Brulé**) 31, rue du Haut-Chemin ☎ 37-32-25-67 → 10 attached to Hôtel de Tourisme. Closed Mon; 2 weeks in Feb. Full-board 139F per night. Coaches welcome (rest. seats 80). Evening meals.

YSSINGEAUX LA GUILDE 43200 Haute-Loire **RN 88 - RD 105 Map 18-A3**
Ⓨ ⊗ ⌂ **LA PETITE AUBERGE** (N° RR JUN 16 996) (Mme **Delabre**) ☎ 71-59-05-32 → 5 Closed Sun low season; Aug. Full-board 140–160F per night. Coaches welcome (rest. seats 70). Evening meals. English spoken.

YUTZ 57110 Moselle **RN 53 Bis Map 10-A1**
Ⓨ ⊗ ⌂ **RELAIS ROUTIERS** (N° RR DEC 26 754) (M. Noël **Rubeillon**) 140, rue Nationale ☎ 82-56-00-28 → 10 Closed Sat, Sun; Aug.

YVETOT 76190 Seine-Maritime **RN 153 Map 4-A3**
Ⓨ ⊗ ⌂ **HÔTEL DE FÉCAMP** (N° RR MAR 26 838) (M. Didier **Feray**)

Y

Yvetot continued

25, rue Clovis Cappon ☎ 35-95-17-76 ⊷ 6 Closed Sun; Aug. English, Spanish spoken. Filling station nearby.

YVRE-L'ÉVEQUE 72530 Sarthe **RN 23 Map 8-B2**

♀ ⊗ **LE RELAIS DU BON CAFÉ Grocery** (N° RR JUN 25 007) (Mme Annick **Simon**) 25, route du Mans ☎ 43-84-54-63 Closed Wed 2.00pm; Aug. Coaches welcome (rest. seats 80). Evening meals (no meals on Sun).

GERMANY

IMMERT (RFA)

♀ ⊗ 🏠 **ZUR BARRIÈRE** (N° RR JUIN 27 297) (M. Patrice **Le Guillou**) Ortsstrasse 31 ☎ 0 6504/1779 Closed Tues and German and French spoken. Evening meals.

BELGIUM

ANTWERPEN (2040)

♀ 🏆 **Total Service Station DELWAIDEDOK ANTWERPSEBAAN – HOEK LAAGEIND STABROEK DELWAIDEDOK KAAI 730** (N° RR 550000109) ☎ 03/568-88-08 – 03/568-88-09 – 03/568-88-10 **Minitel** Closed Sat evening, Sun evening 8.00pm–6.00am. Free showers and coffee. Shop, credit cards accepted. French, Dutch, English, German spoken.

BANDE 6951 **Maquel**

🏆 **LES ROUTIERS SERVICE STATION** (N° RR 550000114) Nle 4,47 Nationale 4 (direction Luxembourg) ☎ 084/34-44-24 **Minitel** Closed Mon. Credit cards accepted. Shop open 7am–10pm, free coffee. French spoken.

BARCHON 4511

♀ 🏆 **SERVICE STATION RESTAURANT LES ROUTIERS** (N° RR 550000115) rue Lieutenant Jungling, 1 Autoroute E 40 Barchon exit (No 36) ☎ 041/87-47-27 Shop open 24 hours, credit cards accepted, free showers and coffee. French, Dutch, German spoken.

BRULY DE COUVIN 6402 Prov. Namur

♀ ⊗ **CHEZ PIERRE** (N° RR AVR 22 759) (M. Pierre **Libens**) 65, rue

BELGIUM

Grande ☎ 060/37-72-02 Closed Mon. English, German, Dutch spoken.

BRUXELLES 1210

⊗ ☕ **Total Service Station**, (N° RR 550000104) Port de Bruxelles, avenue du Port 132, Porte de Bruxelles TIR, ☎ 02/426-0-54, Closed Sat 1.00pm to Sun. Free showers and coffee. Shop, credit cards accepted. Dutch, French spoken.

FOSSES LA VILLE (5660 Province Namur

♈ ⊗ **CAMPING LES VIVIERS 2** (N° RR SEPT 27 026) (Mme Liliane-Andrée **Charlier**) route de Mettet, 175 ☎ 07171-30-74/71-10-38 English and Dutch spoken.

GENT 9020

☕ **Total Service Station**, (N° RR 550000107) Port Arthurlaan Gent/Zeehaven ☎ 091/51-61-44 Shop open 7.00am to 9.00pm. Closed Sun. Free coffee. Credit cards accepted. Dutch, French spoken.

GERPINNES 6280 Prov. Hainaut **RN 5**

♈ ⊗ **LE RELAIS ROUTIERS COMME CHEZ SOI** (N° RR MAR 23 690) (M. François **Le Pauw**) 251, chaussée de Philippeville ☎ 071/21-65-22 German, Italian, English spoken.

GOETSENHOVEN 3311

⊗ ☕ **Total Service Station AE 40**, (N° RR 550000102) Direction Bruxelles/Liège ☎ 016/76-72-45 Open 24 hours. Free coffee. Credit cards accepted. Shop. Dutch, French spoken.

HAVAY 7091

♈ ⊗ **RELAIS ROUTIERS** (N° RR MARS 26 852) (M. Philippe **Nef**) 35, Chausée de Maubeuge.

HORION-HOZEMONT 4230

♈ ⊗ **AU PETIT PARADIS** (N° RR JUIN 27307) (M. Joseph **Paquay**) 11, rue Bihet ☎ 041/501614 Closed Sun morning and Sept. Italian and Dutch spoken. Evening meals.

KALKEN 9288 Anvers-Grand

⊗ **ACCOR** (Belgique) Autoroute E3 ☎ (32) 09/167-64-08 and (32) 09/167-64-09 Self-service restaurant, rest room, showers, TV, telephone. **Fina Service Station** (DKV-VTA) Tobacconist, shop.

KWAADMECHELEN 3968

⊗ ☕ **Station Service Total LES ROUTIERS** (N° RR 550000112) Sluis-straat 1 A-autoroute A13 sortie n° 25 Slwisstraat ☎ 013/66-54-06 Free showers and coffee, shop open 7am to 1pm. Credit cards accepted. Closed Sun. French, Dutch, German spoken.

LAAKDAL/EINDHOUT 3999

⊗ ☕ **Total Service Station LES ROUTIERS** (N° RR 550000111) Heze-meer 1 Autoroute A13 sortie nr 24 ☎ 014/30-19-35 Shop open

BELGIUM

Laakdal/Eindhout continued

7am–10pm. Free showers and coffee, credit cards accepted. Closed Sun. French, Dutch, English, German spoken.

MARCHE EN FAMENNE 5400 **DURUISSEAU**

♨ **Total Service Station LES ROUTIERS** (N° RR 550000113) Rte de Namur 73 Nationale 4 (direction Bruxelles) ☎ 084/31-17-25 Shop open 7am–10pm, credit cards accepted, free coffee. French, Dutch spoken.

MEER HOOGSTRATEN 2321

⊗ ♨ **Total Service Station GRENSEWEG** (N° RR 550000106) E 19 D2 Grenszone, Industriezone ☎ 03/315-88-98 Closed Sat, Sun. Free showers, and coffee. Shop open 6.00am to 10.00pm. Credit cards accepted. Dutch, French spoken.

MENEN-REKKEM 8530

♟ ♨ **Total Service Station KORTRIJK/LAR**, (N° RR 550000108) Rii-jksweg 746 Pecq/Geluwe N 746, Transportzone LAR ☎ 056/40-00-02 **Minitel** Open 24 hours. Closed Sat midday to Mon 6.00am. Rest room, free showers, shop, open 24 hours, credit cards accepted. French, Dutch spoken.

NOIREFONTAINE 6831 **RN 26, 28 and 47**

⊗ **LE RELAIS DES ROUTIERS** (N° RR MAI 19 777) (M. **Marqua**) 5, route de Bouillon ☎ 061/46-63-74 Closed Sun (except Jul/Aug).

ROTSELAAR 3110

⊗ ♨ **Total Service Station ROTSELAAR**, (N° RR 550000105) AUT A2 ☎ 016/44-82-70 Open 24 hours. Shop, credit cards accepted. Free coffee. Dutch, French spoken.

RUISBROEK 1610

♨ **Ruisbroek Total Service Station** (N° RR 550000110) Autoroute Bruxelles-Paris Autoroute Paris-Bruxelles ☎ 02/378-34-00 (Brussels); 02/876-73-63 (Paris). Free coffee and showers, shop, open 24 hours, credit cards accepted. French, Dutch, English, German spoken.

SENEFFE 6198 Prov. Hainaut

♟ ⊗ **RELAIS DE LA MARLETTE** (N° RR SEPT 26 314) (Mme Clémentine **Le Burn**) 4, rue du Rivage ☎ 064/54-87-72 ⊸ 4 Closed Mon; Aug. French, Dutch, English spoken. Evening meals until 11pm.

VILVOORDE 1800

♟ ⊗ **MONICO** (N° RR JANV 25 253) (M. **Pollet**) Schaarbeeck Lei 548 ☎ 02/252-06-85 Closed weekend. Evening meals.

ZEEBRUGGE 8380

⊗ **Total Service Station Baron** (N° RR 550000103) N 31 de Maerelaan 74 ☎ 050/54-54-61 **Minitel** Open 24 hours. Free showers, shop, free coffee, credit cards accepted. Dutch, French, English, German spoken.

Spain

MARTORELL (Prov. Barcelona) Autoroute A2
Y ⊗ **Bar-Restaurant-Cafeteria AUTOSERVICIO – RESTAURANT LLOBREGAT** (N. RA 26) (Monsieur Francisco **Chumilla**) Autoroute A 2 Barcelona-Tarragona PK 18 ☎ (93) 772-01-30 Open 24 hours. Shop, grocery, souvenirs, telephone.

Netherlands

MOERDIJK
Y ⊗ **RELAIS E 10** (N° RR MAI 21 539) (M. J. **Kanters**) Steenweg 2, ☎ 01683-310 Closed Sun. Coaches welcome (rest. seats 50). Evening meals.

Italy

To reach Italy faster, use the Alpine tunnel from Fréjus.

CAMPODARSEGO
Y ⊗ **LES ROUTIERS** (N° RR MAR 23 163) (M. Diégo **Savaretto**) Via Antoniana 128, Padova ☎ 040 55 41 13.

FRATTA DI PORTOGRUARO 30026 Venezia
AUTOGRILL PAVESI 56 Km from Mestre est Autostrada A4.

NOVARA 2811
AUTOGRILL PAVESI 89 Km from Torino Autostrada A4.

STRADELLA 27049 Pavia
AUTOGRILL PAVESI 130 Km from Torino Santena Autostrada A21.

SANT-ANTONINO 10050-Torino
OFFICINA MECCANICA (dei Fratelli **Rebolla**) Via Moncenisio 127 ☎ 011/9649963.

TORINO 10134
BAR RISTORANTE DOGANA (di Giuseppina **Ferrera**) Via Giordano Bruno 114 ☎ 011/694617.

Luxembourg

WILTZ 9560 Grand Duché de Luxembourg
♉ ⊗ ⌂ **AUBERGE AMSTER4DAM WILTZ** (N° RR JAN 24 078) (M. Quirinus **Van Vugt**) 144, rue du Dix-Septembre ☎ 95-73-24 ⇌ 5 Closed Mon. Full-board 975–1200 FB per night. Evening meals until 8pm; menus 280–475FB. Dutch, German, English spoken.

YOUR OPINION

If you are dissatisfied or alternatively would like to praise a Relais Routiers, please write and tell us. Although our establishments are reinspected regularly, your comments help us maintain Routiers' high standards. All correspondence will be treated in confidence.

Send to: ROUTIERS, 354 Fulham Road, LONDON SW10 9UH

Name of Relais Routiers:

_____

Address

_____

_____

on (date) _____ for lunch/dinner/bed and breakfast

Comments

_____

_____

_____

_____

_____

Your Name:

_____

Address:

_____

_____

YOUR RECOMMENDATION

If you know of an establishment not already a Relais Routiers but worthy of nomination, please send us details on the form below. We will arrange for an inspector to call.

Send to: ROUTIERS, 354 Fulham Road, LONDON SW10 9UH

Name of Establishment:

_____

Address

_____

_____

Name of Proprietor (If known):

_____

Restaurant/Pub/Hotel/Bed and Breakfast
(Please delete as applicable)

Comments

_____

_____

_____

_____

Your Name:

_____

Address:

_____

_____